STANLEY GIBBONS

Postcard Catalogue

Second Edition, Summer 1981

Stanley Gibbons Publications Ltd
391 Strand, London WC2R 0LX

By Appointment to Her Majesty The Queen
Stanley Gibbons Ltd, London
Philatelists

© Stanley Gibbons Publications Ltd 1981

ISSN 0144–249X   ISBN 0 85259 341 4

Compiled by
TONIE and VALMAI HOLT

1st edition—September 1980
2nd edition—July 1981

Item No. 2829

Printed in Great Britain by Spottiswoode Ballantyne Ltd.
Colchester and London

CONTENTS

CATALOGUE CLASSIFICATION

CONTENTS (contd.)

CONTENTS (contd.)

PREFACE

With the announcement in May 1980 that Stanley Gibbons were to publish a postcard catalogue it was immediately clear that the postcard world had eagerly been awaiting the appearance of this first new British catalogue for several years. Comment on the first edition has been abundant, ranging across a spectrum from unbridled praise to mild hostility, yet the general consensus has been that the catalogue made a significant and innovative contribution to the existing literature on the subject. We have been greatly encouraged by the majority of press reviews and by the letters that have been received from users (both collectors and dealers).

Having stated our intention with the first editon to lay a framework on which to build, our aim with this second edition has been to strengthen certain sections by adding new material in accordance with a development programme drawn up with Mr. and Mrs. Holt when the catalogue was first planned. In particular we are pleased to include much more substantial Animals (Cats), Artists, Cinema, Modern Cards, Philatelic, Railways, Shipping, Social History/Topographical and Theatre sections which we know will be welcomed by a large number of readers. A new Publishers section is now included and we set out—with specimen entries—our plans for a Local Publishers section which it is hoped to develop in future editions. Work on this is now in active progress and is a joint effort between the compilers and the members of several local postcard clubs. We are delighted with the ready and enthusiastic response from postcard clubs to help in this project which is, we feel, indicative of the friendly co-operation amongst postcard collectors. Long a feature of the philatelic world, it is good to see this joint approach to research and the publication of much needed information developing in the postcard fraternity. Full details are found on page 144. The Artists section is one where the compilers have added much new material in line with the importance it holds for the collector.

On the editorial side we were not satisfied with the layout of illustrations in the first edition and have rectified this detail for the convenience of users. Specialist colleagues within the Stanley Gibbons Group have examined all the prices in this volume, making adjustments where necessary in accordance with the very healthy postcard market presently prevailing. They remain the S.G. selling prices, current at the time of going to press.

Some commentators have asked to which audience the catalogue is aimed and a few words on this subject might not be out of place here. Clearly no catalogue can yet cover in detail all the many different postcard themes or list (as does a stamp catalogue) every one of the items issued over the years. To do so would require a huge multi-volume work rather like the telephone directories and its cost would render it outside the reach of nearly all collectors. Thus the Stanley Gibbons catalogue must remain of a general, rather than a specialised, nature giving sufficient background information, listings and guidance that will satisfy the new and average collectors and those who aim to take their collecting to a slightly more advanced stage. The specialist collector will find much to interest him in subjects outside his own particular field. There might be a good case later for Gibbons to publish specialised catalogues on particular postcard themes; meanwhile we are concentrating on developing this catalogue to be as accurate and comprehensive as we can make it for the generality of collectors. The reception given to the first edition encourages us in this work.

Among the many letters we received about the first edition were a good number from collectors in North America and the catalogue was well-received by the reviewers in several respected journals. In this edition the compilers have, wherever possible, included details of cards published in the USA. We hope that this will prove useful to collectors both in the USA and those elsewhere who collect American cards. We should be pleased to hear from readers whether they would like us to develop this theme and possibly include a separate section on American cards.

Last time we invited readers to write to Mr. and Mrs. Holt with information and suggestions for the second edition. We have been very gratified by the response and where possible have acted upon the suggestions made. Mr. and Mrs. Holt acknowledge this help elsewhere in the catalogue.

J.N.
J.R.H.

HOW TO USE THIS CATALOGUE

Unlike coins and postage stamps which, because of their accountability, are carefully recorded on issue, picture postcards have few birth records. Collectors have therefore created their own descriptive language in order to name and hence identify their cards. This language is explained in the GLOSSARY.

But a single picture postcard may have many names. To one collector it may be 'Comic'; to another a 'McGill'; to another, 'World War 1'; to another, 'Inter-Art', and to yet one more, 'Ethnic'.

Thus in order to consult the INDEX for a particular card, the card must first be named, and this process will be made much easier if the reader is familiar with the major collecting themes. These themes constitute the framework of this catalogue and are set out on page iii under CONTENTS. The process then is simple:

1. **Name the card.**

2. **Locate that name in the index and follow the references.**

NAMING A CARD

There are three descriptive bands within which a name may be found:

1. *Artist's Name*, the signature on the card, e.g. Cassiers.
2. *Publisher*, e.g. Dietrich of Brussels.
3. *Thematic*, based upon the reason for issue or picture content of the card, e.g. COMIC, EXHIBITIONS, RAILWAYS, etc.

For this edition indexes to Artists and Themes are given (to be extended later to Publishers).

Example 1

Name—by artist—'Tom Browne'. Consult 'Browne' in index and refer to page quoted for listing and value.

Example 2

Name—by theme—'Zeppelin'. Consult 'Zeppelin' in index and refer to page quoted for listing and value.

Where a card has a value because of its thematic content, that value will be increased if the picture is the work of a collected artist or publisher.

THE INDEX

The index is the key to the whole catalogue. It contains, in alphabetical order, all the major references to Artists and Themes and is placed at the back of the catalogue.

THE ILLUSTRATIONS

This catalogue contains more illustrations than any British catalogue to date. Each illustration is referred to in the text. Cross-reference is indicated by the sign ■.

ARTIST INFORMATION

Artists are not listed in the ARTISTS section unless some useful item of information can be given about them. As many details as are currently available have been provided on the following pattern—Name; nationality; dates of birth and death; education and artistic training; style or genre; main publishers; series; price range.

Where appropriate, however, lists of artists occur throughout as sub-divisions of the main sections. Those individuals with a biographical entry under ARTISTS are marked with the † sign, e.g. Barribal, W.†

THE THREE BAND PRICING SYSTEM

Much has been written and discussed over the past twelve months about the subject of prices. Further intensive research into the question by the compilers has convinced them of the wisdom of continuing a Three-Band Pricing System: conversely to give one single price only would be inaccurate, inadequate and misleading.

The hobby and business of postcard collecting are still in their infancy, and developing week by week. At this stage of their growth it is unrealistic to give one definitive price for a particular postcard. Unlike stamps or coins, postcards have not been catalogued as they have been produced. The numbers that were printed of any one postcard were rarely recorded. The same applies to any variations in print runs or re-issues.

Postcards have, therefore, had to prove their saleability over the years and cataloguers can only report on what is being asked and paid for a particular postcard. Throughout the collecting world today there are wide fluctuations and extremes in the prices being asked and paid for postcards.

The variations are sometimes geographic. Certain types are more prized in different countries, or even parts of the same country.

For instance: the fine British comic cards are little collected in France, very popular in the UK. Fairly featureless postcards of Canterbury are eagerly sought after, and dearly bought, by collectors in the Canterbury area but would have virtually no value in Edinburgh. The classic *Art Nouveau* cards of the turn of the century have almost no price ceiling in the United States where there is a strong contingent of wealthy 'investor' collectors, yet they often sell in auction in Britain at well below average catalogue prices.

Sometimes the variations are fashionable or seasonal. That is to say that interest is sometimes stimulated in certain types of card by a new book or article which features them. Collectors rush to buy these types, which pushes up the price, although it may then settle down again at a lower level.

Some collectors will only buy cards in excellent condition. This will always have the effect of placing a premium on cards in virtually mint condition. Other collectors are willing to purchase a card in fairly poor condition in order to have an example of a particular artist's work (to complete a series), but usually in the hope of being able to replace that substandard card with a better example in the future. This means that there *is* a market for less than good quality cards, but at a low price. In the middle of those two factors is the reasonable price for a card in good, collectable condition.

Another factor which governs the price of a card is the amount a dealer has had to pay for that card and this, too, can fluctuate wildly. Some dealers do not change the price of cards already in their stock even though the price of those cards is generally accepted to have increased. But as they buy in new cards of the same type they mark them at the new price. Therefore in one dealer's stock collectors often find two examples of the same card, in similar condition, at two very different prices.

At auction, too, prices vary enormously. If two or more potential purchasers are bidding for a card they each urgently want, an uncharacteristically high price is bound to be paid. On the other hand, superb, normally high-priced postcards, often sell in auction at well below their current average price if no-one bidding is particularly interested in them.

What the Three Band Pricing System can therefore imply is:

1. Left Hand Band
This is the lowest price you will probably be asked to pay for this card. It is priced thus because of a combination of the following factors:
a. It is in fairly poor condition
b. It is being sold in an area where such a card is little collected
c. The dealer selling it has had it in stock for a long time
d. The dealer selling it does not know the true value of it
e. It is an inferior example of the artist's work
f. It is poorly printed, or is not a particularly clear photograph, or is a very long distance view of the featured subject (e.g. a tram)
g. The design has been obscured by writing, postmark, etc.
h. It is a modern card

2. Middle Band
This what you will normally be asked to pay for this card. It is the average, reasonable, current market price that is being paid for it because of a combination of the following factors:
a. It is in good, collectable condition
b. The dealer selling it has studied the market and marked it at the current average price being paid for it

c. It is a good example of the artist's work/a good, clear, middle distance photograph/well printed

d. Any writing/postmarks do not detract from the design

3. Right Hand Band

This is the highest price you will probably be asked to pay for this card. It is priced so highly because of a combination of the following factors:

a. It is in virtually perfect condition

b. It is a fine/rare/early example of the artist's work/perhaps it forms part of one of the classic *Collections*

c. It is a superb, close-up, sharp real photograph of an interesting/unusual event, building or location

d. It is a particularly early example of its type

e. It is unique or special in some way (e.g. signed by subject/artist; only very few were issued; was dropped from a balloon, etc.)

Single Price

Where one price only is printed for a card, this means:

a. It is probably a modern card, with a standard retail price, or

b. This card only attains the minimum quoted valuation in this catalogue (25p) in virtually perfect condition, or if it has some outstanding feature. In some cases several examples of the postcard would be required together to attain that minimum.

Prix d'Amateur (P/A)

The card concerned is so rare/attractive that its price has not been sufficiently tested at auction or in dealers' stocks and its price ceiling is only determined by the collector's desire and means.

How The Valuations In This Catalogue Were Arrived At

In order to decide upon the valuations quoted here, the compilers used a variety of techniques including (a) showing a particular postcard to several dealers and asking them how much they would charge for it; (b) showing that same postcard to several collectors and asking them how much they would pay for it; (c) comparing several auction results obtained for that same postcard; (d) comparing the price asked for that same postcard in several sales lists; (e) comparing the price asked for and paid in several different locations for the same postcard.

These exercises have confirmed that there is today *no one finite price for any one postcard—hence the* THREE BAND PRICING SYSTEM.

ABBREVIATIONS

ad	advertisement	It	Italian
art.	artist drawn	LH	left hand
Aust	Austrian	Maxi	Maximum
Austral	Australian	nos.	numbers
b & w	black and white	o/s	oversize
Belg	Belgian	PHQ	Postal Headquarters
Br	British	PMC	Private Mailing Card
Bulg	Bulgarian	PS	Postal Stationery
Can	Canadian	PU	postally used
chromo	chromolithographically printed	Pub.	Publisher
chromo-litho	chromolithographically printed postcard	RH	right hand
		RP	real photo
col.	coloured	Rum	Rumanian
Du	Dutch	Russ	Russian
Fr	French	UB	undivided back
GB	Great Britain	UPU	Universal Postal Union
Ger	German	u/s	undersize
HTL	Hold-to-light	USA	American (United States)
Hung	Hungarian	WW1	World War 1
illus	illustrated/illustration	WW2	World War 2
incl.	including		

GLOSSARY

Appliqué. Material attached to a postcard to embellish it, e.g. dried flowers, hair, velvet.

Artist drawn. Cards that originate from an artist's drawing, e.g. Tuck's 'Oilette' series, although that drawing may not have been originally or exclusively drawn for the postcard, but may be reproduced from a poster or magazine etc. They are usually printed by an ink process.

Back. That side of the postcard which carries the address.

Chromo-litho. A term used to describe high quality, lithographically printed coloured picture cards such as early Gruss Aus (*qv*) examples, where up to sixteen different colours were sometimes applied separately. Such cards are almost always from Period 1 or very early Period 2 and were ousted by the introduction of the cheaper three-colour process from around 1900. Chromo-litho cards exhibit a depth of colour that can almost be felt with the fingers and possess fine detail.

Composite. Collective name for a number of individual picture cards that fit together to make a larger picture. Most composites consist of a dozen or less cards which may or may not be pictures in their own right.

Court size. Cards measuring approximately 115 mm × 89 mm, which were officially recognised in Britain on 21 January 1895.

Divided back. Cards where the back has been divided by a line into two sections. One is for the address, and the other for the message. The idea originated in Britain in 1902.

Front. That side of the postcard which does not carry the address and which normally carries the picture.

Full out. A picture which covers the whole of one side of a postcard and does not share it with either the address or a message space.

Full size. Private postcards in Britain had to be the same size as the official (*qv*) postcards sold at Post Offices. On the Continent much larger cards were permitted by the UPU agreement and these allowed the rapid development of the picture card. The UPU 'full size', 140 by 89 mm (5½ by 3½ inches), became legal in Britain on 1 November 1899.

Gruss Aus. Literally 'Greetings From' in German, the term is used to describe early Continental greetings cards with vignetted pictures.

Hold-to-light. A card which, when held up to the light, displays additional colours or pictures.

Local publisher. A publisher whose premises are located inside the area depicted on his picture postcards. The term implies a production generally limited to that one area. It may also be used to describe the issuing house named on the card (e.g. a local store), although the card itself may have been manufactured by a jobbing photographer or a national company specialising in such work.

Maximum card. Postcard whose illustration corresponds to that of a postage stamp, usually affixed on the same side and sometimes cancelled with a first day of issue postmark.

Name. The identity given to a card by a collector. It may be based upon artist, publisher or theme.

Novelty. A postcard which deviates from the normal rectangular item made of standard board.

Official. A card produced by an official organisation, usually a Government Post Office. Also used to describe cards issued by official non-Government committees for specific events such as exhibitions, political rallies, Olympic Games etc. *See also* 'Postal stationery'.

Oversize. Also referred to as 'Continental' size, these are squarer and larger than the UPU full size cards. PHQ cards and German and Italian Period 5 official cards are typically 'oversize', being around 147 mm × 105 mm.

Philatelic. An item whose *raison d'être* or valuation depends more upon its postage stamp and transmission through the mail than upon its artistic or physical nature.

Photo-origin. The picture found on postcards derive from two main sources—an artist's drawing (*see* 'Artist drawn') or a photograph. Those that originate from photographs are referred to here as 'photo-origin'. They may be printed in one of two ways—photographically, or by some 'normal' printing process involving the transfer of ink, e.g. Tuck's 'Photochrome' series. Normally those cards printed photographically (*see* 'Real photo') give a clearer picture and better detail than other photo-origin cards and are therefore valued more highly. Photo-origin cards as a whole tend to be more valuable than artist drawn varieties, except where the drawings can be attributed to 'collectable' artists.

Postal stationery. Cards carrying pre-printed stamps. The term may also apply to issues made by national post offices for use with adhesive stamps. Postal stationery cards are essentially Government issued, while 'Official' (*qv*) cards may not be. The terms overlap.

Postcard. A card produced with the intention of meeting the regulations concerning the appropriate Postcard Postal Rate.

Poster Ad. A card whose picture is a reproduction of a poster advertisement. The term is often loosely used to describe cards for which there is no firm connection with a known poster, but whose style suggests that an equivalent poster exists.

Printed stamp. The impressed or imprinted postage stamp on official (Post Office) postcards.

Private mailing card. Commercially produced American picture postcard for use with an adhesive stamp. Cards carry the words, 'Private mailing card' on the address side and were introduced on 1 July 1898.

Publisher. A term used to identify the issuing house. Strictly it may not identify the publisher in the dictionary sense of the word, but may also refer to the agent, importer, photographer or printer. The names used for Publishers in this catalogue are those in common usage, e.g. 'Tuck', rather than 'Raphael Tuck & Sons'.

Real photo. A card whose picture originated from a photograph and which has been printed by a photographic process, e.g. Tuck's 'Real photograph' series.

Thematic. The identification of a card by naming its theme, e.g. Advertisement, Comic, Royal, War, etc.

Under size. Applied to cards smaller than UPU 'Full size', but which are not 'Court size' (*qv*).

Undivided back. Cards without a dividing line on the back. The term is generally accepted as denoting an early card.

Vignette. A picture without ruled borders. Typically seen on Gruss Aus (*qv*) cards in twos or threes.

THE SEVEN POSTCARD PERIODS

In the past the collecting of old picture postcards was confined to the years from about 1890 to 1918—'The Golden Age'.

Now, the extraordinary growth in popularity of the hobby has widened collecting horizons, and a cataloguing system capable of dealing with all the years from 1869 has become necessary. The 'Seven Postcard Period' system has been developed with this in view.

The ways in which each of these Periods uniquely defines its postcards are explained in *A Brief History of the Picture Postcard*, following. The Seven Periods and their precise dates are:

Period 1. 1869–1899. The first day of issue of the postcard (1 October 1869) to the last day of the 1800s (31 December 1899).

Period 2. 1900–1914. The first day of the 1900s (1 January 1900) to the last day of peace for Britain (3 August 1914).

Period 3. 1914–1918. The first day of war (4 August 1914) to the cessation of hostilities (11 November 1918).

Period 4. 1918–1939. The first day of peace (12 November 1918) to the last day of peace (2 September 1939).

Period 5. 1939–1945. The first day of war for Britain (3 September 1939) to the day of German unconditional surrender (7 May 1945).

Period 6. 1945–1969. The first day of peace (8 May 1945, VE Day) to the 100th Anniversary of the postcard (1 October 1969).

Period 7. 1969–today. From 2 October 1969 onwards.

A BRIEF HISTORY OF THE PICTURE POSTCARD

Covering Its Seven Periods

PERIOD 1: 1869–1899

On 1 October 1869 the Austrian postal authorities issued the world's first postcard (Fig. A).

Cards had passed through the post earlier than 1869 but they were not 'post' cards because the cost of their transmission was the same as for a letter. The true postcard, designed to stimulate the business of the post office, was carried at a special price which was half of the letter rate. Therefore, postcards did not exist prior to 1 October 1869.

The cards were enormously popular and other countries quickly followed suit—Britain 1870 (Fig. B), Canada 1871, America and France 1873, Italy 1874, and so on. At first the cards were for transmission inside the issuing country only, but negotiations within the Universal Postal Union soon produced agreements allowing international use.

The advertising potential of an open card handled by so many people between sender and recipient was quickly seized upon, particularly by hotels and resorts catering to the fast-growing tourist business. On the Continent, where official restrictions on the uses of postcards were few, the simple line-drawn advertisements of the early years were replaced by beautiful lithographic printings. Today these coloured cards are known as 'chromo-lithos' while on the Continent their official forerunners are called *precursors*.

The other stimulus which led to the growth of picture postcards was the popularity of Exhibitions. Picture cards proved to be excellent mementos of a visit, and the first photographic-origin view card is sometimes claimed to be the one made by the lithographer Zrenner for the 1882 Nuremberg Exhibition (■126a). Exhibitions, or 'Expositions', proliferated—1884 Turin, 1889 Paris, 1893 Chicago (■126b) (*see* EXHIBITIONS). In 1894, in Venice, came one of the earliest Exhibitions devoted to postcards. The world was about to be flooded with pieces of cardboard.

The most widely produced Continental type of picture postcard before 1900 was the Gruss Aus ('Greetings from') variety and this, bearing small vignetted views, was certainly amongst the earliest picture cards made whether for Exhibitions, Hotels or Resorts. Here too the early line drawings (■5a) were replaced by chromo-litho printings and the term 'Gruss Aus' is interpreted by a postcard collector to mean 'vignetted views printed by chromo lithography' (Fig. C). By 1898 illustrators like Kirchner, Cheret and Mucha (■106a) were appearing on Continental cards.

In Britain the Post Office retained a tight monopoly over the printing of postcards, but despite this monopoly a variety of claims have been made for Britain's First Picture Postcard although there are widely differing opinions as to what constitutes a 'picture'. The most popular claimant is probably a card produced in March 1872 by Grant & Co. to advertise a book on London by the artist Doré (■10a). This card was an official issue which had been overprinted with the advertising design. A few official issues

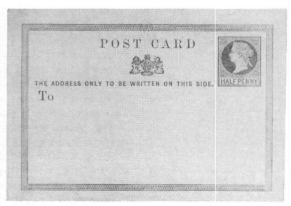

A (*Period 1*): *1869. Austria, the world's first postcard.*

B (*Period 1*): *1870. Britain's first postcard.*

carrying illustrations (rather than 'views') were made—the Guildhall Postal Jubilee card on 16 May 1890 (Fig. D) and The Royal Naval Exhibition Eddystone Lighthouse card in June 1891 (Fig. E). However, commercial British production of picture cards was essentially zero and it was not until 1 November 1899 that the Post Office gave up its monopoly and British firms were allowed to produce full Universal Postal Union size postcards. It was on that day that Raphael Tuck & Son entered the postcard

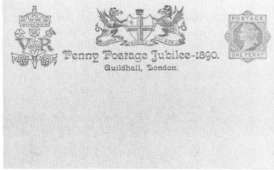

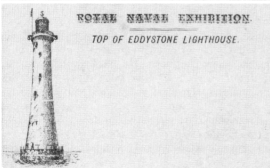

C (*Period 1*): *1897. Typical chromo-litho 'Gruss Aus'. This one from Karlsbad.*

D (*Period 1*): *1890. Penny Postage Jubilee, red printing. Limited issue of 10,000.*

E (*Period 1*): *1891. Eddystone Lighthouse. Royal Naval Exhibition.*

business, neatly anticipating the end of the 1800s and the start of Period 2.

PERIOD 2: 1900–1914

In just a year the Victorian Age was over. Britain's beloved Queen was dead. Now it was Edward's turn at last and changes rapidly flowed in the picture postcard world. By the second year of Period 2 at least a dozen firms were producing cards in London. In July 1900 the *Picture Postcard* magazine had been founded and in December 1900 John Evelyn Wrench, a postcard giant-to-be, had issued his first cards.

The Edwardian entrepreneurs flourished. The collecting fever spread from the Continent. Well-known illustrators like Henri Meunier, John Hassall and Kokoschka drew especially for the new medium and *Art Nouveau* reproductions reigned supreme. When the British idea of dividing the back of the card into two was introduced in 1902, the flood gates opened for British home-grown talent and production. Until then the picture and the message had been forced to share the same side, leaving the other clear for the address. Now the message and the address shared one side, and the picture could spread over the whole of the other. It would take only four years for the idea to gain the approval of all UPU members. Catalogues of postcard issues world-wide had been published by Stanley Gibbons and by Bright & Sons, but the endless stream was impossible to keep up with. The catalogues stopped, Gibbons's last edition being dated 1899.

By 1902 the rotary presses developed in Germany in the mid-1890s for chromo-litho printing, were being applied to photographic cards, and actresses, bishops and politicians featured in their thousands. Postcard clubs were formed, postcard magazines were founded, special postcard pens, posting boxes, blotters and wallets were made and every ounce of ingenuity went into creating new and original cards and designs. There were artistic cards, vulgar cards, squeakers and smellies, humorous cards and topical cards, three-dimensional and hold-to-lights. Royals and commoners had postcard albums proudly displayed. The market seemed insatiable.

But production went to excess. By 1914 the fever was in decline. Production had been too enormous and printing and design standards had fallen from the superb heights of Period 1. The rotary presses were producing illustrated magazines that captured the attentions of both talented artists and the buying public, and the magazines supported by their advertising often cost little more than a single postcard. That small piece of card was about to decline into a common carrier of short messages. It was the end of an era.

PERIOD 3: 1914–1918

The postcard was a natural message carrier for wartime. It was economical in its use of paper; it could be used to say 'I'm O.K.' when there was no time to say more; it was easily censored. But, once again, it was to become more than a carrier of written messages.

The war settled into a confrontation between millions of men arranged behind trenches that stretched from the North Sea to Switzerland. Both sides realised the patriotic and propaganda value of pictures that linked the men at war with those at home—just as in Period 1 the commercial advertising potential of the picture postcard had been understood and exploited. Thus Period 3 saw not just a resurgence in the popularity of the postcard but probably the years of greatest production. The value of Period 3 cards as documentary records of Europe's painful change from autocracy to democracy is only just being understood. In this catalogue the cards of WW1 are set out in considerable detail, reflecting the horrors of trench warfare, the bitterness of the invaded nations, the devotion to King and Kaiser—indeed reflecting the whole panorama of the conflict.

As the war ended, the artificial stimulus died, and when in 1918 in Britain the postcard rate was doubled to one penny, volume postcard production almost disappeared overnight. Another phase was over. Period 3 gave way to the inter-war years.

PERIOD 4: 1918–1939

It is often supposed in Britain that few postcards of note were produced in Period 4. That supposition is wrong.

Certainly, British publishers did not produce much that was collectable and the quantity of cards manufactured was minuscule compared to Period 3. Bread-and-butter viewcards continued in production and in an attempt to revive business the seaside postcard became ever more vulgar That type of card must, inevitably, become collectable. Nursery artists like Jessie M. King, Millicent Sowerby and Shand reflected the height of the *Art Deco* movement for publishers such as Faulkner, the Medici Society and Millar and Lang; Tucks produced their fine 'Queen's Dolls House' series, but we have to look overseas to find real signs of life. Nevertheless, the changing tastes

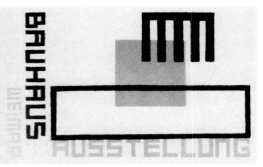

F (*Period 4*): *1923. Bauhaus design by Kurt Schmidt.*

of the world of art are reflected in cards which are considered to be collectable at any given time. *Art Deco* is now accepted as a desirable art form. For many years it was not. This desirability will bring out of hiding an increasing number of Period 4 cards.

France was much concerned with surrealism and towards the end of Period 4 produced an excellent series of cards titled 'La Carte Postale Surréaliste' with such august contributors as Dali, Magritte and Picasso. The main action, however, was with the burgeoning dictatorships.

In Italy, probably the most active Period 4 postcard country of all, *Art Deco*, cubism and futurism found expression through glamorous designs by Brunelleschi (■31b), Mauzan and Montedoro. The impetus was provided by the fascist movement for whom Busi did splendid propaganda works.

By the early 1930s National Socialism had taken control in Germany and the picture postcard featured as a major plank in their propaganda. Artists like Willrich drew both official and commercial propaganda and major photographic series were produced by such publishers as Hoffman of Munich. Numerous series promoting the image of the Nazi party were published from around 1932 and collectors nowadays seem mesmerised by the swastika and by Adolf Hitler. However, there are other interesting cards, including those issued for the Olympic Games in 1936 and the series produced by the Bauhaus movement in Berlin (Fig. F).

As the European climate became more warlike so the postcard found cause to comment. When war began for Britain on 3 September 1939 all the Period 3 reasons for producing picture postcards were once again valid. Another revival began.

PERIOD 5: 1939–1945

Of all postcard periods this one is probably the least understood so far. The postcards of World War 2 have as many varieties and as much vigorous design in this Period 5 as there had been in Period 3.

Very few cards of Period 5 are currently available in Britain, although international trading is feeding an increasing number of German and Italian examples into the collecting circuit. This scarcity should not encourage the deduction that few cards were manufactured. There are few cards around in Britain because here, until now, they have not been defined and therefore could not be sought for. Remarkable catalogues have been published in Germany by Willi and Irma Bernhard which set out an astonishing range of National Socialist picture postcards and as a result these cards are familiar sights in dealers' stocks there. There is another reason too.

During Periods 2 and 3 postcards were considered to be worth collecting and they were therefore assembled together in albums. When the same cards became collectable again in the late 1960s and the 1970s, they were generally found still in their albums and several hundred at a time. In Period 5, however, when the war often waged more fiercely at home than it did at the Front, nothing ephemeral seemed worth collecting. Postcards were not placed in albums, but if kept at all were dumped in a drawer with the letters and ration books. Therefore, when they are discovered today it is usually only in ones or twos. As yet those ones and twos have not been greatly disturbed.

A framework for World War 2 has been established in this catalogue in the section WAR. The categories closely match those of Period 3—political, propaganda, air warfare and so on. There is more concern with the machine and less concern for the man than in Period 3 and the propaganda seems more orchestrated, particularly in Germany and Italy. In Britain there is an overwhelming abundance of humour, often depicted through appealing children by artists like Mabel Lucie Attwell and Dinah. From Europe, as the liberating armies fought their way out of the landing beaches, came a stream of 'Liberation' cards. In the end, however, once the war had ended, it was the same as before. The picture postcard fell by the wayside. It was 1945. Period 5 was over.

PERIOD 6: 1945–1969

To date, the early years of Period 6 seem very quiet in postcard terms. Anniversary cards of Liberation events were published in the former occupied countries and fund raisers of various kinds were issued, including some for the victims of Nazi Concentration Camps. The Iron Curtain countries, less sophisticated in their communication systems than the capitalist regimes, made great use of wall posters—and postcards. Cards were issued to commemorate popular events and gatherings like the great Czechoslovakian gymnastic festivals (Sokols) in which as many as 10,000 people performed simultaneously (Fig. G). But, so far, few postcard examples have reached Britain.

The economies of Europe recovered remarkably quickly and one of the new symptoms of general affluence, the motor car, prompted a resurgence of viewcards for the mobile populations to send home. Street scenes showing those motor cars are now beginning to be popular. In Italy in the 1950s there was a growth in the poster advertising card featuring the petrol company AGIP and commemorating a number of exhibitions. The real stimulus, however, was an approaching anniversary—1969, the Centenary of the Postcard.

In Britain a series of events leading to the Anniversary foreshadowed the collecting explosion which was to follow. Those events were:

1958   A. J. (Jim) Butland & E. A. (Ted) Westwood started the magazine '*Postcard Collectors Guide and News*'.

1959   *Pictures in the Post, The Story of the Picture Postcard*, by Richard Carline, was published.

1959   *Picture Postcards and All About Them*. Limp back publication by A. J. Butland & E. A. Westwood was published by the authors.

1961   Drene Brennan started the Postcard Club of Great Britain.

1966   J. H. D. Smith began a postal sales list; *The Picture Postcard and its Origins*, by Frank Staff, was published.

Interest was accelerating, not in new postcards but in those from Periods 1, 2 and 3—the Golden Age. Oddly, in 1968, Britain lost its true postcard. On 16 September, the two-tier postal system was introduced and there was no longer a 'Postcard Rate' for inland mail. The purist may therefore consider that the British inland postcard lived for 98 years, i.e. from 1870 to 1968.

However, for incoming and for overseas mail there was still a 'Postcard Rate'. But in 1969 the old postcard suddenly joined the world of 'antiques'. It became 100 years old and Period 7 had arrived.

PERIOD 7: 1969–today

The first British event in Period 7 was an exhibition at Reed House, Piccadilly, entitled 'A Century of British Postcards', for which the Postcard Association of Great Britain issued a commemorative card (■115c). This was followed by a travelling postcard exhibition sponsored and arranged by the Victoria & Albert Museum. In 1971 a collectors' guide, *Picture Postcards of the Golden Age*, by Tonie and Valmai Holt, was published after which they exhibited some of their cards on BBC Television's antiques programme, 'Collectors World'. The collecting hunt was on in earnest—and for the same cards that had been sought in the Golden Age.

Since then a great deal has happened— Maurice Hewlett compiled Picton's *Handbook*, the first priced postcard publication in 1971, and was followed by J. H. D. Smith's *I.P.M. Year Book*, Bernhardt's German 'Katalog' and Neudin's *Argus* in France. Postcard fairs escalated from the early initiative of 'RF Postcards' to regular weekly events around the whole country, organised by a dozen or more promoters.

In 1972 Mr. Ken Lawson opened the Middlesex Collectors' Centre and in response to the accelerating interest from collectors, moved on to postal sales in 1974 and to postal auctions in 1976. Today his Specialised Postcard Auctions organisation has clients in 19 different countries.

The growth in the market also led to the emergence of sophisticated postcard magazines, beginning with Valerie Monahan's *Picture Postcard Collector's Gazette* in 1974 and continued today by Brian and Mary Lund's *Picture Postcard Monthly* in Britain, and by Don and Sue

Bodow's *Picture Postcard News* and *American Postcard Journal* in the United States.

Perhaps one of the most significant events was the 1975 formation by dealers in old picture postcards in the UK of the Postcard Traders' Association (PTA). The development of the PTA's annual British International Postcard Exhibition (BIPEX) confirmed the international interest in the hobby, matching similar events held in Paris and now in New York. Even the general auction houses, such as Phillips, Sotheby's and Christie's in London and Neales in Nottingham feature postcards regularly, and during 1980 a single postcard, albeit one with philatelic/postal history attributes, realised over £1000.

There has been a recent strengthening in popularity of Period 7 cards and some adventurous publishers have entered the market with cards that reflect all the old virtues of initiative and topicality that were so typical of the Golden Age—for example, Carousel Limited Editions and Veldale Covers in the UK and Coral-Lee in the USA. The burgeoning of interest in the collection of Period 7 cards has resulted in a greatly expanded MODERN (*qv*) section in this catalogue.

In 1980 Stanley Gibbons published the First Edition of this postcard catalogue and such was its impact on the market that it quickly sold out. Reaction from collectors and dealers around the world was overwhelmingly favourable and many wrote in with suggestions and additions for Edition 2. A good number of these suggestions was acted upon and are reflected in the expanded ARTISTS section, the detailed RAILWAYS section and several other major expansions. The Index has also been extended to become more comprehensive.

Despite a general decline in activity in other collecting fields, the picture postcard hobby remains healthy and vigorous. The publication by Stanley Gibbons of Edition 2 of this catalogue, less than 12 months after Edition 1, is ample proof of this.

BIBLIOGRAPHY

The following is a list of publications to which the compilers have referred and/or which are recommended for further reading.

1. Books

Frederick Alderson. *The Comic Postcard in English Life* (1970).

Allan Anderson & Betty Tomlinson. *Greetings from Canada* (Canada, 1978).

Barbara Andrews. *A Directory of Postcards, Artists, Publishers and Trademarks* (1975).

Brian & Mary Lund. *Annual of the Picture Postcard* (1980 & 1981).

Ronnie Barker. *Book of Bathing Beauties* (1974).

Ronnie Barker. *Book of Boudoir Beauties* (1975).

Ronnie Barker. *Sauce* (1978).

Ronnie Barker. *Gentleman's Relish* (1979).

David Q. Bowers & Mary L. Martin. *The Postcards of Alphonse Mucha* (1981).

Anne Bradford. *The Animal Magic of Harry Whittier Frees* (1977).

Anne Bradford. *More Animal Magic* (1978).

J. R. Burdick. *Pioneer Postcards* (USA, 1957).

A. J. Butland & E. A. Westwood. *Picture Postcards and All About Them* (1959).

A. Byatt. *Picture Postcards and Their Publishers* (1978).

Bygone Series (of local Southern Counties Postcards) 11 titles 1970s/80s.

Michael Cane & R. G. Harris. *The Career of Harry Payne* (1978).

Richard Carline. *Pictures in the Post* (1959, revised 1971).

Elizabeth Carter. *Sydney Carter* (1948).

Sally Carver. *The American Guide to Tuck* (1977, revised 1980).

Dawn & Peter Cope. *Illustrators of Postcards from the Nursery* (1978).

David Cuppleditch. *The London Sketch Club* (1978).

David Cuppleditch. *The John Hassall Lifestyle* (1980).

Rodney Dale. *Louis Wain. The Man Who Drew Cats* (1970).

William Duval & Valerie Monahan. *Collecting Postcards in colour 1894–1914* (1978).

Eric J. Evans & Jeffrey Richards. *A Social History of Britain in Postcards* (1980).

F. A. Fletcher & A. D. Brooks. *British Exhibitions and their Postcards* (1978).

F. A. Fletcher & A. D. Brooks. *British & Foreign Exhibitions and their Postcards* (1980).

John Geipel. *The Cartoon* (1972).

Benny Greene. *I've Lost My Little Willie!* (1976).

Paul Hammond. *French Undressing* (1976).

C. W. Hill. *Discovering Picture Postcards* (1978).

C. W. Hill. *Edwardian Entertainments* (1978).

Tonie & Valmai Holt. *Picture Postcards of the Golden Age* (1971, reprinted 1978).

Tonie & Valmai Holt. *Till the Boys Come Home: The Picture Postcards of the First World War* (1977).

Tonie & Valmai Holt. *The Best of Fragments From France* (1978).

A. K. Huggins. *British Postal Stationery* (1970).

John Kaduck. *Rare and Expensive Postcards* Books I & II (USA, 1975, 1979).

Ivy Millicent James: A Children's Postcard Artist (1980).

Gerald King. *Alice through the Pillar Box* (1978).

Ken Lawson & Tony Warr. *Tom Browne* (1978).

Ken Lawson & Tony Warr. *Lance Thackeray* (1979).

George & Dorothy Millar. *Picture Postcards in the United States* (1976).

Valerie Monahan. *Collecting Postcards in colour 1914–1930* (1980).

Erik Norgaard. *With Love—the Erotic Postcard* (1969).

William Oulette. *Fantasy Postcards* (1976).

William Oulette & B. Jones. *Erotic Postcards* (1977).

Alan Roger Quinton. *The England of A. R. Quinton* (1978).

John Rawlings & Michael Passmore. *The Postal History of the Nuremberg Rallies* (1980).

C. Radley. *Collecting Silk Postcards* (1976).

C. Radley. *The Embroidered Silk Postcard* (1977).

C. Radley. *The Woven Silk Postcard* (1978).

Dorothy Ryan. *Philip Boileau. Painter of Fair Women* (USA) (1980).

Reginald Silvester. *Railway Postcards of the British Isles, Vol. 1* (1978).

Frank Staff. *The Picture Postcard & its Origins* (1966, reprinted 1979).

Frank Staff. *Picture Postcards & Travel* (1979).

Alain Weill. *Art Nouveau Postcards* (1978).

2. Catalogues

Frederico Bartoli & Ivo Mataloni *Cartoline d'Epoca e gli Illustratori Italiani* (Rome, 1979).

F. Baudet. *Encyclopedie Internationale de la Carte Postale* (Paris, 1978).

Irma & Willi Bernhardt. *Travemunde Bildpost-karten Katalog* (Hamburg, 1977).

Irma & Willi Bernhardt. *Bildpostkarten Spezial Katalog Weihnachtsen* (1974).

Irma & Willi Bernhardt. *Bildpostkarten Spezial Katalog Automobil* (1978).

Irma & Willi Bernhardt. *Bildpostkarten Spezial Katalog National Sozialismus* (1975).

Andre Fildier. *Catalogue des Cartes Postales Anciennes de Collection* (Annual).

Klaus W. Gruner. *Postais Antigos Portugueses* (1980).

Mario Mordente. *Catalogo delle Cartoline Illustrate Italiane* (1980).

Joelle & Gerard Neudin. *Cartes Postales* (Paris, Annual).

M. R. Hewlett, B. H. Swallow *et al. Picton's Priced Catalogue and Handbook of Pictorial Postcards and their Postmarks* (1971 *et seq.*).

J. H. D. Smith. *I.P.M. Catalogue of Picture Postcards* (1975 *et seq.*).

3. Journals

American Postcard Journal (USA). Eds. Sue and Don Bodow.

British Postcard Collectors magazine. Ed. Ron Griffiths (1980–).

La Carte Postale (France). Ed. Jehanno.

Hertfordshire Postcard Magazine. Ed. Ron Griffiths (1979–80) (renamed *British Postcard Collectors magazine* 1980).

International Postcard Mail. Eds. Maurice Bray and Colin Rhodes Doughty (1978–80) (now incorporated in *Picture Postcard Monthly*).

Picture Postcard Collectors Gazette. Ed. Valerie Monahan (1975–1977).

Postcard Collectors Gazette. Ed. David Pearlman (1978–1980) (now incorporated in *Picture Postcard Monthly*).

Picture Postcard Monthly Eds. Brian and Mary Lund (1980–).

Picture Postcard News (USA). Eds. Sue & Don Bodow.

Postcard World: Journal of The Postcard Club of Gt. Britain. Ed. Drene Brennan (1975–).

Reflections. Eds. Brian and Mary Lund (1978–1980) (renamed *Picture Postcard Monthly* 1980).

4. Articles

F. C. Dixon, 'Dublin Picture Postcards.' *Dublin Historical Record* (1978).

C. W. Hill. 'Balloon Postcards.' *Stamps* (Nov., 1980).

Tonie & Valmai Holt. 'Lure of the Postcard.' *Everything Has a Value* (Oct., 1980).

Jack House. 'Wish You Were Here—Valentine's.' *Scotland's Magazine* (Dec., 1963).

Harold White. 'Fred Judge.' *The Photographic Journal* (May/June, 1979).

ACKNOWLEDGEMENTS

Since the renewal of interest in postcard collecting which began in the 1960s, a large number of books on the subject have been published, supplemented by numerous articles in both the postcard and philatelic press.

Naturally all authors refer to the work of others—and especially to the work of established experts on particular aspects of a subject. In compiling this catalogue we have referred to many such works and are pleased to express our admiration for the work of our fellow collectors and writers and to acknowledge with thanks our debt to them. We list those books—and more—in the Bibliography.

In addition we are happy to acknowledge the assistance of Postcard Clubs, of several eminent collectors and dealers in compiling the listings for this second edition; the section on which they helped is given in brackets after their name.
Reg. Auckland (Author *British Black Propaganda to Germany*) (*War*); Eric W. Baldock (*Local Publishers*); Dave & Christie Bowers (*Artists*); James & Wendy Brazier (*Artists*); A. Brooks & F. Fletcher (Authors *British Exhibitions & their Postcards* and *British & Foreign Exhibitions & their Postcards*) (*Exhibitions*; *Historical, etc.*); Frank Burridge (Curator, Big Four Railway Museum) (*Modern Cards*); Heather Cavell (*Local Publishers*); Barry C. Church (*Local Publishers*); Olive M. Clark (*Artists*); Ray E. Collier (*Publishers*); Michael Day (*Local Publishers*); Chris Easton (Principal, Crest Collectors Centre) (*Artists et al.*); F. Fletcher (*Local Publishers*); Fred G. Foley (*Modern Cards*); Klaus W. Gruner (*War*); Mark Haddon (Theatrical designer) (*Cinema*; *Theatre*); Joan Humphreys (*Artists*); Alan A. Jackson (*Artists et al.*); Ken Lawson (Principal, Specialised Postcard Auctions; Chairman, Postcard Traders' Association) (*Comic*; *Publishers*); Brian & Mary Lund (Editors & Publishers, *Picture Postcard Monthly*) (*Sport*); Norma Manning (USA) (*Modern Cards*); Dr. Mike & Mrs. Pat McMullen (Canada—*The McMullen Album*) (*Publishers*); Ron Menchine (USA) (*War*); Anne Mobbs (*Animals*; *Artists*); Valerie Monahan (*Modern Cards*); Derek Morley (*Local Publishers*); William J. Nelson (*Local Publishers*); Percy Oliver (Australia) (*Commemorative*); Graham S. Orr (*Modern Cards*); Maurice & Joyce Palmer (Authors *Wellingborough Album*) (*Artists*); Michael H. Passmore (Joint Author *The Postal History of the Nuremberg Rallies*) (*War*); John Rotheroe (Shire Publications) (*Modern Cards*); Reginald Silvester (Author *Railway Postcards of the British Isles*) (*Railways*); Angela & Michael Steyn (Principals, 'Recollections') (*General*); Roger Storey, (*Artists*); Robert G. Woodall (Publisher *Magpie's Nest*) (*Artists*)

They are all remarkably busy people and yet they gave generously of their time and knowledge. This is, we believe, indicative of the dedicated postcard collector, and is one of the chief factors that makes the hobby so enjoyable. Postcard collecting is after all not just about amassing postcards—it is finding out about them, sharing one's knowledge and pleasure with other collectors and in so doing the hobby progresses.

Since the publication of the first edition we have received many letters of praise, encouragement and constructive criticism from users of the catalogue. We are grateful to all who took the trouble to write and for the many helpful suggestions and useful information supplied and to whom, as promised in the first edition, we record our acknowledgements and thanks: A. S. Allen; Mrs. P. E. Bevan; B. J. Brockes (Italy); Michael Clark; Jillian Collins; David Cook; W. E. G. Dive; G. F. Eynott; William Eyre; Mrs. S. French; Rex Haggett; John P. Haynes; Francis Heaney (Ireland); Lt. Col. James Hewgill; Dr. S. Hingston (Ireland); Andrew H. Hinrichs (Canada); Barbara Holland; R. W. Hudson; Robert Ireland; D. J. MacLaurin; Ian McDonald, Derrick Neave; Mary G. Ramsay; Mrs. Y. Reeman; John Rosser; J. H. D. Smith; Phillip J. Standley; Col. & Mrs. B. S. Turner and Mrs. K. Watson.

It may well be that we have accidentally omitted someone to whom acknowledgement should have been made. If so, we apologise and, given the full details, promise to make correction in a future edition.

Permission to reproduce the postcards published by them has been kindly granted by the following, to whom grateful acknowledgement is made: Bamforth & Co. Ltd.; Jarrold & Sons Ltd.; J. Salmon Ltd.; Raphael Tuck & Sons Ltd.; and Valentines of Dundee Ltd.

TONIE AND VALMAI HOLT

POSTCARD CLUBS

1. National Clubs

Postcard Club of Great Britain
Mrs. Drene Brennan
34 Harper House
St James's Crescent
LONDON SW9 7DW

Irish Picture Postcard Society
T. D. Rose
Cathair Books
South King Street
DUBLIN 2

2. Local Clubs

Avon Postcard Club
Marion Freeman
24 Cherry Orchard
PERSHORE
Worcs. WR10 1EL

Bedfordshire Postcard Club
Warden Hill Community Centre
LUTON
Beds.

Bradford & District Postcard Society
A. E. Wood
26 Front View
Shelf
HALIFAX
West Yorkshire HX3 7JU

Cambridge University Deltiologists
M. Ellison
Clare College
CAMBRIDGE CB2 1TL

Canterbury & East Kent Postcard Club
Joanna White
27 Milton Ave.
MARGATE
Kent

Hertfordshire Postcard Club
Neil Jenkins
113 Bramble Road
HATFIELD
Herts. AL10 9SD

Huddersfield & District Postcard Society
D. Armitage
202 Hebble Lane
Wheatley
HALIFAX
West Yorkshire

Hull & Humberside Postcard Collectors Society
C. J. Ketchell
Flat 2
105 Princes Ave.
HULL HU5 3JL

Leeds Postcard Club
Mrs. A. Whitelock
9 Brentwood Grove
LEEDS LS12 2DB

Lincoln Collectors Club
Peter Rowlett
3 Wickenby Close
North Hykeham
LINCOLN

Maidstone Postcard Club
Mrs. I. Hales
40 Hildenborough Cres.
MAIDSTONE
Kent ME16 0NR

Manx Postcard Association
David Wilson
52 Julian Road
Glen Park
DOUGLAS, I.O.M.

Mercia Postcard Club
M. L. Palmer
5 Saxon Rise
Earls Barton
NORTHAMPTON NN6 0NY

Merseyside Postcard Club
P. W. Woolley
7 Patrick Ave.
BOOTLE
Merseyside L20 6EP

Newcastle-upon-Tyne Postcard Club
Frank Fletcher
35 St. George's Terrace
EAST BOLDON
Tyne & Wear NE36 0LU

Norfolk Postcard Club
P. J. Standley
63 Folly Road
WYMONDHAM
Norfolk NR18 0QR

Northern Ireland Postcard Club
Roy Campbell
70 The Green
Dunmurry
BELFAST BT17 0QA

North of England Postcard Club
Frank Fletcher
35 St. George's Terrace
EAST BOLDON
Tyne & Wear NE36 0LU

North Wales Postcard Club
Michael Day
39 Links Ave.
Little Sutton
SOUTH WIRRAL L66 1QS

Pickering Postcard Club
Mrs. B. Hood
21 St. Peter Street
Norton
MALTON
North Yorkshire YO17 9AL

Rushden Collectors Circle
Barry Church
2 Meadow Drive
HIGHAM FERRERS
Northants NN9 8EZ

Somerset Postcard Club
Heather Cavell
36 Kingsway Road
BURNHAM-ON-SEA
Som. TA8 1ET

Suffolk & Essex Postcard Club
Stephen Andrews
30 Millers Lane
Stanway
COLCHESTER
Essex CO3 5PS

Surrey Postcard Club
S. Burke
7 Sandfield Terrace
GUILDFORD
Surrey GU1 4LN

Sussex Postcard Club
R. Cairns
2 Shelley Road
Ringmer
BRIGHTON
East Sussex

Postcard Club of Tayside
Sydney Mitchell
36 Bruce Road
Downfield
DUNDEE DD3 8LL

Tees Valley Collectors Club
Joan Lambert
24 Beechwood Ave.
DARLINGTON
Co. Durham DL3 7HP

Wyre Forest Postcard Club
Derek Gallimore
The Grange
30 Pinewoods Ave.
Hagley
STOURBRIDGE
West Midlands DY9 0JF

3. Specialist Postcard Clubs
Canal Card Collectors Circle
A. K. Robinson
56 Henley Ave.
DEWSBURY
West Yorkshire WF12 0LN

Exhibition (Cards) Study Group
A. D. Brooks
'Fairhaven'
Sunderland Road
EAST BOLDON
Tyne & Wear NE36 0NA

Oilette Research Group
Derek Gallimore
The Grange
30 Pinewoods Ave.
Hagley
STOURBRIDGE
West Midlands DY9 0JF

Tuck Collectors Circle
D. Pinfold
7 Glenville
NORTHAMPTON NN3 1LZ

Study Circle for Early Numbered Tucks
Tony Warr
'Fairview'
Ickford Road
Shabbington
AYLESBURY
Bucks HP18 9HN

THE COMPILERS

The compilers of this catalogue, Tonie Holt and his wife, Valmai, are well known to postcard collectors around the world. Their first postcard book, *Picture Postcards of the Golden Age*, is widely regarded as one of the classic works on the hobby. Since publication of that volume they have published two other postcard-orientated books, one of which, entitled *Till the Boys Come Home*, looked at the First World War through its picture postcards, and was described by *The Times* as, 'head and shoulders above the rest (of military books of the year), unique in content and treatment and produced superbly.' Their most recent book, now in the press, is a study of World War Two. To be called *I'll be Seeing You*, it uses over 800 contemporary WW2 postcards to chart the course of the war.

As well as contributing to postcards journals in Britain and America and lecturing on the subject, Tonie and Valmai Holt have made many radio and television appearances in connection with postcards.

Their writing activities are not confined to postcards, but include fiction for print and radio, as well as contributions to a variety of magazines. Although their major occupation is arranging and conducting tours of the battlefields of Europe and America (which enables them to study the postcard market in about half a dozen different countries each year) they consider the compilation of the *Stanley Gibbons Postcard Catalogue* to be amongst their most absorbing and challenging tasks to date.

The great success of the First Edition brought them letters and suggestions from around the world, many of which have been incorporated in this edition. Mr. and Mrs. Holt continue to invite readers to send them details of their collections as they say there is more scope for collectors in today's hobby than there has ever been before.

"And 'ere's the actual 'ole where I was asked if I knew of a better one."
(With apologies to Bruce Bairnsfather.)

Pub. T. & V. Holt. Artist David Langdon. Battlefield Tour version of Bairnsfather's 'Better 'Ole' cartoon. Period 7. Limited Edition of 1000.

2 NEW POSTCARD ALBUMS FROM STANLEY GIBBONS

Two large albums with different pocket formats have been developed by Stanley Gibbons to provide you with the range of pocket sizes and formats you require to enhance your collection.

The **'Golden Age'** Postcard Album with four crystal clear top loading pockets (sizes 145 x 100mm) per leaf with backing inserts, 10 leaves per album, with index card and slip box is for the standard **'Golden Age'** sized postcard, still in use after nearly a century.

The SG **'Picture Postcard'** Album has four larger 'top loading' pockets, sizes 155 x 110mm, per leaf also with backing inserts. Again 10 crystal clear leaves per album, with index card and slip box. For British Post Office Picture Cards issued since 1973, and other larger size 'maximum' cards. Ask your dealer for details of extra leaves and binders!

STANLEY GIBBONS PUBLICATIONS

Always look for products bearing the STANLEY GIBBONS name!

ACCESSORIES

During the 'Golden Age' of collecting, many postcard related products were made for collectors' convenience and to stimulate their interest in the hobby. Today many of these products are collectable items, and the need for albums to suit today's collectors' needs still exists.

ALBUMS

Golden Age Albums
With Art Nouveau covers .. .. £1/**£2**/£4
With intact 'linen-finish' pages .. 75p/**£1.50**/£3
Daily Mail WW1 albums .. .. £1/**£2**/£3.50
German WW1 albums .. .. .. £1/**£2**/£4
Japanese lacquered albums with silk hand embroidery/ivory decoration .. £10/**£25**/£40

Modern Albums
A range of albums with polythene sheets of envelopes exist for today's collections, including 56-pocket albums that take the oversize cards of Periods 5 to 7.

AUTOMATIC VENDING MACHINES
These can still be found in operation on the Continent.
Golden Age versions .. .. .. £5/**£10**/£15

CONTAINERS
Simulated leather boxes .. .. .. £2/**£3**/£5
Art Nouveau copper boxes .. .. £10/**£20**/£30
Mock 'books' to carry postcards .. £1/**£3**/£5
Pocket wallets for postcards, various materials .. .. £1/**£2**/£3

PACKETS
Original packets for postcard sets are now beginning to be sold separately by some dealers. Often listing other series published by the manufacturers, they are valuable items for postcard research .. .. 50p/**75p**/£1

PENS
During the Golden Age special 'Postcard Pens' were made by the main fountain pen manufacturers .. .. .. £2/**£4**/£6
Blotters were also made in postcard size with a variety of decorative backs .. 50p/**75p**/£1

VIEWERS
Stereoscopic viewers of the Golden Age (with a premium for elaborate cabinets) .. .. £12/**£15**/£30
Reflectoscopes (concave mirror in viewing box) .. .. £3/**£5**/£7
Modern episcopes .. .. **£85+**

ADVERTISING

There were advertisements on postcards from the first day that they were issued in 1869. The simplest advertisement was the company mark, name and address pre-printed on the non-address side of an official issue.

Currently these are little collected in Britain and a median value would be £2. Continental superiority (particularly in Germany), in printing techniques, and an official attitude less restricting than that in Britain, soon led to the appearance of simple line drawings as advertisements. Hotels, having used illustrated notepaper for many years, were quick to employ the postcard, and entrepreneurs in towns and regions catering to the rapidly growing tourist trade issued picture cards with the pre-printed title *Gruss Aus* (Greetings From). ■5a shows an early Period 1 (*c.* 1880) German card on which is an etching of the 'Curhotel' in Bad Neuenahr with the greeting 'Gruss Schonen vom Ahrthal'. A median value for this is £15. Colours came on to cards around 1890 and the coloured lithographic *Gruss Aus* type accounted for the majority of the Continental production. *See also* EARLY CARDS and GREETINGS.

The theme of advertising covers almost every human activity and needs careful subdivision. Thus the use of propaganda and morale-boosting advertising cards for causes have their own sections, e.g. RELIGION, and self advertising cards for individuals come under headings such as CINEMA, CURIOUS, SPORT and THEATRE. Transport advertising is divided between MOTORISED TRANSPORT, RAILWAYS and SHIPPING, while trade shows and expositions are contained under EXHIBITIONS.

The value of an advertising card is built up from several elements which include premiums for designs by well-known artists, signed designs, cards forming part of a known series, advertisements for products with social history connotations, such as bicycles, or items no longer sold, and broadly the older the card the more valuable it is. However, Period 4 *Art Deco* designs are beginning to rival Period 2 prices. Overall, poster style cards currently command the highest prices because they very often derive from, or are copies of, advertising posters which are themselves artist designed and collected in their own right.

In this section we confine ourselves to general 'Trade' advertising and the widest range is that concerned with products. Small shopkeepers and businessmen would often buy proprietary cards and overprint their sales message upon them. More enterprising and larger firms had their own cards especially designed, and on the Continent the long tradition of poster art, particularly of the late 1880s, is reflected in the artistic quality of some of their Period 1 and early Period 2 cards. A notable example is the 'Concours Byrrh' (*see also* COLLECTIONS where the winning entries are listed).

British cards reproducing already issued poster designs are much sought after, particularly the Tuck's 'Celebrated Posters' series (*see also* COLLECTIONS). Chocolate, cocoa and tea companies are well to the fore in what are currently taken as collectable categories.

Two particularly interesting cards are the Australian Victoria State 'Beer & Baccy' card ■5b, and the Grant Doré card which is sometimes claimed to be the first British picture postcard. The former was an official card, issued in 1896, upon which lager and tobacco advertisements were printed. This caused a public outcry that almost toppled the State Government. The Grant card was issued in 1872 to promote the sales of a forthcoming London picture book by the illustrator Doré. In 1904 the Collectors' Publishing Company published what was to be the first of only three issues of a magazine called *Postcard Connoisseur*. With that first issue, a facsimile of Grant's card was given away (as an insert). ■10a.

There are six parts to this section and these are listed below. Within each part the entries are not thematic but strictly alphabetical.

ALCOHOL/TOBACCO
ANIMAL FOODS/FOODS/MEDICINES
BOOKS/MAGAZINES/NEWSPAPERS
CHOCOLATE/COCOA/COFFEE/TEA/NON-ALCOHOLIC
    BEVERAGES
COMMERCIAL/HOUSEHOLD/INDUSTRIAL
GENERAL POSTER TYPE ADVERTISING

ALCOHOL/TOBACCO

Dewars, James Buchanan, Thornes & Ogdens all have cards in the Tuck 'Celebrated Posters' series. (*See also* COLLECTIONS.)

Austria Cigarettes (Zurich)

Poster types	..	..	..	..	£5/**£8**/£12

Bacardi

Comic designs	..	..	..	..	£1/**£2**/£3

Beer
Pull outs .. .. –/**50p**/75p
Walker's Lager. Poster types for Warring-
ton & Burton brewery .. .. £10/**£15**/£20

Beer & Baccy
Victoria State (1896). ■5b .. .. £20/**£25**/£30

Cavanders Army Mixture
Poster type. Period 3 .. .. .. £7/**£8**/£10

Chairman Cigarettes
Old English Pottery & Porcelain .. £1/**£1.50**/£2

Chateau Loudenne
Lancet ad. Period 2. ■5c .. .. £3/**£4**/£5

Chianti
Italian wine bottle design .. .. £2/**£4**/£6

Cider
Schweppes poster type. Glamour. Period
4 .. .. £15/**£20**/£22

Cinzano
Dutch costume studies. UB .. .. £2/**£2.50**/£4

Claymore Whisky
Pub. Tuck. Artist Harry Payne. Defenders of
the Empire (1924) .. .. .. £2/**£4**/£6

Codorniu Champagne
Ten card composite by artist Lorenzo
Brunet. Per set .. .. £30/**£35**/£45

Cognac Bisquit
Pub. Bru Fils. Poster type. ■6a .. £6/**£7**/£9

Dewars Whisky
Pub. Dewars. Artist Albert Hammond.
Gems of Art series. Period 2 .. 50p/**£1**/£1.50

Distillers Co.
Joseph Chamberlain silhouette .. £7/**£11**/£13

Dubonnet
Grand Prix 1900. Col. UB .. .. £4/**£5**/£6
Period 7. Rare card by artist Cassandre
.. .. £10/**£20**/£40

Fernet Branca
Pub. Chappius Italy. Series of 10 chromo-
litho fashion studies. Period 2 UB
.. .. £40/**£45**/£50

■5a

*Period 1. German. Gruss vom Ahrthal. Probably
printed from a line block* £15

■5b

*Period 1. Official card. Victoria State, Australia
1896. 'Beer & Baccy' advertising* £25

■5c

*Period 2. Chateau Loudenne claret advertise-
ment with* Lancet *recommendation on back* .. £4

5

Gallaghers Park Drive
Poster type. Period 3 .. .. .. £3/**£5**/£6

Gancia
Bottle vignette UB .. .. £3/**£4**/£5

Gitanes Cigarettes
Poster type. *Art Deco.* Artist René Vincent
.. .. £18/**£25**/£35

Godfrey Phillips
Period 5 inserts in large cigarette packets. 127 × 89 mm.
Beauty Spots of the Homeland (30 cards)
.. .. **50p**
De Reszke series (24 cards) **50p**
Famous paintings (26 cards) .. **50p**
Garden studies **50p**

Grapevine Cigarettes
Southend Imperial Lifeboat (1906) £2/**£3**/£4

Guinness
Brewery scenes. Period 4. Photographic
.. .. **£1**/£1.50/£2
Period 6. Oversize **£1**
Poster ads. Periods 2, 3 .. .. ..
Poster ads. Periods 4, 7. Oversize ('Alice', Strength, etc). ■6b .. .. ..75p/**£1**/£1.50

Hofbrauhaus, Munich Beer House
Early Period 2. Gruss Aus type vignettes
.. .. £1/**£2**/£2.50
Period 2. Pub. Karl Wittermuller. Comic types. ■6c .. .. ..75p/**£1.50**/£2
Period 4. Poster type .. .. £2/**£4**/£6
Periods 6, 7 (incl. 'Beer Mat' postcards)
.. .. 25p/**50p**/75p

Job Cigarette Paper
Poster type. Chromo-litho. Pub. Vercasson, Paris .. .. £15/**£20**/£22

Kempinski Champagne
Chromo-litho designs of ladies and *bon viveurs* with wine bottles. At least 14 designs. Period 2 .. .. £6/**£9**/£10

Kupferberg Gold Champagne
Bottles and *bon viveurs*. Chromo-litho
.. .. £3/**£6**/£7

■6a

Pub. Bru Fils. Cognac ad. Poster type. Period 4 .. .. £7

■6b

Period 7. Guinness poster advertisement. Oversize £1

■6c

Pub. Karl Wittermuller. Hofbrauhaus. Comic ad. 'Gruss Aus Munich's finest beer house' £1.50

Löwenbrau, Munich Beer
Col. poster type. Period 4 .. .. £6/**£9**/£12

Mercier Champagne
Vignettes of bottles and leisure activities
UB .. .. £4/**£7**/£10

Mitchell's 'Prize Crop' Cigarettes
Chromo-litho vignettes. Glasgow Exhibition
1901 .. .. £12/**£15**/£18

Park Drive Cigarettes
Poster type, e.g stagecoach .. .. £12/**£15**/£18

'Principe di Piemonte' Cigarettes
Poster type. Artist A. Scorzon .. £4/**£6**/£7

Ruinart Père et Fils Champagne
Overprint on a series of at least 6 cards
depicting revels at a masked ball. Pub. J.
Goffin Fils, Brussels .. .. .. £5/**£7**/£10

Sandorides 'Lucana' Cigarettes
Poster type .. .. £12/**£16**/£20

Vino Aroud
Comic situations .. .. £1.50/**£2**/£3

White Horse Whisky
Pub. Alf. Cooke. Maggs coaching studies.
Period 2 .. .. −/**50p**/£1

Wills
Poster types for Capstan, Gold Flake, Three
Castles, and Westward Ho! .. £15/**£26**/£30

ANIMAL FOODS/FOODS/MEDICINES
Colman's Mustard is represented in Tuck's
'Celebrated Poster' series (*see also* COLLEC-
TIONS).

Banana Bread & Flour Co.
Bananine poster type. ■7a .. .. £6/**£8**/£10

Beechams Pills
Blue card. 'Thanks' .. .. .. £3/**£4**/£6
Others .. .. .50p/**75p**/£1.50

Birds Custard
Poster type. Ed. VII series .. .. £10/**£12**/£15
Other poster types .. .. £11/**£13**/£16

Buttapat Margarine
Poster type .. .. £10/**£13**/£15

Carnine Lefranc Health Food (1908)
Artist Weal. French Public Figures. (6
cards) .. .. £3/**£5**/£7

Cerebos Salt
Poster type. Chromo-litho. Multi-vignettes
.. .. £12/**£24**/£28

Champions Vinegar
Poster type. Chromo-litho .. .. £15/**£20**/£24

Chanteclair Embrocation
Poster type. Artist Mich .. .. £5/**£9**/£11

Chivers & Sons
English fruits .. .. 50p/**75p**/£1
Aerial views of Histon .. .. .. −/**50p**/75p

Crawfords Cream Crackers
Russo—Japanese war map (1905) £1/**£2**/£3
Poster type .. .. £2/**£4**/£6

Force Cereal
Special offer cards. Early period 2 £3/**£5**/£9

Glaxo
Various subjects .. ..75p/**£1**/£1.50

■7a

*Period 2. Bananine banana bread poster type
advertisement* £15

7

Harrison & Garthwaite Biscuits
VC winnners. Action scenes with inset
portraits. Set consists of Burt, Dorrel,
Holmes, Leefe Robinson, O'Leary and
Pollock .. .. £2/**£3.50**/£5

Hartley
Productions scenes at Aintree. Interior and
aerial .. .. 50p/**75p**/£1
Poster type. Marmalade .. .. £3/**£5**/£7

Huntley & Palmer Biscuits
Poster type. The Very Best Available
.. .. £3/**£5**/£7
Poster type. *Art Deco*. Artist René Vincent
.. .. £18/**£23**/£35

Jacobs Biscuits
Biscuit production scenes .. .. 50p/**75p**/£1
Cream crackers. Chromo-lithos .. £7/**£10**/£12

Jaffa Oranges
Poster type. Jaffa genie .. .. £14/**£22**/£25

Johnston's Corn Flour
Court size. Twenty-four cards .. £15/**£17**/£20

Lemco
Coronation series .. .. .. £5/**£8**/£10
Poster type. Artist Hassall. Set of 'Types of
Lemco Cattle' (6 cards) .. .. £3/**£4**/£5

Liebig Fray-Bentos
Meat processing scenes .. .. .. 75p/**£1**/£1.50
Oxo Shackleton Expedition. ■8a £2/**£4**/£6

Lustucru Pâtes. ■8b
Poster type. 1924 Centenary .. £3/**£4**/£6

MacFarlane Lang & Co.
Poster type. 'Sultana Sandwich' series
.. .. £2/**£4**/£6

Mellins Food
Poster type .. .. £2/**£4**/£5

Melox
Poster types. Animal and poultry food.
Numbered sketches. .. .. £2/**£3**/£4

Millenium Bread and Flour (1905)
Poster type. Series 2. Artist Cock £2/**£4**/£6
Poster type. Party invitation. Series 3 £3/**£5**/£7

Molassine Meal Animal Food
Various sketches .. .. £1/**£1.50**/£2

Neaves Baby Food
Poster type .. .. £10/**£12**/£18

New England Maple Syrup Co.
Poster type. 'Uncle John's Golden Tree',
'The Real Flavour from the Maple
Grove,' etc. .. .. £7/**£10**/£16

Peark's Butter
Various .. .. 50p/**75p**/£1

Peek Frean
GB views .. .. –/**50p**/75p

Pitman Health Food Co.
Ideal food series .. .. .. 75p/**£1.50**/£3

■8a

*Period 2. OXO advertisement showing Lt.
Shackleton's Nimrod and with a quotation from
him on the back £5*

■8b

*Pub. Moullot. Lustucru ad. 100 years of egg
pasta, Period 4 .. .. £4*

Quaker Oats

Poster type. 'Smiles' Set of 10 (Postman,
Grandpa, Sailor, Cook, Tramp) £8/**£10**/£12
Smiles, text on front .. .. .. £4/**£5**/£6

St. Ivel

GB views .. .. –/**50p**/75p

Sainsbury's Margarine

Crelos overprint of Tuck's 'Early days of
Sport' .. .. 75p/**£1**/£1.50

Scotts Emulsion

Ninety-two cards in series, one for each
Department in France, Corsica & Algeria.
Period 2. ■9a .. .. £2/**£4**/£6

Shippams

Food production scenes .. .. .. 50p/**75p**/£1

Spratts Dog Food

Dog studies .. .. 50p/**75p**/£1

Virol

Children of all Nations. Ideal Home Exhibition (1910) .. .. £1/**£1.50**/£2

Walker, Harrison & Garthwaites

City Meat Dog Biscuit. Viscan. Dog studies.
Poster type .. .. £2/**£4**/£6
Phoenix Poultry Foods. Poultry studies.
Poster type. ■9b .. .. £2/**£4**/£6

BOOKS/MAGAZINES/NEWSPAPERS

Publications of all sorts frequently contained
postcards. This was particularly so in Period 2
and is again prevalent today (Period 7), when the
reply-paid advertisement card, generally on very
thin board, is much used. Sometimes the inserted
card was intended to be an attractive giveaway
that would encourage sales of the publication
concerned. On other occasions insert cards advertised quite independent products. Almost all
postcards associated with books, magazines and
newspapers are insert giveaways, the major
exception being the *Daily Mail* battle scenes listed
under WAR. Period 2 inserts are not highly valued
and Period 7 varieties are not yet collected.

Answers

Poster type .. .. £1/**£2**/£3

Bazaar, Exchange & Mart

Bazaar, Exchange & Mart series, drawings
each side. ■9c .. .. £2/**£3**/£4

Hutchinson

Period 1. Court size. Ads for novels £10/**£12**/£14

■9a

Pub. Emulsion Scott. One of series of 92 cards.
Period 2 .. .. £4

■9b

Period 2. Walker, Harrison & Garthwaites
Phoenix Poultry Foods advertisement £6

■9c

Period 2. The Bazaar, Exchange & Mart series.
Pictures both sides £3

Inserts

These are little collected. Delittle, Fenwick and Co. produced vast quantities for Shurey's Publications (*Smart Novels*, *Dainty Novels*, etc.) with a few lines of overprint on the address side of topographical cards. The views are now likely to be the most valuable element, otherwise the inserts listed are worth a maximum of 50p except where stated.

Bretts publications .. ..
Canary & Cage Bird Life .. ..
Caperns Bird Foods .. .. ..
Captain magazine. Artist Tom Browne
.. .. £1/**£2**/£3
Christian Novels .. ..
Connoisseur .. ..
Daily News Wallet Guide .. ..
Dainty Novels .. ..
Family Reader .. ..
Feathered World .. ..
Field. Military sketches .. .. ..50p/**£1**/£1.50
Gentlewoman .. ..
Girls Own Paper. Hand cut from sheet of 4.
UB .. .. £1/**£1.50**/£3
Home Words .. ..
Idle Moments .. ..
Mirror Novels .. ..
My Pocket Novels .. .. ..
My Queen & Romance .. .. ..
Postcard Connoisseur
Facsimile of Grants Doré card. ■10a
.. .. £30/**£35**/£50
Others .. .. £10/**£12**/£15
Princess Novels .. ..
Red Letter .. ..
Shureys Publications. Artist drawn Tube
Stations. ■10b .. .. £1/**£2**/£3
Sketchy Bits .. ..
Smart Novels .. ..
T.A.T. 'The Months' Series .. 50p/**75p**/£1.25
Others .. .. –/**50p**/75p
Time Magazine. Uncreased only. Period 7.
■10c .. ..
Tiny Tots .. .. –/**50p**/75p
Ward Lock. Naval .. .. .. 50p/**75p**/£1
Weekly Tale Teller .. .. ..
Weldon's Bazaar .. ..
Yes or No .. ..
Other Inserts .. ..

■10a

Period 2. Pub. Postcard Connoisseur. Facsimile of Dore advertising card originally issued in 1872 and sometimes claimed as the first English picture postcard. Facsimile issued 1904 .. .. ..£40

■10b

Period 2. Pub. Shurey's Publications. Insert card. One of set of 6 underground stations £3

■10c

Period 7. Time *magazine subscription card, No. 9927 (1977)* 50p

CHOCOLATE/COCOA/COFFEE/TEA/ NON-ALCOHOLIC BEVERAGES

Cadbury's, Frys, Rowntrees, Mazawattee, Milkmaid, Idris, Schweppes, Bovril, Appolinaris, Edwards Soup are represented in the Tucks 'Celebrated Posters' series. Price range £15 to £40 (*see also* COLLECTIONS).

Arlatte Chicory
Pub. Tuck. Periods 1, 2. Flowers UB
.. .. £3/**£4**/£5

Banania drink
Poster type .. .. £15/**£17**/£20

Bensdorps
Dutch art .. .. £1/**£2**/£3
Dutch artist drawn views UB. Poster type,
    free sample offers .. .. £3/**£5**/£7
Dutch views. Brightly drawn. PMC backs.
    12 cards in set .. .. .. £4/**£6**/£9

Boon's Cocoa
European views .. .. .. –/**50p**/75p

Bovril
Art reproductions .. .. .. 75p/**£1**/£1.50
Pub. Moss. Famous posters in
    miniature .. .. £14/**£16**/£18

Broma Cocoa
Plantation sketches .. .. .. –/**50p**/75p

Cadbury
Bourneville village scenes .. .. 50p/**75p**/£1

Camp Coffee
Poster type Artist Harry Payne .. £25/**£30**/£40
Poster type. Others .. .. £20/**£25**/£30
Write-Away type .. .. .. £6/**£9**/£12

Chocolat Lombart
Poster type. *Art Deco.* Artist René Vincent
    .. .. £10/**£12**/£15
Scenes of boys, carts, railways, ships.
    Chromo-litho .. .. .. £8/**£11**/£15

CWS Packet Tea
Dickens scenes and others .. £2/**£3**/£4
Plantation scenes. Poster type .. £12/**£14**/£16

De Beukelaer's Cocoa
Topographical sketches **50p**

Epps Milenia Milk Chocolate
Poster type .. .. £12/**£18**/£23

Formosa Ooolong
Japanese types .. .. .. £2/**£3**/£4
Japanese landscapes .. .. £1/**£1.50**/£2

Fry's Chocolate or Cocoa
Artists Chas. Pears, Hassall, Maud Fabian.
    Poster types .. .. £15/**£20**/£35
Artists Reg Carter, Tom B. .. .. £6/**£8**/£12
A. W. Ford 'Celebrated Advertisement'
    series .. .. £17/**£24**/£30
Captain Scott at South Pole. Poster
    type .. .. £20/**£30**/£40
G. H. Elliott (the 'Chocolate Coloured
    Coon') .. .. £2/**£4**/£6
Hancock & Corfield series .. .. £25/**£30**/£35
Joseph Causton Showcard Replica
    series .. .. £18/**£26**/£32
Kingsway Press series .. .. .. £2/**£3**/£4
Views of Somerdale Works .. 75p/**£1**/£1.25
Vivian Mansell series. Poster type.
■11a .. .. £25/**£30**/£35

■11a

Period 2. Pub. Vivian Mansell. Fry's poster advertisement series 7 .. ..£25

George Payne Tea
GP Government Tea. Poster type £12/**£14**/£16
Military vignettes .. .. .. £2/**£3**/£4
Composite set of King at Windsor **P/A**

Hornimans Tea
Poster type, e.g. Edward VII .. £5/**£11**/15
Views .. .. 75p/**£1**/£1.50

Kathreiner's Kaffee
Artist Henri Meunier. Advertisement tas-
    tefully printed, front and back, onto the
    exquisite 'Girls of 1900' series, e.g.
    'Aubépine', 'Iris', etc. .. .. **P/A**

Kohler Chocolate
This Lausanne manufacturer of chocolate
    and cocoa issued a series of 22 or more
    col. litho UB cards. Period 1/Early Period
    2 .. .. £2/**£3**/£4

Liptons
American UB. Language of flowers £10/**£12**/£14
Pub. C. W. Faulkner. Estate sketches
.. .. £1/**£2**/£3

Maggi
General views .. .. –/**50p**/75p
Pub. Maggi. Artist G. Fraipont. Our
Churches series .. .. £1/**£2**/£3

Menier Chocolate
Periods 2, 3. Views of Paris. Numbered.
Probably over 100 cards .. .. £1/**£2**/£3

Moxie
Cola type drink. Period 4 .. .. 50p/**75p**/£1

Nestlés
Animals and birds. Series 575. 12 card
set .. .. 75p/**£1**/£1.50
'Famous Posters in Miniature'. Series 4421
.. .. £7/**£15**/£20
Military vignettes. Poster type .. £15/**£20**/£22
Pub. Williams. Patriotic Empire designs,
incl. New Zealand, Australia, etc. £2/**£3**/£3.50
Signed artists. Poster types .. .. £20/**£22**/£24

Ovaltine
Poster type (incl. Phyllis Cooper. Period 4.
Art Deco) .. .. £12/**£14**/£16

Pearks
Various .. ..75p/**£1**/£1.50

Ridgways Tea
Artist John Hayes. Pub. Norman Davy
.. .. £2/**£3**/£5
Estate scenes .. .. £1/**£2**/£3

Rowntree
Rowntrees postcard series .. ..75p/**£1**/£1.50
Various .. .. 50p/**75p**/£1

Salutaris Table Water
Poster type. Artist Hassall, o/s .. £10/**£14**/£16

Schweppes
Soda Water. Artist FS. Period 4 .. £17/**£20**/£24

Suchard Chocolate
There is a wide range of advertising cards from
before 1890 until early Period 2. Valuation must
take into account the quality of the design as well
as the subject matter and age.

Period 1. Souvenir series UB .. .. £17/**£20**/£24
1900 Paris Exhibition .. .. .. £1/**£1.50**/£2
Period 2. UB. Chromo-litho .. .. £7/**£8**/£10
Chromo-litho. PS back .. .. .. £2/**£3**/£5
Vignettes. Children, etc. .. .. £1/**£2**/£4

Symingtons
Foreign views .. .. 50p/**75p**/£1

Tower Tea
Poster type. Artist John Hassall .. £12/**£16**/£18
Proverb series
Hassall type .. .. £5/**£7**/£8
Others .. ..75p/**£1**/£1.50

Van Houten's Cocoa
European views .. .. 50p/**75p**/£1

COMMERCIAL/HOUSEHOLD/ INDUSTRIAL

The total number of firms who either issued their
own cards or overprinted their message on to
already published cards is enormous. Here we list
together, in alphabetical order, those companies,
products and activities that currently attract
collectors.

Allentown Adpostals
Between 1911 and 1913 the Allentown Adpostal
Corporation (Pennsylvania) issued several different advertising cards. They carried a mixture of
advertisements (on both sides of Government
postal cards) for a number of commercial organisations (*see* OFFICIALS—USA).
1 cent green printed stamp. 2 cards
.. .. £9/**£13**/£15
1 cent red printed stamp. 5 cards. ■12a
.. .. £8/**£12**/£15

■12a

*Allentown Adpostal. Red stamp. Address side ad.
for Kellogg's Corn Flakes. Message side ads. for
Dr. Price's Extract, Ingram's Cream, etc. Period
2* £12

Bicycles

Humber Beeston. ■13a. Self-addressed
    series (1907)   ..   ..   ..   £10/**£12**/£14
Regent Cycles. Poster type. Vienna UB
    ..   ..   £16/**£18**/£20
Royal Enfield UB   ..   ..   ..   £2/**£4**/£6
Rudge Whitworth   ..   ..   ..
    Cycling magazine inserts   ..   75p/**£1**/£1.50
    RP personalities. 'Lighting up Times'
    ..   ..   £5/**£7**/£10
Singer. Poster type   ..   ..   £16/**£18**/£20
    Others   ..   ..   ..   £6/**£8**/£10

Boot Polish

Berry's Diamond. Poster type. Artist P.
    Lehmann   ..   ..   ..   £12/**£18**/£20
Kiwi. Emblem cut in chalk. Period 3
    ..   ..   75p/**£1**/£1.50

Candles and Lamps

Bray Gas Burner.
    Poster type   ..   ..   £2/**£4**/£5
Edison Lamps
    Poster type   ..   ..   £4/**£6**/£7
Philips Lamps
    Fr. designs   ..   ..   £1/**£2**/£4
Prices Candles
    Military studies   ..   ..   ..   £2/**£2.50**/£3
Primus
    It. Period 4. ■13b   ..   ..   ..   £2/**£4**/£6
Veritas Mantles
    Poster type. Artist Hassall   ..   £2/**£3**/£5

Carriers and Removers

Carter–Paterson Express Carriers
    Chromo-litho   ..   ..   ..   £15/**£19**/£22
Others
    Photographic   ..   ..   ..   75p/**£2**/£5
    Artist drawn   ..   ..   ..   50p/**£1**/£3

China and Pottery

Foley. Pub. E. Brain. Examples of Foley art
    china   ..   ..   £1/**£2**/£3
Goss. Pub. S. Oates. Goss china/Roman
    vases   ..   ..   £2/**£4**/£6
Goss. Natgarw. Pub. R. & J. Lea   ..   £1/**£2**/£3
Trent. Pub. Trent Bridge. Trent china/
    Roman vases   ..   ..   ..   50p/**75p**/£1
Others   ..   ..   50p/**75p**/£1

Coal

Clay Cross. Mining scenes   ..   ..   £2/**£3**/£4
Haydock. Art reproductions/views   50p/**75p**/£1
Others   ..   ..   –/**75p**/£1

Dentifrice

Erasmic   ..   ..
    Col.. poster type. Period 4   ..   £2.50/**£4**/£5
Odol ..   ..
    Series A112, b & w adverts, recom-
    mendations by famous stars—Camille
    Clifford, Zena Dare, Marie Studholme,
    etc, ...   £1/**£1.50**/£3

■13a

*Period 2. Pub. Humber Ltd. Miss Ellaline
Terriss. Self-addressed catalogue request series
  ..   ..£10*

■13b

*Original Primus. The Ultimate Novelty. It. Period
4   ..   ..   £5*

Engineering Products

Capewell Horse Nails

    Poster type. b & w .. .. .. £5/**£8**/£9

Continental Aeroplanstoff (Aircraft fabric)

    Poster type. Comic .. .. £6/**£10**/£12

Continental Ballonstoff (Balloon fabric)

    Poster type. Comic .. .. £12/**£20**/£23

North British Rubber Co. 'Chick' golf
  balls

    Rules of Golf, Artist Elcock .. £2/**£3**/£5

Friendly Societies/Insurance Cards & Companies

Friendly Societies. Period 2 (1907 onwards) 'Self-Help' associations formed to provide financial assistance to members in time of need.

Grand United Order of Oddfellows £3/**£5**/£8

Hearts of Oak Benefit Society .. £3/**£5**/£8

Independent Order of Rechabites .. £3/**£5**/£8

Order of the Sons of Temperance .. £3/**£5**/£8

Twentieth Century Equitable Friendly
  Society .. .. .. £3/**£5**/£8

Others, including Ancient Shepherds,
  Manchester Unity, etc. .. £1.50/**£5**/£6

Eagle. Head Office building. ■14a £1/**£2**/£3

Illustrated *Sunday Herald*. Period 4. Free
  Insurance scheme with Lloyds 50p/**75p**/£1

King Insurance Co. Royalty sketches
  .. .. £3/**£4**/£5

    Kings of England. Probably 50 in series
  .. .. £1/**£2**/£3

Norwich Union. Pub. Scott Russell. Motor
  Fire Engine .. .. .. £6/**£8**/£10

Ocean Accident. Insurance postcard
  series .. .. .. £1/**£1.50**/£2

'Tit-bits' £1000 Insurance. Poster
  type .. .. £2/**£3**/£5

Wrench. Early Period 2 Insurance
  cards .. .. £3/**£5**/£7

Others .. .. 75p/**£3**/£8

Hotels/Restaurants

Many cards showing hotels and restaurants are photographic in origin or printing. Therefore there is often a street scene or transport item associated with the picture, and this can greatly increase the value of the card (*see also* ROAD TRANSPORT and SOCIAL HISTORY/TOPOGRAPHICAL). Railway hotels are listed under RAILWAYS.

Foreign. Period 2 DB .. .. –/**50p**/75p

Foreign. 2 UB, not *Gruss Aus* .. 50p/**£1**/£1.50

London. Artist drawn. H. M. Bateman/
  Harold Oakley/T. Stephenson. ■14b.

  Periods 2 to 4 .. .. .. £1/**£3**/£5

London. Artist drawn. Others .. 50p/**£1.50**/£2

London. Photographic origin .. .. –/**50p**/£1

Poster type .. .. £1/**£3**/£5

Provincial. ■14c .. .. .. 50p/**75p**/£1

US. Jack Dempsey Restaurant
  Artist Montgomery Flagg. Period 4
  .. .. 75p/**£1**/£1.25

Industrial Scenes

Cammell Laird. Period 3 .. .. £1/**£1.50**/£2

Harland & Wolff. Pub. Valentine. Period
  2 .. .. £1/**£1.50**/£2

Others .. .. –/**75p**/£1

■14a

Period 2. Eagle Insurance Co. Advertising card—head office buildings 50p

■14b

Period 2. Artist Harold Oakley. Marble Arch Hotel advertising card £2.50

■14c

Period 2. Advertisement for London Hotel, Taunton. Value increased due to splendid motorised transport £10

Kitchen Equipment
Produits du Lion Noir
    Pub. Edition R.D.C., Seine. Artist
       Beatrice Mallet. Set of 6. Period
       4 .. .. £1.50/**£3**/£4
Fonderie Nestor Martin   .. ..
Pub. Goossens, J. G., Bruxelles. Artist
       Beatrice Mallet. Set of 6. Period 4
    .. .. £1.50/**£3**/£4

Lever Bros.
Artist drawn views of Port Sunlight
    .. .. –/**50p**/75p

Motor Cars
Period 2 .. .. £1.50/**£3**/£5
Period 3, 4, ■15b .. ..£2.50/**£5**/£10
Periods 5, 6 .. .. £1/**£1.50**/£2
Period 7 .. .. **50p**

Motor Shows
Period 2. ■15a .. .. £5/**£10**/£15
Period 4. Berlin (1937–9) .. £3/**£5**/£7.50
Period 6. Berlin .. .. .. £1.50/**£3**/£5
Others .. .. £1/**£2.50**/£4

National Insurance–*see* POLITICS

Oils
Castrol
    Sir Malcolm Campbell in *Bluebird*. World
       Record 1935. 301 mph .. 50p/**£1**/£1.50
Mex Motor Spirit (Bowring Petroleum Co.)
    Poster type. These have attained over £30
       in auction but normally they attract the
       following range .. .. £5/**£10**/£15
Oilzum Motor Oil
    Poster type .. .. £8/**£12**/£14
Pratts Motor Spirit
    Artist drawn scenes showing use of
       Anglo-American oil products £3/**£5**/£7
Shell
    Poster type general. Period 2 .. £15/**£25**/£30
    Poster type suffragette theme. Period
       2 .. .. £15/**£20**/£25
    Reproductions. Period 7 .. .. –/**25p**/50p
Sternol Oil
    Poster type. Comic. Artist Hassall
    .. .. £12/**£16**/£20
White Rose Kerosene
    Hold to Light .. .. £8/**£10**/£15

Overprints
These are proprietary cards upon which an additional advertising message has been printed. They vary from one line additions, on either side of the card, to full out pictures. They should be valued on the basis of the original card, plus a premium (from 50p) for the advertising overprint according to its rarity or interest. ■15c

Phonographs
Edison
    USA. Poster type .. .. .. £1/**£2**/£4
    Others .. ..75p/**£1.50**/£3

■15a

Pub. P.P. Press, Liverpool. J. A. Lawton's promotional postcard for the 1906 Motor Show at Olympia. The latest Panhard. PU *Nov. 1906* £10

■15b

Pub. Dueck-Nicoll Motors, Vancouver, B.C. Vancouver Co. form 542. Advert for 1939 Hudson. PU *May 1939* £10

■15c

Period 2. Blum & Degen overprint advertisement on a poor view card 50p

Schools

(*See also* SOCIAL HISTORY/TOPOGRAPHICAL for non-advertising cards.) Many British schools were, and are, partly or fully supported by the fees paid by their pupils. Schools, therefore, had a need to advertise their facilities to the parents of potential pupils. This was often done by picture postcards, particularly in Period 4.

Commercial schools, e.g. Pitmans	£1/**£3**/£4
General views. ■16a	£1/**£1.50**/£2
Science laboratories with pupils ..	£2/**£3**/£4

Shampoo/Soaps

Pears are represented in the Tuck 'Celebrated Poster' series classified under COLLECTIONS.

Amami shampoo	50p/**75p**/£1
CWS soaps	75p/**£1**/£1.50
Fields Toilet Soap. Childhood series	£1/**£2**/£3
Gossages. 'The Right Sort'. Royalty and others	£4/**£6**/£8
Hudsons: Queen Victoria	£3/**£4**/£5
Vignette studies	£10/**£12**/£14
Lux: Ger. Period 4. Poster type ..	£2/**£3**/£5
Pears: 'Bubbles'	–/**50p**/75p
Poster types	£5/**£7**/£10
Other types	£1/**£2**/£3

Shops and Stores

Throughout Europe interest has grown in recent years in pictures showing the way that things used to be. Shop fronts, showing goods displayed for sale, are a popular collecting category, and as with HOTELS/RESTAURANTS photographic cards have added value.

London stores. Artist drawn. ■16b	£1/**£2**/£3
Photographic origin	75p/**£1.50**/£2
Provincial stores	£1/**£2**/£3
Shop fronts. British or foreign. Close-ups	£6/**£8**/£10
Shop interiors. Particularly collected in the USA	£3/**£5**/£8

Singer Sewing Machines

Aviation studies	£2/**£3**/£4
Battleships	£1/**£1.50**/£2
Others	50p/**75p**/£1

Starch

Colmans. GB sketches	50p/**75p**/£1
Postmen of the Empire	£3/**£4**/£5
Remy	
Maps with vignette views	£1/**£2**/£2.50

Sutton Seeds

Flowers and vegetables	–/**25p**/50p

Swan Fountain Pens

Artist Harrison (1906). Comic historical types	50p/**75p**/£1

Thomas Cook

Periods 1, 2. UB Chromo-litho multi-vignettes	£20/**£25**/£30

(Madame) Tussauds

Pub. Tuck	£2/**£3**/£5

Typewriters

Oliver. Writing through the Ages ..	£1/**£2**/£3
Remington. Poster types	£3/**£5**/£7
Underwood. Poster types. Period 3	£3/**£5**/£7

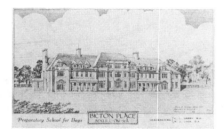

■16a

Period 4. Bicton Place School, Bexhill. Advertising card £1

■16b

Period 2. Swan & Edgar advertising card £2.50

Tyres

Scottish tyres are represented in the Tuck 'Celebrated Poster' series classified under COLLECTIONS.

Continental Pneumatique
Periods 2, 3. Col. litho/*Gruss Aus* types
   ..   ..   £6/**£8**/£12
Dunlop
    Periods 2, 3. Litho   ..   ..   £5/**£7**/£8
Engelbert
    Poster type. Period 4   ..   ..   £5/**£9**/£11
Excelsior. ■17a. Period 4   ..   ..   £3/**£4**/£5
Goodyear. Blimp. Pub. Technor USA.
    Period 6   ..   ..   £1/**£2**/£3
John Bull   ..   ..
    1910 First International Cycle Show,
      Olympia ..   ..   £5/**£8**/£10
Palmer. Poster type. Period 2   .. £14/**£15**/£18
Others   ..   ..   £1/**£7**/£15

Wood-Milne Rubber Heel

Artist Sager. Period 3 pin-up types   £2/**£3**/£4
GB views. 40 numbered cards   ..   –/**25p**/50p
Poster ads. Unnumbered   ..   ..   £1/**£2**/£3

GENERAL POSTER-TYPE ADVERTISING
Various   ..   ..   £2/**£10**/£25

■17a

Pub. Curt Behrends, Berlin. Artist L. Zabel. Advert for Excelsior tyres. Period 4   ..   .. £5

Stanley Gibbons Postcard Album

Attractively presented in a rich deep red PVC padded binder blocked in gold, this album contains 20 crystal clear double pockets, each designed to hold four postcards to a maximum size of $6\frac{1}{2} \times 4\frac{1}{8}$ in. each. The pockets are held in a quick release spring-arch fitting incorporating a special locking device.

Stanley Gibbons British Post Office Picture Card Album

This album is designed specifically to house the attractive series of picture cards— popularly known by collectors as PHQ's— produced by the British Post Office. The compact, fully padded, royal blue PVC two-ring binder contains 2 single pockets to hold the first two cards, PHQ 1 and 2, and 13 double pockets to hold cards PHQ 3 onwards. Binder gold blocked on spine. Space for additional pockets. Packs of extra pockets are also available.

Readers are cordially invited to send in details to Mr. and Mrs. Holt of cards, series, publishers, artists ... indeed any relevant information which they may have upon any postcard topic which adds to what appears in this edition. All correspondence addressed to them at the publishers will be answered and all contributions will be formally acknowledged in the next edition.

As it is often difficult to date a card precisely, a period system has been used in this catalogue— see the introductory notes for details.

ANIMALS/BIRDS/FISH/ INSECTS

Taking the theme of a particular animal, bird, fish or insect can give a varied collection of artist-drawn or photographic postcards covering the 7 periods.

As many of them drew a variety of animals, they are listed under the animal for which they are best known. In the case of Louis Wain, as the bulk of his designs were of cats, his work is listed here, rather than under his biography in the ARTISTS section.

† The section on ARTISTS gives details of the individual concerned.

BEARS

Performing Bears
Real Photo. Period 2 .. .. .. £3/**£5**/£8

'Roosevelt' or 'Teddy' Bears
Particularly collected in the USA. Pubs. include Collins Baking Co. (Ad); Albert Hahn; Illus. P.C. Co. (embossed); Kaiser Co.; Medici Society (Artist Margaret Tempest); National Art Co. Rotograph (Artist Rose Clark); Tower; M & N etc.
Price range .. .. 75p/**£2.50**/£4

BIRDS

Artists
Scrivener, Maud
Pub. Tuck. Oilette, e.g. 'British Birds' (at
    least three series). Period 2 .. 50p/**75p**/£1
Pub. Wrench. Period 2 .. .. .. –/**50p**/75p

West, A. L.
Pub. Tuck. Oilette, e.g. 'Birds and
    Blossoms', No. 3191. Period 2 .. –/**50p**/75p

British Museum of Natural History
Several series of British Game Birds, British
    Resident birds, Summer Visitors, Artist
    Grunewald. Period 4 .. .. .. –/**50p**/75p
Add a premium of £1 per series if the original descriptive leaflets still exist.

Canary and Cage Bird Life Series and Capern's Bird Foods Series: *See* ADVERTISING

Doves/Love Birds
Often found on highly embossed cards, usually of Continental origin, in the GREETINGS category. Publishers include: Stewart & Woolf, Tuck, Wildt & Kray. Periods 2 to 4 .. .. 50p/**£1**/£2

Parrots
A highly collectable category.
Artist Lawson Wood. Parrots. Period 4
    .. .. £1/**£1.50**/£2
Photographic or lesser known artist drawn
    .. .. –/**50p**/75p
Pub. Tuck. 'Pretty Polly' series. Period
    2 .. .. 50p/**75p**/£1
    Educational series .. .. .. 75p/**£1**/£1.50
Other miscellaneous, anonymous artist
    drawn, photographic studies, etc.
    .. .. 25p/**50p**/£1.50

Real Feathers: *see* NOVELTY

Swans
Often featured in photographic view cards to add interest to a static scene, and much collected. Publishers include Frith, Valentine, Wildt &
    Kray and many local publishers. Periods
    2 to 4. Value varies according to whether
    the swans are in the foreground or in the
    distance .. .. –/**50p**/75p
Pub. Tuck 'Birds on the Wing' Mechanical Series: *see* NOVELTY.

■18a

Pub. Tuck. Artist Helena J. Maguire. 'Animal Studies' 6714. Embossed. PU *1906* £3

CATS

Of all the ANIMAL postcards these are, and have in the past been, the most collectable, and is one of the categories which have proved very popular over the last two years. This is mainly due to new information about artists becoming available. Cat-card expert Anne Mobbs has identified over 50 'cat artists', of which some of the better known are listed here.

The Artists

Anonymous
Owing to the popularity of cats as a subject for many Victorian and Edwardian artists, literally thousands of unsigned, but extremely attractive and beautifully printed, chromo-litho cat designs exist, firstly used on greetings cards (Period 1) and later transferred to the postcard medium. They are highly collectable and become more and more appreciated each year.

Barnes, G. L.
Pub. Tuck. 'Oilette' series. 'Cat Studies' series I and II (9301 and 9402). Col.
.. .. £2.50/**£4.50**/£6

Pub. Tuck. 'Oilette' series. 'Pussy in Fairyland' series III and IV (9477 and 9504). Col. .. .. £2.50/**£4.50**/£6

These sets were reproduced in 'Glosso' series, both photographic and col. Period 2. .. .. £1/**£2**/£3

Boulanger, Maurice ■23a
French artist who produced some superb, imaginative, 'catty' sets. Originally published in France, many were later used by Tuck in Britain with English captions.

Pub. Anon
Set 'Cats with Rats'. Period 2. Col.
.. .. £1.50/**£3**/£5
Period 2—Set of 12 cards of Continental origin depicting 'Months of the Year'. Col. .. .. £4/**£6.50**/£8
Set of 12 cards of Continental origin titled 'A Happy Christmas and a Bright New Year', col., using cards as above £4/**£5**/£6

Set of 12 cards by Tuck with English titles, e.g. 'Splashing', 'Shopping', Chestnuts', etc. using cards as above .. .. £5/**£6**/£7

Pub. E.P. Paris
Period 2—'Cats in Love' (col.) and 'Christmas' series (col.) .. .. £4/**£5**/£6

Pub. H.M. & Co. (Henry Moss)
Early Period 2—Events 'In Catland' series—collo-types or tinted .. £2.50/**£4**/£5

Pub. J.M. Paris
Early Period 2—Set of 10 cards 'Gambling Party' (culminating in a duel) and 'Catland Characters'—Gourmand, Coquette, etc. (tinted) .. .. £5/**£6**/£7

Pub. K.F. Editeurs, Paris
Early Period 2—Beautiful chromo-litho col. sets of 10—many themes incl. 'Cat portraits with hats', series 586 and 898 and 'Language of Flowers', series 897 .. .. £4/**£5**/£6

Others .. .. £1.50/**£3**/£5

Butcher, Arthur
Pub. E. T. W. Dennis—Black cat humour. Periods 2, 3 .. .. £1.50/**£2**/£3

Pub. Inter-Art Comic—Black cat humour. Periods 2, 3 .. .. £1.50/**£2**/£3

Other artists may have also drawn these studies.

Carter, Reg.†
The Southwold artist best remembered for his 'Sorrows of Southwold' (cartoons of the Southwold narrow gauge railway) and WW1 humour and patriotic cards. Also produced superb studies of cats in Edwardian dress and cat characters.

Pub. E. Mack. Series 437, and 438, 455 and 993 (includes 'One of the Knuts') .. .. £1.50/**£2**/£3

Pub. J. Salmon (similar to above) (includes 'Let 'em all come!') .. .. .. £2/**£3**/£4

Pub. A. Stiebel. 'Wiggle-Woggle' cards. Humorous cats with mechanical parts .. .. £2/**£4**/£5

Pub. Valentines. Hobble-skirt humour (includes 'The Glad Eye' and 'The *Cat*-ch of the Season') .. .. £1.50/**£2**/£3

Cobbe, B.
Pub. Tuck. 'Oilette' series of 6 cards. 'Catland' series I (8883), series II (8884). 'When Cats are Kittens', series III (9538). 'When Cats are Kittens', series IV (9766) .. .. .. £1/**£1.50**/£2

Cats also feature prominently on 'Oilette' series such as 3467, 9099, 9157, 9361, 9537, 9538, 9539 and 9765 .. £1/**£1.50**/£2

Ellam, W. H.†
Period 2, 3—Alfred Stiebel & Co. 'Modern Humour' .. .. £1.50/**£2**/£3

Period 2—E.F.A. Black and White series 18 .. .. £2/**£3**/£4

Period 2—Philco Publishing Co. series 4032 .. .. £1.50/**£2**/£3

Periods: 2, 3—Pub. S. H. & Co. Ltd. London. Tommy C (Atkins) series .. .. £1.50/**£2**/£3

Periods 2, 3—Pub. Tilley & Son, Ledbury. Novelty pull-out .. .. £1.50/**£2**/£3

Period 2—Tuck. 'Oilette' humorous. 'Breakfast in Bed' (9321), 'Tales of the Seaside' (9685), 'Mixed Bathing', series II (9636) and 'Breakfast in Bed', series IV (9786) .. .. £2/**£3**/£4

Others—Printed in Saxony—grey background cards, e.g. 'Is yer Ma Out?' .. .. £2/**£3**/£4

Series 522, black backgrounds—'The Gibson Girl', etc. Series 534, red backgrounds—Pantomime cats—'Dick Whittington' etc. .. .. £2/**£4**/£6

Kennedy, A. E. (A. E. K.)
Pub. Faulkner. Three Little Kittens Who Lost Their Mittens .. .. .. £2/**£4**/£5

Pub. Faulkner. Series 1538. Kittens playing, also panel cards .. .. .. £2/**£4**/£5

Pub. Faulkner. Series 1195. Cats and Dogs at Play. White bordered cards. Some with French titles .. .. £1/**£2**/£3

Pub. Faulkner. Series 1317. Cats playing 'Ring A Ring O' Roses', etc. Grey bordered .. .. £2/**£4**/£5

Pub. Faulkner. Series 1241. Pop eyed cats. Cards have a very light grey border. 'Admiration' etc. .. .. .. £2/**£3**/£4

Pub. Faulkner. Series 1507. Cats in Love. Cards are white bordered .. .. £2/**£3**/£4

Pub. Faulkner. Series 1789. Lucky Black Cats .. .. £1/**£2**/£3

Knight, M. & Kennedy, A. E.
Pub. Faulkner. Series 1338. Pop-eyed cats. 'I Am Fifi', also panel cards. .. £1/**£2**/£3

Pub. Faulkner. Series 1646. WW1 themes, white bordered, also published with French titles. 'A Food Controller' .. .. £1.50/**£2**/£4

Pub. Faulkner. Series 1659. White background cards—'She Loves Me', etc. .. .. £1/**£2**/£3

Kennedy, Charles
Pub. Gale & Polden. 'Our Domestic Pets'. WW1 humour, incl. 'Are You a Tank'. Period 3 .. .. £1.50/**£2**/£4

Pub. A. M. Davis. 'Comic Animals' (565). WW1 humour. Period 3 .. .. £1/**£2**/£3

Kennedy, T.
Pub. Humoresque. Animal humour. Period 4 .. .. £1/**£2**/£3

Lydon, A. F.
Pub. A. & M. B. Series 125. Chromo-litho. Early Period 2 .. .. .. £1.50/**£4**/£6

Maquire, Helena
One of the most prolific artists of Victorian greetings cards, many of which were later transferred on to postcards. Period 2—early. Chromo.

Pub. Hildersheimer. Period 2 .. £1.50/**£4**/£6

Pub. Tuck. 'Animal Studies', series 6174.
  Period 2. Chromo ■18a .. .. £1.50/**£4**/£6

Pub. Misch & Stock. Snow scenes, set 69.
  Period 2. Chromo .. .. .. £1.50/**£4**/£6

Roberts, Violet (VR)
Mostly Photochrom. Cards. Periods 3, 4.

Pub. Photochrom. 'All the World and His
  Wife at Harrogate' (yellow card)
  .. .. £2/**£4**/£6

'Song Titles' (b & w sketches) .. £2/**£4**/£6

Celesque series', 2 sets WW1 Regiments
  (un-numbered and 517). Various humour
  (un-numbered and 600), 2 sets—Seaside
  humour (blue border). Christmas series,
  e.g. 'I'm Awfully Keen on Xmas'
  .. .. £2/**£4**/£6

Duotype series. Lucky Black Cats, Black
  Cats and Rhymes, etc. (series 1226–
  1231 and 1831) .. .. .. £2/**£4**/£6

Pub. Alfred Stiebel & Co. Modern humour,
  series 4161, 4162 and 4205 .. £2/**£4**/£6

Pub. Tuck. 'Oilette' series. 'Khaki and Fluff'
  (8895), 'Khaki and Fluff' series II
  (3104), 'Some Cat' (3202) 'Christmas'
  series 8427, 8436. Chromo-litho
  .. .. £2/**£4**/£6

Schropler, L.
Style reminiscent of Thiele. Published in Germany.

Pub. Anon. School series. Period 2 £1.50/**£2**/£3

Pub. Tuck. Oilette. 'Kitty's Little Love
  Affair' (9938). Period 2 .. .. £2/**£3**/£4

Thiele, Arthur† ■23b
More popular with many collectors than Wain, certainly more versatile. He also drew dogs, hens, horses, pigs, monkeys, rabbits. His prolific output spanned the years 1899 to 1919, and his animal studies ranged from striking, colourful heads to whole scenes (nursery rhymes and fairy stories) of animals in human dress and situations. Publishers of his feline studies include:

Pub. Faulkner, C. W. Snow Scenes (Tobog-
  ganing), series 1067. Musical Cats in
  Snow, series 1298 and At School, series
  1373. Springtime in Catland, series
  1378 .. .. £4/**£6**/£8

Pub. Klaus & Co. Ladies Hats, series 486
  and The Nursery, series 474 .. £4/**£6**/£8

Pub. Tuck. Several sets incl. 'Catland',
  series I and II (9818 and 9819
  'Playtime') .. .. £4/**£6**/£8

B.K.W.I. Period 3. Series 323. 'Sporting
  Types' .. .. £4/**£6**/£8

Pub. T.S.N. (Theo Stroefer, Nuremberg)
  (sets of 6 cards)
  710 Be-ribboned Cats
  851 Life At Home
  918 The Six Ages of the Cat (male)
  945 Kittens with Bouquets (later Solomon
       Bros)
  947 Diabolo
  962 School Kittens
  975 Tears & Joy
  995 Winged Cats (Fantasy)
  1012 A Mewsical Party (later Tuck
        Oilette 9797)
  1016 Cats at Play*
  1018 Classic Loves
  1077 Events at Home
  1113 Haute Cat-ure
  1194 Cats Tobogganning
  1214 A Tennis Tournament (later Tuck
        Oilette 9983)
  1229 The Subscription Ball (later Tuck
        Oilette 9782)
  1404 New Year Greetings
  1405 New Year Greetings
  1408 New Year Gifts
  1412 Kittens at Play
  1421 Cat's Heads/Scenes
  1423 School Kittens
  1425 Just Like Dad (kittens)

1469 Fun in Snowland (later Tuck
     Oilette 8604)
1601 Cats at Play*
1602 Street Scenes
1667 Cats at Play*
1830 In Kittendom (later Tuck Oilette
     4091)
1876 Ice Skating
1892 Just Like Mother (Kittens)
Price range   ..   ..   £4/**£6**/£8

* Some interchange of cards between sets, probably later Tuck Oilette series 9818 and 9819.

Note
No series of T.S.N. postcards have titles, and the
ones given here are those thought most appropriate by the compilers. Where T.S.N. series were
taken by Tuck, the 'Oilette' title has been given.
Other un-named T.S.N. Thiele series include:
949, 1010, 1017, 1225, 1326, 1427, 1428,
1450, 1893, 1999 (Snowmen), 2030.

Travers Pope, Dorothy
Pub. Misch & Co. 'Our Cats' (series 807)
(A. & M. B. No. 531). 'Kitties Family'
(series 858) (A. & M. B. No. 561)
Chromo-litho, Period 2, 'Pretty Puss'
(series 865) (A. & M. B. No. 533)
   ..   .. £1.50/**£3**/£5

Wain, Louis William† ■23c
Well known cat artist and caricaturist. Started
making sketches at the age of 19 for the *Sporting
and Dramatic News*, which included animals other
than cats, e.g. fishes, birds and even human
heads.
A cat—named 'Peter the Great'—bought for his
wife to keep her company during an illness·
aroused his interest in producing life-like cat
drawings. Sir W. Ingram published a double page
of his 'Cats' in the *Illustrated London News*, thus
establishing Wain as a household word. He was a
brilliant artist but unlike contemporary Continental animal artists, his style of drawing was more
the cartoon than the character drawing. Use was
made of his drawings in childrens' books, many of
which were published by Ernest Nister, and his
talents were soon taken up by the postcard
publishers of the day. Many thousand of postcard
designs exist incl. those purchased by publishers
or merely pirated by them, the same cartoons may
be found in many publishers' lists. He had a

somewhat unhappy life, suffering from mental
illness and financial difficulties, and often sold his
drawings for a meal or a train fare. He died in
Napsbury Mental Home in 1939, having been
confined there for some years.

Pub. Alphalsa Pub. Co. At least 2 designs
   ..   .. £4/**£7**/£10

Pub. Anon. Advertisements for Jackson's
Hats and Boots   ..   ..   .. £14/**£16**/£20

Superb, rare WW1 set, incl. a cat 'Kaiser'
   ..   .. £14/**£16**/£20

Many hundred cards, often pirated, often
with Wain's signature removed   £8/**£10**/£12

Pub. Beagles. Period 2. Col. and photographic. At least 4 sets, incl. 'Matri-
monial Cats'   ..   .. £8/**£10**/£12

Pub. Boots. Famous Picture series of 12
   ..   .. £3/**£5**/£8

Pub. Collins, Wm. Set of 6 'Animals'
   ..   .. £4/**£7**/£10

Pub. Davidson Bros. Period 2. At least 9
sets   ..   .. £8/**£10**/£12

Pub. Davis, A. M. & Co. At least 1
set   ..   .. £3/**£5**/£8

Pub. Dennis, E. T. W.. At least 1 design
   ..   .. £4/**£7**/£10

Pub. Dutton, N. Y. Period 2   .. £10/**£12**/£14

Pub. Ettlinger & Co. Series 5226 and 5376
'Father Christmas' cats. Period 3
   ..   .. £8/**£10**/£12

Pub. Faulkner, C. W. & Co. Includes series
such as 182, 183, 189, 190, 374, 453,
454, 484, 485, 503, 515, 541 and 1596,
plus many others. Periods 2, 3   £12/**£14**/£16

Pub. Gale & Polden. At least 1 design
   ..   .. £5/**£8**/£12

Pub. Hartmann. Manx cats (3069) and
Fluffikins Family (3068). Sporting Cats
and some fine embossed cards. Period
2 ..   .. £8/**£10**/£12

Pub. Mack, W. E. The Cats Academy series
(not all Wain designs) .. .. £8/**£10**/£12

Pub. Millar & Lang. At least 1 design
.. .. £4/**£7**/£10

Pub. Moss, Henry (Pre-1905). 'Start off'
series .. .. £5/**£8**/£12

Pub. Nister, E. Series 353, 355 etc. Early
Period 2 .. .. £10/**£12**/£14

Pub. Osborne. At least 1 design .. £4/**£7**/£10
Pub. Pascalis, Moss. At least 1 design
.. .. £5/**£8**/£12

Pub. Philco. At least 3 series .. £5/**£8**/£12

Pub. Rowntree. Advertising design £4/**£7**/£10

Pub. Solomon Bros. *c.* 1918 designs
.. .. £4/**£7**/£10

Pub. Stroefer, Germany. Usually unsigned
designs .. .. £6/**£8**/£10

Pub. Taylor, A. & G. At least 1 design
.. .. £4/**£7**/£10

Pub. Tuck. Periods 1, 2, early b & w
undivided back Raphael Tuck et Fils
series 130. .. .. £12/**£14**/£16

Theatre series b & w cards 3885–3895.
Period 2 .. .. £8/**£10**/£12

Write-aways series 539, 956, 957, 1003
and 1004. Period 2 .. .. £8/**£12**/£14

Chromo-litho's Early Period 2. Series 1260,
1261, 1262, 1735, 1748, 1749, 1782,
5802, 5892 .. .. .. £8/**£12**/£16
Chromo-litho Nursery Rhymes/Pantomime/
Christmas. Period 2. Series 297, 298,
8126, 8127 .. .. .. £8/**£12**/£16
Diabolo Set 9563 .. .. .. £10/**£12**/£14
Dressing Dolls Fairy Tales 'Oilette' 3385
.. .. £12/**£16**/£20
Oilette and similar series 1412, 3266,
6075, 6084, 6401, 6444, 8515, 8612,
8613, 8614, 8615, 8816, 8817, 8826,
8850, 8864, 9396, 9540, 9541
.. .. £10/**£12**/£14

Others, Various odd cards, parts of sets (not
completely Wain's designs), etc. including Series C132, 133 .. .. £8/**£10**/£12

■23a

Maurice Boulanger. Pub. Anon. Decembre—part of sought-after set of months of the year. UB   £8

■23b

Pub. T.S.N. Series 918. Cat's Head. Artist Arthur Thiele £6

■23c

Pub. Anon. Artist Louis Wain. The Kaiser. Period 3 .. ..£20

Pub. Valentines Coloured series (un-numbered) Period 2 .. .. .. £8/**£10**/£12
Charlie Chaplin card. Periods 3, 4 £10/**£14**/£16

Pub. Wrench Black cat's series, Pantomime
.. .. £10/**£12**/£14

The sets and series listed here do not in any way constitute a complete list of Wain postcards. They are included here to stimulate interest in the variety and scope of Louis Wain's work, and to show that even to obtain the cards from a single publisher such as TUCK or VALENTINES could be a lengthy and difficult task.

Black Cats
A common and popular theme in Periods 2 to 4. Many series were published by Inter-Art, and often re-printed with greetings overprints or French captions in WW1. Most catland artists produced some postcards of this genre, in particular Boulanger, Roberts, Thiele and Wain, whose cards command a premium of up to £5. Values according to artist and period.

Pub. Dennis, E. T. W. Periods 2, 3
.. .. £1.50/**£2**/£3

Pub. Inter-Art Comic Periods 2, 3 £1.50/**£2**/£3

Comic Cats
Cats in humorous situations were featured by many of the well known postcard artists, such as Tom Browne, G. F. Christie, Donald McGill and Lawson Wood. Unfortunately many of the best cards of this type produced by the popular publishers were drawn by artists who will perhaps forever remain anonymous. Typical of the anonymous humour of this genre of card are those produced by the Scottish publishers Millar & Lang who reproduced their famous series 'When Father Says Turn' depicting cats.
Price range .. .. £1.50/**£3.50**/£6

Felix the Cat—*see* CINEMA

Photographic Studies

Frees, Harry Whittier (1879–1953)
Born in Reading, Pennsylvania, he soon specialised in animal photography and became famous for his cats, often kittens, in human dress and situations. Published in New York by the Rotograph Co. and in Britain by the Rotary Co. Periods 2 to 4 .. .. £1.50/**£2.50**/£3

Landor
Cat studies (also dogs). Periods 2 to 4. Publishers include Hildesheimer, Tuck and Wrench, incl. b & w, col. and sepia .. .. £1.50/**£2**/£3

Other Photographic Studies
Periods 2 to 7 .. .. £1/**£2**/£3

Taber Bas Relief Co.
Photographic studies .. .. .. £2/**£3**/£4

The Publishers
Faulkner, Hildesheimer, Stewart & Woolf, Tuck, Wrench and others all produced countless 'cat' cards, incl. some fine, early chromo-litho cards, often embossed. Periods 1, 2 .. .. .. £1.50/**£3.50**/£6
Davidson Bros., Ettlinger, Inter-Art, Rotary, Tuck, Wildt & Kray and others produced many amusing, sentimental cards, many photographic, often on greetings cards. Periods 2 to 7 .. .. £1/**£2**/£3

Stanley Gibbons Postcard Album
Attractively presented in a rich deep red PVC padded binder blocked in gold, this album contains 20 crystal clear double pockets, each designed to hold four post-cards to a maximum size of $6\frac{1}{2} \times 4\frac{1}{8}$ in. each. The pockets are held in a quick release spring-arch fitting incorporating a special locking device.

Stanley Gibbons British Post Office Picture Card Album
This album is designed specifically to house the attractive series of picture cards— popularly known by collectors as PHQ's— produced by the British Post Office. The compact, fully padded, royal blue PVC two-ring binder contains 2 single pockets to hold the first two cards, PHQ 1 and 2, and 13 double pockets to hold cards PHQ 3 onwards. Binder gold blocked on spine. Space for additional pockets. Packs of extra pockets are also available.

DOGS

Artists

Aldin, Cecil†
Intelligent, characterful dogs, hunting scenes. Tuck and other publishers. Period 2 .. .. £1/**£2**/£4

Daws, F. T.
Spratts 'Champion Dog' series. Printer Johnson, Riddle & Co. Period 2 .. .. 75p/**£1.25**/£1.75
Series for Birn Bros. High gloss finish. Periods 2 to 4 .. .. –/**50p**/75p

Drummond, Norah
Many finely drawn series for Tuck. Oilettes, e.g. 'With Dog & Gun', No. 9273, 'On the Moors', No. 9327. Period 2 .. 50p/**£1**/£1.50

Muller, Augustus
Worked in Munich. Specialised in Dachsunds. Pub. Hildesheimer. Periods 1, 2 .. 50p/**£1**/£1.50

Pope, Dorothy Travers
Fine chromo-litho series, e.g. Misch & Co. Series 806. 'Our Dogs'. Period 2 £1/**£2**/£3

Stokes, Vernon
Superb, early chromo-litho series on fine board (incl. Bulldog, Husky). Series 11825. Pub. Anon. Periods 1, 2. ■25a .. .. £1/**£2**/£4

Studdy, George†
The famous Bonzo dog. Publishers include Valentine's and 'RPS' Series. Period 4 .. .. £1/**£1.50**/£2

Wardle, Arthur
'Dog' series J1. 'Sporting Dogs & Birds', series J2. Pub. James Henderson. Period 2 .. .. 75p/**£1**/£2

Watson, Maud West
Tuck. Oilette, e.g. Sketches of Dogs, No. 9681. Period 2 .. .. 75p/**£1**/£1.50

Comic Dogs

Dogs in humorous situations were featured by many fine artists, like Tom Browne, Hassall, etc.: *see* ARTISTS.

Publishers

Eyre & Spottiswoode, Hildesheimer, Wrench, etc., produced many early b&w series of photographic and art productions of dogs and other animals by artists like Stanley Berkeley and photographers like Reid. Periods 1, 2 .. .. –/**50p**/£1
Tuck produced countless series of Oilette and photographic studies of varying worth. Periods 2 to 4 .. .. .. 50p/**75p**/£1
There are also many Periods 2 to 4 series and single cards of photographic studies of animals in a sentimental vein, often with actresses and pretty girls, often on greetings cards, by Ettlinger, Rotary, Valentine, etc. .. .. –/**50p**/75p

■25a

Artist G. Vernon Stokes. Chromo-litho dog. UB *1903* £3

■25b

Swiss. Lucerne milkman with dog cart. UB. *Period 2* £4

Working Dogs

Swiss St. Bernards. Period 2. ■191a
.. .. 50p/**75p**/£1.50

Dog Carts

Belgian milk carts	£1.50/**£3.50**/£5
Belgian military carts	£2.50/**£4**/£6
Belgian other carts	1.50/**£3.50**/£5
French milk carts	..£4/**£7.50**/£12
French other carts	£6/**£8**/£12

Dutch, German, Russian, Swiss carts. ■25b
.. .. £2/**£4**/£6

Military Dogs

Red Cross/Transport Dogs in WW1
.. .. £1/**£1.50**/£3

FISH

Angling Cards

Photographic studies, many local publishers. Periods 2 to 4 .. .. –/**£1**/£1.50
Tuck. Oilette. Various series. Period 2
.. .. 50p/**75p**/£1

Poisson d'Avril:

Pub. Hawaii & South Seas Curio Co.,
Honolulu Chromo-litho tropical fish.
Large, colourful series .. .. 75p/**£1**/£1.50
Pub. Hawaii Jas. Steiner series Probably
over 30 in series .. .. ..75p/**£1**/£1.50

Stranded Whales and Other Fish Curiosities

Many local photographers and publishers.
Periods 2 to 4 .. .. .. 50p/**75p**/£1
Tuck Oilette/Connoisseur series, e.g. 'British
Fresh Water Fish', 'British Fish'. Period
2 .. ..50p/**£1**/£1.50

Three Band Pricing System

Left Hand Band: *The lowest price you will probably be asked to pay for this card.*

Middle Band: *What you will normally be asked to pay for this card: its average, reasonable price.*

Right Hand Band: *The highest price you will probably be asked to pay for this card.*

For a full explanation of the system, see page viii.

FROGS

Adverts. Much collected in the USA,
especially for throat pastilles (e.g. 'Frog in
Your Throat Co.') .. .. .. £1/**£2**/£4
Alice in Wonderland frogs—*see* 'LITERARY'
Frog Bands .. .. 50p/**75p**/£1
Pub. Meissner & Buch. Series 170 and
283 .. .. 50p/**75p**/£1
Others .. .. 25p/**50p**£1

HORSES

The most collectable cards in this sub-section are
undoubtedly race horses and allied cards.

Ancient White Horses

An interesting category—early British White
Horses carved in chalk on hillsides.
Publishers Wilkinson & Co., Trowbridge and
many other local publishers .. 50p/**75p**/£1

Artists' Impressions of Horses

Periods 2 to 5. Various publishers –/**50p**/75p

Horse Studies

Pub. 'P.F.' Artist Kocj (signed 'G.K.').
Embossed heads .. .. .. £1/**£2**/£4

Harry Payne Horses

Rural Studies

Pub. Tuck Oilette series. Period 2. ■26a
.. .. £1/**£2**/£4

■26a

Pub. Tuck. Artist Harry Payne. 'By Mead and Stream'. Oilette 9337. PU *1910* £1.50

Pub. Tuck early chromolithographed heads.
Period 2 .. .. £1.50/**£2**/£3
Pub. Tuck Oilette, e.g. 'Horse Studies',
'Man's Best Friend'. Period 2 .. 75p/**£1.50**/£2

Horse Fairs
In Britain and Eire (e.g. Buttevant) Periods
2 to 4 .. .. £1/**£2**/£4

Hunting Scenes

Photographic Studies
Specified hunts, e.g. Compiègne (LL), Surrey Union. Period 2 .. .. .. 75p/**£1**/£2

Artists' Impressions
Many Tuck Oilette series, e.g. 'A Hunting
We Will Go'. Also E. T. W. Dennis
'Dainty' series. Periods 2 to 4 .. 75p/**£1**/£1.50

Military Horses

Boer War
Artists Caton Woodville, Harry Payne.
Periods 1, 2 .. .. £1/**£2**/£4
Photographic. Periods 1, 2 .. .. £1/**£2**/£4

WW1
Artist Matania, Frederick .. .. 75p/**£1**/£2
Cavalry horses, Officers' horses, pulling gun
limbers, military transport 50p/**75p**/£1.50

General Military
Pub. Gale & Polden type, etc. Period 2
.. .. 75p/**£1**/£1.50

Named Race Horses—*see also* SPORTS & PASTIMES
Pub. Tuck. Derby Winners. UB. Periods 1,
2 .. .. £1/**£2**/£3
Pub. Walker & Co. 'Celebrated Racers'
series. Period 2 .. .. 50p/**75p**/£1
Pub. Wrench series. Period 2 .. 50p/**75p**/£1

Point to Point Races
Periods 2 to 4. Artist drawn .. .. 50p/**75p**/£1
Real photographic .. .. .. 50p/**£1**/£3

Races and Race Courses (British)
Ascot, Goodwood, Epsom, etc.
Photographic studies. Publishers Frith,
Valentines and Wrench and many local
publishers. Value varies according to
clarity and detail. Periods 2 to 4. Artists'
Impressions .. .. 50p/**£1**/£1.50

Races and Race Courses (Foreign)
Chantilly, Le Havre, Ostende, etc. Period 2
.. .. 50p/**75p**/£1

Royalty at the Races
Photographic. Various Publishers. Periods 2
to 4 .. .. £1/**£2**/£3

Spanish Riding School, Vienna
Period 4. Photographer H. Schuhmann
.. .. 75p/**£1**/£1.50

Working Horses
Ploughing, Drawing Cabs, Fire Engines, etc.
Various Publishers. Value increases
according to rarity of occupation/vehicle
and whether the picture is close-up or
distant. Periods 2 to 5 .. .. 75p/**£1.50**/£2

See also ROAD TRANSPORT.

INSECTS
Many early Continental chromo-litho cards,
often embossed, featured beetles, ladybirds, etc. Periods 1, 2 .. .. 75p/**£1.50**/£2

Butterflies

British Museum of Natural History
'British Butterflies'. Probably 100 cards.
Printed by Waterlow/Henry Stone &
Sons. Period 4 .. .. –/**50p**/75p

Tuck Oilette
'Butterflies', 'British Butterflies & Moths'.
Period 2 .. .. 50p/**£1**/£1.50

Tuck 'Butterflies on the Wing'. ■28a—*see
also* NOVELTY .. .. .. £3/**£4**/£5

Fleas
Fleas were the subject of countless humorous
cards of Periods 2 to 4, by artists like
'FS', Donald McGill, and many unnamed
artists. Value varies according to
artist .. .. –/**75p**/£1.50

Performing Fleas/Circuses
Period 2 .. ..   £1/**£3**/£5

MISCELLANEOUS

Animals on Greetings Cards
Greetings cards are, perhaps, the most prolific source for animal card collectors (bunnies and chicks on easter cards, robins on christmas cards, kittens, puppies, horses, etc. on birthday cards, fish on April Fool cards): *see* GREETINGS.

Circus and Performing Animals

Dogs, Elephants, Fleas, etc.
Barnum & Bailey and other named Circuses: *see* CIRCUS

Domestic Animals
Pub. Tuck. Educational series No. 4. Embossed. Late Period 2 .. ..   £3/**£4**/£5

Monkeys on Barrel Organs
British and Continental. Period 2 ..   £1/**£2**/£4

Mickey Mouse, Donald Duck: *see* CINEMA.

Nursery Animals
Many artist drawn cards, often published by the Medici Society in the 1920s–1950s, feature animals. This is a small selection of some of the named artists. *See also* CHILDREN.

Folkard, Charles
Periods 4, 5 .. ..75p/**£1**/£1.50

Tempest, Margaret
Periods 4 to 6 .. .. £1/**£1.50**/£2

Thompson, G. H.
Publisher Nister. Period 2 .. ..75p/**£1.50**/£2

Pigs
Pigs were regarded as good luck symbols on the Continent and often appeared on greetings cards.
Early chromo-litho, artist drawn pigs.
Periods 1, 2 .. ..75p/**£1.50**/£3
British humorous cards of pigs. Periods 2 to
5 .. .. –/**75p**/£1.25
Modern French cards with 'dubious' captions. Period 7 .. .. –/**25p**/50p

Wild Animals

Pub. Tuck's Oilette series, e.g. 'Wild Animals'. Period 2 .. ..   50p/**75p**/£1.50
Pub. Wrench and other b & w photographic series of lions, polar bears, etc. Period 2
.. .. –/**25p**/50p

Artist Rankin, George
Studies of lions, tigers, etc. Tuck's Oilette series, e.g. 'Wild Animal' series. Period 2.
■28b .. ..   50p/**75p**/£1.50

Artist Scrivener, Maud
Tuck's Oilette series, e.g. 'In the Jungle'.
Period 2 .. ..   50p/**75p**/£1.50

■28a
Pub. Tuck. Oilette 3390. 'Butterflies on the Wing'—novelty card to push out. Artist R. J. Wealthy. Period 4 .. .. £5

■28b
Pub. Tuck. Artist George Rankin. Tigress 'Wild Animals' series 8785. Period 2 .. .. .. £1

■28c
Pub. Tuck. Baby Jumbo's toilet. 'Our Pets' series 1426. PU *1904* 50p

Zoo Animals

'LL' photographs of London—*see* PUBLISHERS, 'LL'

Many 'Zoological' cards exist in long series, e.g. 'From the Gardens of the Zoological Society Regents Park', b & w photographic studies by W. S. Berridge, Henry Irving, etc. Period 2 ..   ..   ..   –/**50p**/75p

Zoo Berlin

Col. chromo-litho set 1900 ..   ..   £1/**£3**/£4

Zoo Buildings and Keepers

Zoo Dresden
Col. chromo-litho series. Vignettes. 1897
..   ..   £2/**£4**/£5
Other types through to Period 7. ■28c
..   ..   25p/**50p**/£1

Photographic studies of zoos and their keepers were produced by popular publishers of most of the famous zoos in Britain and on the Continent. Value increases with age and rarity of subject as well as clarity of photograph. Periods 2 to 7 ..   ..   –/**£1**/£1.50

Other Animals

Cows, Donkeys, Mice, Monkeys, Oxen, Rabbits, Squirrels, Stags, etc. often appear on cards. Some fine early Continental chromo-litho cards (often imported by C. W. Faulkner) some embossed, are well worth collecting. Later photographic designs are of little interest or worth. Value increases with age, quality of reproduction. Periods 2 to 7 ..   ..   **50p**

The Stanley Gibbons Postcard Department is at 391 Strand London WC2. Open Mon.–Fri. 9 a.m.–5.30 p.m.; Sat. 9.30 a.m.–12.30 p.m.

ART DECO

As ART NOUVEAU (*qv*) wilted, so a new style began to take its place, a style which in some of its forms was a reaction against the florid aspects of *Art Nouveau*. The new style, which came to be known as *Art Deco* (from *Art Decoratif*) derived from the more austere and abstract forms of *Art Nouveau*. It was evident in the orientally inspired designs by Leon Bakst for the Ballet Russe in Paris in 1909 and in the work of J. Hoffmann who, with Koloman Moser, founded the Wiener Werkstätte. They in turn had been influenced by the work of Mackintosh in England. The movement was characterised by the love of the symmetry in design that recalled the classic style. After an early emphasis on stylised garlands, roses and fruit, the style was more and more inspired by cubism and the geometric form. As with *Art Nouveau*, the style was applied to many branches of the arts, both useful and decorative. Exponents of *Art Deco*, in love with 'the machine', influenced 'streamlining' of racing cars (Bugatti), furniture and interior design. The décor of the Park Lane Hotel, Piccadilly, London, is an outstanding example of the genre.

Couturiers like Paul Poiret put a strong *Art Deco* feeling into ladies' fashion and used artists of the new style to illustrate their creations in albums and magazines.

Art Deco reached its apogee in 1925 with the Paris Exposition des Arts Decoratifs et Modernes, and died out in the mid-1930s.

To a lesser extent than with *Art Nouveau*, *Art Deco* influences can be seen in the borders and decorations of postcards in several general categories, such as Greetings cards and Adverts. ■17a. Some of the most interesting examples of the *Art Deco* architectural style are to be found on postcards of New York skyscrapers, like the Chrysler Building. ■31a.

The film sets and décor of Hollywood movies of the late 1920s and 1930s reflect the style. A prime example is 'The Wizard of Oz', postcards of which exist. As *Art Nouveau* degenerated into convoluted excesses as its strength as an art form waned, so *Art Deco*, when it strived to appeal to the mass market, developed into 'kitsch'.

It is difficult to generalise, but *Art Deco* styling adds about £2 to the value of cards collectable for other reasons. As the genre becomes more and more popular, the virtuoso exponents of the art command ever higher prices for signed examples of their work. The principal artists are listed below and for details of their work and valuations *see* ARTISTS, CHILDREN, COLLECTIONS and GLAMOUR.

ADVERTISING/GENERAL/GLAMOUR ARTISTS

Bakst, L.†	Iribe, P.
Barbier	Jung, M.
Bentivoglio	Koehler, M.† ■65a
Bertelli, P.	Kokoschka, O.† ■65b
Bompard, S.	Larcombe, E.
Brunelleschi† ■31b	Lendecke
Calderara, C.†	Likartz, M.
Cappiello, L.	Longley, C.
Carrere, R. ■31c	Marty, A.
Chiostri, C.†	Mauzan
Corbella, T.† ■49a	Meschini, G.
Dudovich, M.† ■31d	Monier, M.
Garry, C.	Montassier, H.
Gesmar, C.	Montedoro, M.
Gobbi, D.	Moser, K.†
Gobbo, C.	Nanni†
Graf, M.	Nashnyekov
Grosze, M.	Scattina
Guitry, S.	Singer, S.
Hoffmann, J.†	Vincent, R.

Price range (if unlisted elsewhere) £3/**£8**/£20

† = *see* ARTISTS section.

ANONYMOUS

Many unsigned, or undecipherable artist signed *Art Deco* postcards are now emerging. In particular there are some fine advertising designs of Period 4, many of them French or Italian.

Price range .. .. £2/**£5**/£7.50

Remember that the arrangement of this catalogue is alphabetical—both in main section arrangement and in sub-divisions within the main sections.

The 'Nursery' Artists

In some cases these artists went through an *Art Deco* phase in a more general artistic career. *See also* CHILDREN.

These are the principal artists recognised by British collectors. Many more are listed and collected on the Continent.

Attwell, M. L.† ■36c
Bertiglia, A.† ■40c
Cooper, P.
Cramer, R.
French, A.
King, J. M.†
Mallett, B.
Mercer, J.†
Pinochi
Preston, C.
Rose, F. M.
Shand, C. E.
Smith, J. W.†
Sowerby, M.†
Willebeek Le Mair, H.†
Price range (if not listed elsewhere)   £1.50/**£3**/£5

■31b

Artist Brunelleschi. Bird Woman. Period 4 .. £40

■31c

Pub. Braun et Cie., Paris. Artist Rene Carrere. 'Don Juan'. Period 4   ..   .. £4

■31a

Pub. Wm. France. B & w photo Chrysler and Chanin Buildings, New York. Period 4   .. 75p

■31d

Artist Marcello Dudovich. 'The Hand Kiss'. Period 3   ..   .. £20

ART NOUVEAU

Now perhaps reaching 'over-exposure', this has since the mid-1970s been the most prized style of design illustrated on the postcard. Following from the pre-Raphaelites and William Morris's *Arts and Crafts Movement*, the style emerged almost simultaneously in the mid-1880s in Glasgow and Brussels (where it was known as *le style belge* and mainly applied to architecture). It is characterised by lyrical, flowing, complex, curvilinear designs, often with floral, ivy and clover leaf and peacock feather symbols. The art form spread to Germany and France where it got its name from S. Bing's Paris shop, founded in 1895, *L'Art Nouveau*. It is immortalised in Hector Guimard's entrances to the Paris *Métro* and the glass of Lalique and Gallé. It continued in Glasgow in the form of stained glass and copper work (notably in the superb building that housed Millar & Lang the postcard publishers), and developed in the USA in the glasswork of Louis Comfort Tiffany. Reaching its apogee in 1900–1902, the style faded out about 1910.

Many of the sought after *Art Nouveau* postcards were originally designed for the poster, but the influence of the style is seen strongly in borders and decorations of advertising/photographic/view and many other types of postcards.

All cards in this category are Periods 1 and 2.

PRINCIPAL ART NOUVEAU POST-CARD ARTISTS

† *See* section on ARTISTS for details and valuations.

Abeille, J.† ■97a	Grün, J.
Abbéma, L.	Guillaume
Basch, A.†	Hoffmann, J.†
Beardsley, A.	Jozsa, C.†
Bianchi	Kirchner, R.† ■32a
Bilibine, I.†	Kuhn-Regnier
Bonnet, G.	Laskoff, F.
Boutet, H.† ■41b	Léandre, C.
Cheret, J.† ■47a	Lélée, L.†
Christiansen, H.†■47b	Lessieux, L.
Combaz, G.† ■48c	MacDonald, A. K.† ■66b
Dannenberg	Martini, A.†
Faivre, A.	Mazza, A.
De Feure†	Melina, C. L.
Fredillo	Metlicovitz, L.
Géraud	Meunier, G.
Grasset	Meunier, H.† ■32b

Mignot, V.†	Riviere, J.
Moser, K.†	Sem, J.
Mucha, A.† ■106a	Steinlen, T.†
Noury, G.†	Toulouse-Lautrec, H. ■32c
Patella, B.†	Villon, J.†
Péan, R.	Wanke, A.

Examples of their work range from £15–£750. There are 100 or more artists well known and collected on the Continent. The principal show pieces for *Art Nouveau* artists were the great Austrian, French and German COLLECTIONS.

■32a
Artist Raphael Kirchner. 'Woman in the Sun'. UB *1902* £50

■32b
Pub. E. Tefrich, Brussels. Artist Henri Meunier. UB *1900* £50

■32c
Editions Cinos Collection of Celebrated Posters. Artist Henri de Toulouse Lautrec. UB *1895* £500

ANONYMOUS ARTIST DRAWN ■33a

Some extremely beautiful unsigned, or undecipherable artist signed *Art Nouveau* cards exist. They are highly prized and often fetch high prices. Publishers include:

'A & M, B.' Series of fine heads, printed in Saxony. UB

Davidson's 'Artistic Series', printed in Saxony. UB

Femmes Modernes series

Tuck 'Art' Postcards. UB

Pub. anon. Series 305. Bathing beauties. UB

Others

The highest price is for col. Price range
.. .. £2/**£6**/£12

ART NOUVEAU BORDERS/ DECORATION

Coloured. ■33b	£1/**£3**/£5
b & w	50p/**75p**/£1
Russo–Japanese war. ■33c	£4/**£5**/£6

ART NOUVEAU BUILDINGS/ FURNITURE

Paris Métro in 'Paris Vécu' series.	£1/**£3**/£5
Others	75p/**£1.50**/£3

ART NOUVEAU FANTASY

Large Letter. ■33d	50p/**£1**/£2
Others	50p/**75p**/£1

■33b

Pub. Marcus Ward. Coloured Art Nouveau *border. 'The Yachting Girl'. Period 2* £5

■33c

Pub. Tokyo Printing Co. Russo–Japanese War card with Art Nouveau *border.* UB. PU *1906* £6

■33a

Unsigned coloured Art Nouveau *design.* UB. *Early period 2* £12

■33d

Pub. Rapid Photo Printing Co. b & w Art Nouveau *large letter. Miss Lily Hanbury/Miss Margaret Hulstan. Period 2* 75p

ART REPRODUCTIONS

One of the most under-estimated categories, which can yield some of the very finest colour printing to be found on the postcard. The section includes reproductions of friezes, mosaics, paintings, sculpture and tapestries.

FRIEZES

Pub. Gaddis & Sief, Luxor
Mortuary chapels of the Nobles, Thebes.
Period 2 (premium of 25% for complete
set of at least 30) .. .. .. —/**50p**/75p

Pub. Luca Gentile & Co., Naples
Pompeii scenes with red border. Period 2
.. .. 50p/**75p**/£1

MOSAICS

Pub. A. Reber, Palermo
Mosaic from the Palatine Chapel, gold &
silver print. Cards form a type of 'composite'. Period 2 (a large premium would
be attached to a complete picture)
.. .. 50p/**75p**/£1

PAINTINGS

Pub. Fine Arts Publishing Co.
Royal Exchange paintings. Period 4. Two sets of 6
in original packets with explanatory leaflet.
Set with packet .. .. £2/**£4**/£6
Set without packet .. .. £1/**£3**/£4

Pub. Misch & Co.
World's Galleries series, bearing a Stengel
number, as well as a Misch number.
Brilliant colours on heavy board. From
1905 .. .. 50p/**75p**/£1

**Pub. Misch & Stock/Other Misch & Co.
series/Stengel. From the National Gallery**
Rembrandt series .. .. —/**50p**/75p
Millet's masterpieces. Period 2 .. —/**50p**/75p

Pub. Tuck
Many series throughout Periods 2 to 4 in a
variety of presentations .. .. —/**50p**/75p

Other British publishers—
Alpha, Boots, Cassell's, Ettlinger, Eyre & Spottis-
woode 'Woodbury' series, C. W. Faulkner & Co.,
S. Hildesheimer, W. MacKenzie, Medici Society,
Ernest Nister, Photochrom, Celesque 'Famous
Picture' series, Rotary, Schwerdtfeger, Valentine,
J. Welch, Wildt & Kray, Wrench.
Period 1 .. .. —/**50p**/75p
Periods 2 to 4 .. .. —/**25p**/50p
Per five cards. Periods 5 to 7 .. —/**25p**/50p

Foreign publishers—
Period 1 .. .. —/**50p**/75p
Periods 2 to 4 .. .. —/**25p**/50p
Carlo Bestetti, Rome, Toulouse-Lautrec
reproductions. Period 6 .. .. £2/**£3**/£5

Reproductions from Art Galleries
Birmingham, Lady Lever Art Gallery, Louvre,
Manchester, National Gallery, Prado, etc.
Period 1 .. .. —/**25p**/50p
Per three cards. Periods 2 to 4 .. —/**25p**/50p
Per six cards. Periods 5 to 7 .. .. —/**25p**/50p

SCULPTURES

Alpha/Paris Salon/Others
Period 1 .. .. —/**25p**/50p
Per five cards. Periods 2 to 4 .. **50p**
Per ten cards. Periods 5 to 7 .. **50p**
Pub. Anon. Artist Giris. Personalities like
Farman and the Kaiser. Periods 2, 3
.. .. £1.50/**£3**/£6
Pub. D.M. Italy. Artist L. Rizzi. WW1
satire Tzar, Emperor of Austria, Poin-
caré, etc. .. .. £1.50/**£3**/£6
Pub. A. Noyer, Paris. Artist Mastroianni.
Photographs of sculptured military
scenes. Periods 2, 3 .. .. .. 50p/**75p**/£1

TAPESTRIES

Pub. ND. Photo. Bayeux Tapestry. Period 2.
(large premium for complete set) —/**50p**/75p
Pub. Anon. Southampton. D-Day embroidery by Elsie M. Scudell, designed by
Catriona M. Christison. Period 6. —/**50p**/£1

ARTISTS

This section gives general information about the work of the better-known postcard artists, together with some biographical background. It also gives cross references to the sections where more details and specific valuations of the artists' work are listed. Valuations in this section indicate the price range of the artists' general work, including contributions to the David Allen 'Theatre Poster' series and the Tuck 'Celebrated Poster' series.

If complete information about an artist is available the following sequence is adhered to: name, date and place of birth and death, education, art training, style or genre, main publishers, postcard output, illustration.

Unfortunately, complete entries are possible only in a few cases. It is the intention to expand and complete the entries in future editions, and contributions from readers will be welcome.

ABEILLE, JACK ■97a

One of the earliest French artists to design for the postcard (from about 1898) with delightful vignettes, often featuring lovely ladies (*see also* BATHING). He also designed for the Paris Exhibition of 1900 (*see also* EXHIBITIONS) and went on producing postcards well into Period 3, when he produced some military designs.

Pre-1900 designs	£15/**£25**/£30
Paris Exhibition	£10/**£15**/£20
Period 2. Flower series/Head-dress styles through the ages/'Sins' series ..	£6/**£10**/£18
Later designs	£5/**£10**/£15

ALDIN, CECIL (d. 1935) ■109b

Educated at Solihull Grammar School and then under Calderon in Kensington, he was a popular founder member of the London Sketch Club, of which he was President in 1905. He specialised in dogs, hunting scenes and other animal studies and was a Master of Foxhounds. Publishers include:

Lawrence & Jellicoe	£1/**£2**/£3
Savory, E. W. Ltd., Bristol	£1/**£2**/£3
Tuck 'Celebrated Poster' series No. 1500 (1 card), series No. 1502 (2 cards), Cadbury's Cocoa, Colman's Blue, Colman's Starch	£15/**£17**/£22
Valentine & Sons. The five senses	£1.50/**£2**/£4

ANDERSON, MARTIN (CYNICUS) (1854–1932) ■36a

A rare, original vein of unconventional humour and satire characterised this prolific artist's work. A Scot by birth and breeding, Anderson moved to London to establish himself as an artist. After producing some of the first postcard designs for Blum & Degen he set up his own company in Tayport, Fife (later with a subsidiary company in Leeds). The company produced hundreds of designs, some of them hand-tinted, which dealt with many facets of Edwardian life—bicycling, courtship, marriage, parenthood, the railway, Scottish life, the seaside—with his unique brand of abrasive fun. Many serious topics, like pollution, were also tackled. *See also* COMIC.

Blum & Degen (1899). Three court-sized sets	£1/**£3**/£5
Cynicus Pub. Co., Leeds & Tayport (1902–1916). Many series relating to Scottish, marital and seaside humour themes. Also London and Scottish views, Shakespearian characters, 'Last Train' series, etc.	50p/**75p**/£1.50
Tuck (1914). Set of 'By and Bye' Darby & Joan types	75p/**£1**/£2

ANDERSON, V. C. ■36b

Period 2. American artist. Subjects include children and comic. Publishers include:

Charles Scribner's Sons, Reinthal & Newman, Wildt & Kray	75p/**£1**/£1.50

ARDIZZONE, EDWARD (b. 1900)

Born in Haiphong, China, he came to England to be educated in 1905. He studied at the Westminster School of Art. He is best known as an official War Artist of WW2

Price range	50p/**£1**/1.50

ASTI, ANGELO (1847–1903)

Italian artist who mostly worked in France. He was born in Paris and died in Mantua. His work was exhibited in the Paris Salon between 1890 and 1901. He was mostly known for his bosomy beauties (*see also* GLAMOUR).

Pub. H. J. Smith of Brighton 1902	75p/**£1**/£1.50
Pub. Tuck. Several series of girls' heads, many designs reversed	75p/**£1**/£1.50

ATTWELL, MABEL LUCIE (b. 1879) ■36c

The Queen of the 'cute' child type of illustration, her postcard career spanned at least four decades. Wife of Harold Earnshaw, she started illustrating children's books and many of these drawings were later reproduced as postcards. Her first postcards appeared before WW1 and she continued drawing through the Great War (with many patriotic and morale-raising designs—*see also* WAR)—and between the wars came her most prolific period, during which the *Art Deco* influence could often be seen. During WW2 (*see also* WAR) her kiddies donned uniforms and gas masks and queued for their rations and in Period 6 they reverted to commenting gently on current fashions and mores. *See also* CHILDREN. Her main publishers were Tuck and Valentine.

Periods 2, 3	..	..	..	..	..	75p/**£1**/£1.50
Period 4	..	..	..	..	..	–/**50p**/75p
Period 5	..	..	..	..	..	75p/**£1**/£1.50
Period 6	..	..	..	..	..	–/**50p**/75p

AVELINE, F. ■37a

Portrayer of elegant ladies, often in period dress. Pub. James Henderson & Sons. Periods 3, 4. Head studies/In Hoops & Furbelows, etc. Others .. .. 75p/**£1**/£2

BAIRNSFATHER, BRUCE (1887–1959) ■37b

Best known for his 'Fragments from France' series of postcards (*see* WAR). Bairnsfather, who trained at the John Hassall Art School, also did comic strips on postcards between the wars (*see also* COMIC) and some fine theatre advertising postcards.

Period 3

British Red Cross Society. Surrey Branch fund raiser	..	..	..	£3/**£5**/£8
The Follies. Four Div.	..	..	..	£1/**£3**/£5
Pub. Beagles. Photographic portrait	..	..	..	£3/**£5**/£8

Pub. *The Bystander* 'Fragments from France'
Series One
   a. The Fatalist
   b. Well, if you knows of a better 'ole, go to it
   c. So obvious
   d. Keeping his hand in
   e. There goes our blinkin' parapet again
   f. The things that matter

■36a
Martin Anderson ('Cynicus'). Pub. The Cynicus Art Pub. Co., Leeds, No. C393 'The Road Hog'. Period 2 .. .. £1

■36b
V. C. Anderson. Pub. Charles Scribner's Sons, 'Nobody Loves Me' (1905) 75p

■36c
Mabel Lucie Attwell. Pub. Valentine. Period 4 .. .. 75p

Series Two
- a. That evening Star-Shell
- b. The Eternal Question
- c. Coiffure in the Trenches
- d. The Thirst for Reprisals
- e. No possible doubt whatever
- f. The Innocent Abroad

Series Three
- a. Our Democratic Army
- b. They've Evidently Seen Me
- c. The Tactless Teuton
- d. Directing the Way at the Front
- e. That Sword
- f. Where did that one go to?

Series Four
- a. A Maxim Maxim
- b. The Push—in three chapters
- c. Situation Shortly Vacant
- d. A.D. Nineteen Fifty
- e. My Dug-Out
- f. Gott Strafe this Barbed Wire

Series Five
- a. The Ideal and the Real
- b. In and Out (I)
- c. In and Out (II)
- d. Dear . . . At present we are staying at a farm . . .
- e. . . . these . . . rations
- f. Watch me make a fire-bucket of 'is 'elmet

Series Six
- a. What it Really Feels Like
- b. That 16-inch sensation
- c. Frustrated Ingenuity
- d. The Soldiers Dream
- e. The Same Old Moon
- f. Our Adaptable Armies

Series Seven
- a. My Dream for Years to Come
- b. The Dud Shell
- c. The Historical Touch
- d. Springtime in Flanders
- e. When one would like to start an offensive of one's own
- f. The Conscientious Exhilarator

Series Eight
- a. Happy Memories of the Zoo
- b. The Nest
- c. A Proposal in Flanders
- d. Thoroughness
- e. The Professional Touch
- f. Trouble with one of the Souvenirs

■37a

F. Aveline. Pub. James Henderson. 'In Hoops & Furbelows' series 4. Period 2 .. .. .. £1.50

■37b

Bruce Bairnsfather. Pub. Tuck. 'By Special Arrangement with the Passing Show' Old Bill and Bert. PU *1935* £1.25

■37c

Bantock. Art Deco *design. Period 4* £2

Series Nine
    a. Observation
    b. The Intelligence Department
    c. His Dual Obsession
    d. The Communication Trench
    e. His Secret Sorrow
    f. Nobbled
        Per card .. .. 75p/**£1**/£1.50
Pub. Tuck. Oilette No. 3189. 'Better 'Ole'
    series .. .. 75p/**£1**/£1.50
Theatre advertising (poster types). Pub.
    David Allen. C. B. Cochran's 'The Better
    'Ole' .. .. £10/**£15**/£30
Theatre advertising (poster types). Pub.
    Waddington. 'Flying Colours' .. £10/**£15**/£30

Period 4
British Legion fund raiser. .. .. £1/**£1.50**/£3
Pub. Tuck. Comic strips of Old Bill and Bert
    from *The Passing Show* .. .. 75p/**£1**/£1.50

Period 5
Pub. Valentine. 'Old Bill Again' from *The
    Bystander* .. .. 75p/**£1**/£1.50

BAKST, LEON NIKOLAEVICH (1866–1924)

It is often said that Bakst, more than any other single person, had a profound effect on the development of the decorative arts. Growing up in St. Petersburg he attended the Imperial Academy of Arts and became a member of the Society of Painters in Water Colours. A fashionable success, he taught the Grand Duke Vladimir's children and started to work as a theatrical designer. In 1906 he exhibited in the Russian section of the Salon d'Automne in Paris and two years later made an indelible mark on the future of design with his scenery and costumes for Diaghilev's fabulous *Ballet Russe*. The seeds of *Art Deco* were born. He returned briefly to Russia, but later settled in Paris, assuming the joint role of producer and designer for theatrical and balletic productions in Paris and London. Recently postcards have been discovered of Bakst's revolutionary designs for the *Ballet Russe* in 1908.
Price range .. .. £15/**£30**/£50

BANTOCK ■37c
Stylised *Art Deco* designs. Period 4. 'Bantock' series .. .. £1/**£2**/£3

BARRIBAL, W.
Known as 'Barri', he was best known for his glamorous girls—all based on his wife, Babs. After WW1 he lived at Aston Rowant, where he became friendly with the Bairnsfather family. He was a very successful commercial artist and drew advertisements for many products, designed playing cards and contributed to numerous magazines. A member of the Savage Club, he was President of the London Sketch Club in 1931. *See also* CHILDREN and GLAMOUR.
Pub. David Allen. Theatre Poster Adverts
    for 'The Count of Luxembourg' and
    'Tonight's the Night' .. .. £5/**£10**/£15
Pub. Inter-Art. Periods 2 to 4. Series include
    Fireflies, Artistique, Children
    .. .. £1.50/**£2.50**/£3.50
Pub. James Henderson & Sons. 'Heads' and
    other series .. .. £2/**£3**/£4
Pub. Valentine. Late Period 2. Series
    include 'Girls of the Period' .. £1.50/**£3**/£4
Others, incl. Period 5 glamour .. £1.50/**£3**/£5

BASCH, ARPAD
One of the most spectacular *Art Nouveau* artists working in Paris around the turn of the century.
Set of six 'International Girls' (1900)
    .. .. £40/**£60**/£75
Town Portrait series .. .. £20/**£25**/£30
Others .. .. £15/**£20**/£25

BATEMAN, H. M. ■40a
British cartoonist of the first rank, an admirer of Caran D'Ache (*qv*) and Aubrey Beardsley, his work appeared all too rarely on the postcard. A contributor to a host of magazines and journals, including *Punch*, he specialised in the social 'gaffe'.
Price range .. .. £1/**£2**/£3

BATES, MARJORIE CHRISTINE (1883–1962)
Born in Derbyshire, she moved at the age of 17 with her family to Nottinghamshire and studied at the Nottingham School of Art and later in Paris. Her work was exhibited at the Royal Academy and the Paris Salon. In a working style similar to that of 'Jotter' (Hayward Young) she travelled the British Isles, sketching, mostly in her distinctive style of pencil and crayon. She was a member of the Royal Pastel Society. During Periods 4, 5 her work was published by the British Art Co. (who had a distinctive trademark of the initials 'B.A.C.' around a Grecian-helmeted face, which was later changed to the initials 'F.A.C.'). They printed

Marjorie Bates's postcards by the offset-litho method. As well as the postcards listed below (by B.A.C./F.A.C. and other publishers), Marjorie Bates also illustrated books and her work was reproduced as prints and also as trade cards for Bennet Bros. of Hinckley (who produced 'Tudorose' hosiery) for the coronation of Queen Elizabeth II.

Pub. British Art Co. (B.A.C., later F.A.C.)

Period 4 (some seen PU Period 5). Series of distinctive but delicate pastel/pencil sketches of rural and town scenes. Titles so far identified (with the probable number of cards in the series) are: Cambridge (6); Canterbury (6); Chester (6); Edinburgh (6); London (?18); Oxford (6); Salisbury (6); Scarborough (6); Shrewsbury (6); Stratford-on-Avon (6); Whitby (6); Windsor (6) and Worcestershire (6).

Period 4. Series of Characters from Shakespeare. So far identified are: 1. Lady Macbeth; 2. Romeo & Juliet; 3. Hamlet; 4. Rosalind (*As You Like It*); 5. Clown (*Twelfth Night*); 6. Malvolio (*Twelfth Night*); 7. Falstaff & the Merry Wives of Windsor; 8. Portia (*Merchant of Venice*); 9. Titania & Bottom (*Midsummer Night's Dream*); 10. Katharina (*The Taming of the Shrew*).

Pub. P. R. Series

Period 4. Princess Royal Hotel Whitby, and other adverts for Princess Royal Hotels.

Pub. Phillipson & Golder of Chester

Period 4 Chester designs.

Others, including R. Bolland & Sons Ltd., Restaurant, Chester

Price range (highest price for Shakespeare set and the ad.) .. .. 50p/**75p**/£1

BEIRNE, F. O. ■40b
Superb early UB chromo-litho military vignettes reminiscent of Harry Payne.
Pub. Anon. .. .. £1/**£2**/£3

BELCHER, GEORGE
Royal Academician who specialised in analytical charcoal character studies of cockney life. He contributed to *Punch*, *The Tatler* and many books, working from live, authentic models. Sadly few of his designs were reproduced on the postcard. *See also* COMIC.

Pub. Tuck 'Celebrated Posters', Ogden's Guinea Gold. No. 1501 .. .. £12/**£15**/£22
Pub. Tuck. Period 2. Two humorous sets .. .. £3/**£5**/£6

BERTIGLIA, A. ■40c
Italian artist whose work spanned Periods 2 to 5. Subjects include children, glamour and military subjects for WW1 and WW2.
Price range .. .. £1/**£2**/£4

BILIBINE, B.
Russian artist, whose style resembled the Belgians Cassiers and Lynen. He specialised in sensitively observed local scenes and characters, often with decorative borders. During WW1 he also drew some designs for the Red Cross. Periods 2, 3.
Price range .. .. £5/**£10**/£15

BOILEAU, PHILIP (1864–1917) ■41a
Born in Quebec to a French diplomat and an American society beauty, Philip studied art and music in Milan in 1887, where he married. Following the death of his wife, he travelled in Europe and finally moved to Baltimore in 1897 to live with his brother. He remarried, to a beautiful student, Emily Gilbert, who became his model and inspiration. Success came from Boileau's interpretations of the 'American Girl', the transatlantic rival to the 'Gibson Girl', which were published in *Associated Sunday Magazines* and *Saturday Evening Post*. He used his nieces and nephews as models for the children on his designs, which were reproduced as posters, prints and calendars, in magazines, on china—and on postcards. His cards were widely distributed in Europe as well as in the USA. *See also* GLAMOUR and WAR.

Advertising work. Contrary Mary Book, Flood & Conklin, Metropolitan Life Ins. Co., Nat. Suit and Cloak Co. Period 2 .. .. £2/**£3.50**/£6

Pub. Reinthal & Newman. Periods 2, 3

Absence Cannot Hearts Divide
Anticipating
At the Opera
Autumn
Baby Mine
Be Prepared
Bit of Heaven, A
Blue Ribbons
Boy Scout's Motto
Butterfly
Chic
Chrysalis, The
Chrysanthemums
Chums
Coming Storm, The
(Contrary Mary) book ad
Debutantes
Devotion
Don't Wake the Baby (Boyhood)
Dreamy Hour, The
Enchantress, The
Evening and You
Every Breeze Carries My Thoughts To You
Eyes Say No The Lips Say Yes, The
Fairy Tales (Girlhood)
The Flirt
Forever
From Him
Fruit of the Vine, The
Gift of Love, A
Girl in Black, The
Girl of the Golden West, The
Golden Dreams

Happiness
Haughtiness
Have a Care
Her Soul With Purity Possessed
Here Comes Daddy! (Babyhood)
His First Love
Hundred Years Ago, A
I Don't Care!
I Wonder . . .?
In Confidence
In Maiden Meditation
Joyful Calm
June, Blessed June
Just a Wearying for You
Little Devil, A
Little Lady Demure
Little Neighbors, The
Loneliness
Lullabye (Motherhood)
Mischiefmaker, A
Miss America
Miss Pat
Music
My Big Brother
My Boy
My Chauffeur
My Moonbeam
My One Rose
Need a Lassie Cry?
Neutral, A
Nocturne
Old Home Farewell!
Once Upon a Time . . .
Out for Fun
Parting of the Ways
   The (Maidenhood)
Passing Shadow, A
Peach Blossoms
Pebbles on the Beach
Peggy
Pensive

Poppies
Purity
Queenliness
Question
?! (variation of preceding)
Ready for Mischief
Ready for the Meeting
Rings on Her Fingers
School Days
Secret of the Flowers, The
Serious Thought! A
Sincerely Yours
Sister's First Love
Snowbirds
Spring (Nat'l Art Co. 17)
Spring Song
Summer (Nat'l Art Co. 18)
Sunshine
Sweet Lips of Coral Hue
Sweetheart
Thinking of You
To My Sweetheart
To My Valentine
To-Day?
Token of Love, A
Tomorrow
True as the Blue Above
Twins, The
Twixt Doubt and Hope
Vanity
Waiting for You
When Dreams Come True
When His Ship Comes in
Whisperings of Love (Annunciation)
Winter
Winter
Winter Whispers . . .
With Care for None
Yesterday!
Youth
Young America

Other Pubs. (incl. National Art Co., Wildt & Kray)

Original designs and re-issues of Reinthal titles.

Price range .. .. £2/**£3**/£5

BONZAGNI, AROLDO (1887–1918)

Italian artist who drew both glamorous girls *en déshabillé* and fund-raising designs. These included anti-Austrian caricatures. Periods 2 to 4.

Price range .. .. £3/**£6**/£12

BOUTET, HENRI (1851–1921) ■41b

An important French postcard artist of Period 1/early Period 2. The 1979 *Neudin Argus* lists nearly three hundred cards. His inspiration was in Paris night life, the *midinettes* and artists' models. His 'Corsets' series created a moral furore in England in 1901. Main publishers include Motot, A. D., La Librairie Charles, L'Atelier d'Art, and in England, Southwood. He contributed card No. 8 of the 'Collection des Cent' (*see* COLLECTIONS) and apart from his glamorous art designs, produced some cards with a military theme.

Price range (highest value for the 'Cent'
   card) .. .. £5/**£20**/£60

■40a

H. M. Bateman. Advert for Simpson's-in-the-Strand. Period 4 .. .. £3

■40b

F. O. Beirne. Argyle & Sutherland Highlanders. UB. *Period 1/early Period 2* £3

■40c

A. Bertiglia. Published in Italy. The Laundress. Period 3 .. .. £2

BRADSHAW, PERCY V. ■110a

Born to a totally inartistic family, Bradshaw always had the desire to draw. At the age of 14 he started work with an advertising agency and in his spare time persevered until he sold a picture to *Boy's Own Paper*. He progressed to his firm's Art Department, but at 18 he went freelance, gradually getting work with a number of magazines. He also started writing and eventually started the correspondence art school that made him famous. It grew apace and by 1915 he had over three thousand students a year. During his long productive years, many of his clever and humorous drawings were reproduced as postcards. Over one hundred and fifty designs have been recognised, some signed only with his initials, 'P.V.B.'

Pub. Misch & Co. (Early Period 2)

Series No. 947 Excentricity ..	£2/**£3**/£5
948 Smiles	£2/**£3**/£5
Others	£1.50/**£2**/£4

Pub. Moss & Co. (Early Period 2)

Series No. 4415 Musical Terms up to Date	£2/**£4**/£6
Others	£1.50/**£3**/£5

Pub. Tuck

22 known series incl.:
Early Period 2
Series No. 1001 Market Reports
　　　　　 1002 Tennis
　　　　　 1178 Racing Illustrated
　　　　　 1179 Stock Exchange Notes
　　　　　 1279 Parliamentary Notes
　　　　　 1288 Billiard Terms
　　　　　 1289 Market Reports
　　　　　 1307 Yachting Terms
　　　　　 1308 Business Notes
　　　　　 1324 Cricket Illustrated
　　　　　 1325 Cricket Terms
　　　　　 1365 Football Terms
　　　　　 1366 Weather Reports
　　　　　 1367 Stock Exchange Notes
　　　　　 1624 The Five Senses (6th card 'The
　　　　　　　　 Jester introduces himself')
　　　　　 1767 Newspaper Headings
　　　　　 1768 The Cockney Yachtsman
　　　　　　　　　　　　　　 £3/**£4**/£6
Oilette
Series No. 6142 Fiscal Football
　　　　　 6400 A Telephone Tragedy
　　　　　 9097 Popular Fiction Illustrated
　　　　　 9248 The General Election
　　　　　　　　　　　　　　 £2/**£3**/£5

Pub. Wrench

Nos. 18043–18048 Shakespeare Illustrated by 'Toasts'. £3/**£4**/£6
Others
Various .. .. £1/**£2**/£4

■41a

Philip Boileau. Pub. Reinthal & Newman. 'Sweetheart'. Period 2 .. .. £2

■41b

Henri Boutet. Pub. E.G. Paris. Collection des Cent. *No. 8. Period 2* £60

■41c

Tom Browne. Pub. Alexander Baird. The signed Series. PU *1904* £6

BRETT, MOLLY

Subjects include animals and fairies.

Pub. Faulkner, C. W. .. .. .. 75p/**£1**/£1.25
Pub. Medici Society .. .. .. 75p/**£1**/£1.25

BROWNE, TOM (1870–1910) ■41c, 110b

Born and educated in Nottingham until the age of 11 at St. Mary's National School, his artistic talent soon began to blossom. Passing through local art school he moved to London where his comic style developed. He created 'Weary Willie and Tired Tim', joined the Langham Sketching Club and was published in *Punch*. A co-founder with his friend, Dudley Hardy, of the rip-roaring London Sketch Club (of which he was President in 1907), his work was first exhibited at the Royal Academy in 1897. In 1898 he was made a member of the Royal Society of British Artists and in 1901 a member of the Royal Institute of Painters in Water Colours. His acute but sympathetic observation made him the recorder *par excellence* of the Edwardian working classes at play and at home. On the serious side, his Dutch themes, the result of cycling tours in Holland, are sensitively executed. Two visits to the United States produced some amusing American postcard comments. His untimely death from cancer at the age of 39 deprived postcard design of one of its most natural and outstanding artists. To date his known postcard output is more than 1300 designs. *See also* COMIC.

Pub. Baird, Alexander

Two series of Dutch themes on deep brown mounts; among his finest postcard work .. .. £2/**£4**/£6

Commercial work

See also ADVERTISING, ARTISTS and THEATRE.

Arcadians, The	..	..	..	£4/**£6**/£8
Beechams pills	..	..	..	£10/**£15**/£20
Eucryl soap	..	..	..	£4/**£6**/£8
Fry's chocolate & cocoa	..	..	£10/**£15**/£20
Peak Frean biscuits	..	..	£4/**£6**/£8
Raleigh bicycles	..	..	£10/**£15**/£20
Weekly Telegraph	..	..	£2/**£4**/£6
Others	..	..	..	£2/**£4**/£6

Pub. Davidson Bros.

Comic series. 2500–2648 (excl. the serious sets below). Subjects include: billiards, boating, cats, Mrs. Caudle's lectures, chicks, courting, cricket, cycling, dogs, fishing, football, golfing, holidays, hunting, Ma & Pa, Military, Naval, Uncle Podger, Weary Willie & Tired Tim. Many were overprinted as greetings cards.

Price range .. .. £1/**£2.50**/£5

Serious series. 2529, 2531–2533, 2542–2543. Castles, Cathedrals, Dutch and London views.

Price range .. .. £1/**£2**/£4

Pub. Hartmann

About five series. Subjects include 'Celebrities' and 'Eminent Men in the Days of Their Youth' .. .. £2.50/**£5**/£10

Pub. Landeker & Brown

'Ellanbee Aquasimile' series .. .. £2/**£4**/£6

Pub. Tuck

Many Oilette series, unsigned, subjects include Jokes from *Punch*, Seaside Humour, Dutch Studies, etc. Periods 2, 3 .. .. £2/**£4**/£6

Pub. Valentine

About ten series, of which about half are signed. Subjects include 'Christmas Humour', 'London Studies', 'Proverbs' .. .. £2/**£4**/£6

Pub. Wrench

Three known series. Dutch themes, Humour of Life, *Punch* Illustrations .. £2/**£4**/£6

■42a

Frances Brundage. Pub. Tuck. 'Little Hollanders'. No. 6910, chromolithograph. Period 2 .. £5

BRUNDAGE, FRANCES (1854–1937)
■42a

Born in New Jersey, USA, she started illustrating books for Tuck in their New York offices, progressing to postcard designs for them and for Sam Gabriel. She travelled to England, working for Tuck there. Nearly three hundred signed designs have been identified; in addition there are many unsigned designs attributed to Brundage and some signed only with her initials, F.B. She specialised in CHILDREN and GREETINGS (*qv*).

Pub. Gabriel, Sam (from 1910)
Nineteen sets of 10 cards have been identi- fied, including Halloween and Thanks- giving .. .. £1/**£1.50**/£3

Pub. Tuck (from 1900)
About 25 sets, some unsigned, including 'coons', Dutch children, greetings .. .. £2/**£3**/£5

Others
Various .. .. £1/**£1.50**/£2

BRUNELLESCHI, UMBERTO (1886– 1949) ■31b

Italian artist whose finest work was a series of imaginative girls as birds, butterflies, etc. pub- lished *c.* 1920 in the *Art Deco* style. He also did strong patriotic and military designs and some commercial work, incl. illustrations for the French fashion magazine, *Journal des Dames et des Modes* and the *Guirlande des Mois*.
Price range .. .. £20/**£35**/£45

BUCHANAN, FRED
Comic artist, Periods 2 to 4 ■43a

Pub. Tuck
Taking the Waters, etc. .. 75p/**£1.50**/£2.50

Pub. Woolstone Bros.
Comic series .. .. 50p/**75p**/£1

Others
Various .. .. –/**50p**/75p

BULL, RENE ■43b
Period 2 comic artist, whose humour often had a political flavour. Publishers include Davidson Bros., C. W. Faulkner. Landeker & Brown (Ellanbee)—Humorous & Fiscal series, Chas. Voisey—Humours of Billiards, and others.
Price range .. .. £2/**£3**/£4

BUXTON, DUDLEY ■43c
Period 2 comic artist. Publishers include Inter-Art 'Comique' series, A. V. N. Jones and others
Price range .. .. 50p/**75p**/£1.50

■43a
Fred Buchanan. Pub. Tuck. 'Taking the Waters'. No. 3631. Period 4 .. .. £2.25

■43b
Rene Bull. Pub. Davidson Bros. 'Bai Jove'. PU *1906* £3

■43c
Dudley Buxton. Pub. Inter-Art. War-time Regulations. Period 3 .. ..75p

CALDECOTT, RANDOLPH (1846–1886)
■44a

Born the son of a Cheshire accountant who forced him to stifle his love of art in order to train in a 'sound profession', Caldecott became a bank clerk, in Whitchurch, in 1861. Later promoted he moved to a Manchester bank and studied in the evenings at the Manchester Art School. In 1868 his first drawings were published in a local paper. In 1879 he was befriended by Thomas Armstrong of the South Kensington Museum, and thus encouraged he became a regular contributor to *London Society*, resigned his job and enrolled in the Slade Life Class. He went on to contribute to *The Graphic* and *Punch* and to illustrate the children's books—*John Gilpin* (1878), *The Three Huntsmen* and *Ride a Cock Horse* (1884)—drawings from which were reproduced in postcard form by Frederick Warne & Co. in 1929/30. Heart trouble following rheumatic fever forced him to winter in Florida, where he died in February 1886.

Pub. Frederick Warne & Co. Period 4
Series A & B
    John Gilpin (A1, A2, B1, B2)
    The Three Jovial Huntsmen (A3, A4, B3, B4)
    Elegy on the Death of a Mad Dog (A5, A6, B5, B6)
Series C & D
    The House that Jack Built (C1, C2, D1, D2)
    Sing a Song of Sixpence (C3, C4, D3, D4)
    The Queen of Hearts (C5, C6, D5, D6)
Series E
    Hey Diddle Diddle (E1, E2)
    Baby Bunting (E3, E4)
    The Milkmaid (E5, E6, F5, F6)
Series F
    Ride a Cock Horse (F1, F2)
    A Farmer Went Trotting (F3, F4)
    The Milkmaid (Numbering error by Warne's. See Series E above)
Series G & H
    A Frog he Would . . . (G1, G2, H1, H2)
    Come Lasses & Lads (G3, G4, H3, H4)
    The Frog Jumps Over . . . (G5, G6, H5, H6)
These were packaged in sets of 6. They were also sold as 4 packets, each containing 2 sets of 6.
Price range   ..   ..   –/**50p**/75p

CALDERARA, C.
Italian artist of fashion and glamour with a distinct *Art Deco* flavour, often featuring motor cars in the design. *See also* GLAMOUR and WAR.
Price range   ..   ..   £2/**£4**/£6

CAMARA, LEAL de (1877–1948) ■165b
Spanish artist, most of whose best postcard work was done in Paris. Most famous for his limited edition political caricatures (*see also* POLITICAL). He also contributed many illustrations which were reproduced as postcards for the satirical magazine *L'Assiette au Beurre*. Bicycles and motor cars were favourite subjects (Period 2).
Bicycle themes ..   ..   £8/**£10**/£15
Motor car themes   ..   ..   ..   £10/**£15**/£20
Others   ..   ..   £7/**£9**/£12

CARAN D'ACHE (Emmanuel Poiré) (1859–1909) ■44b
French artist of Russian extraction ('Caran D'Ache' is a gallicised version of the Russian for pencil) he contributed to some of the great early French series (*see* COLLECTIONS) and is most famous for his military designs.
Price range (highest valuation for the 'Cent' cards) ..   ..   £10/**£25**/£100

■44a
Randolph Caldecott. Pub. Warne & Co. 'A Frog he Would A-wooing Go'. Period 4 ..   ..75p

■44b
Caran d'Ache (*Emmanuel Poiré*). *Pub. E.G. Paris*. Collection des Cent. *Period 2* ..   £100

CARTER, REGINALD ARTHUR LEE (1886–1950) ■46a

Carter was born, and lived most of his life, in Southwold, Suffolk. A member of the North British Academy, he contributed to magazines like *The Sketch* and *The Tatler*. His versatile and prolific output of postcards spanned Periods 2 to 4 and was produced by a variety of publishers, including himself ('The Sorrows of Southwold' printed by the Southwold Press). *See also* ANIMALS.

Pub. B. P. & Co. (Period 4)
Birthday greetings for 1–8 year olds. The
set .. .. £2/**£3**/£4

Pub. Dennis, E. T. W.
'Southwold' comic card .. .. .. –/**50p**/75p

Pub. Ettlinger
John Chinaman's Winter Sports (1905)
.. .. 50p/**75p**/£1
Office humour (1906) .. .. .. 50p/**75p**/£1
Other series .. .. 50p/**75p**/£1

Pub. Mack, E. (Period 2)
Various designs including some fine political
cartoons .. .. 50p/**£1**/£2

Pub. Millar & Lang (Periods 2, 3)
Several series, incl. 'At the Seaside'
1910 .. .. –/**50p**/75p

Pub. Salmon, J. (Period 2)
Several series .. .. –/**50p**/75p

Pub. Southwold Press and Reg. Carter (Period 4)
'Sorrows of Southwold'. Two series of
6 .. .. 50p/**75p**/£1.50
Period 7 reprints per set **50p**

Pub. Stiebel, Alfred (Periods 2, 3)
'Modern Humour' series, incl.
'Scouting' .. .. .. 50p/**75p**/£1.50

Pub. Valentine (Periods 2 to 4)
Series include motoring and seaside
themes .. .. –/**50p**/75p

Pub. Verdier (1909)
Hints to Aeroplanists, Hints to Roller Skaters, A Labour of Love, Studies of Paradise (some with adverts for Sunlight soap), The Territorials, etc. .. 50p/**75p**/£2

Pub. Wildt & Kray
Chinamen series (1904) .. 50p/**75p**/£1.50
Fashion series (1910–1914) for men and for
women .. .. 75p/**£1**/£1.50

CARTER, SYDNEY (1874–1945) ■46b

Born in Enfield, Middlesex, he moved shortly to Epping Forest, where his lifelong love of trees started. At 15 he went to Walthamstow Art School, was exhibited at the Royal Academy at the age of 20 and went on to the Royal College of Art. He won several art scholarships and was exhibited at the Paris Salon and the British Institute of Watercolours and Oils. After WW1 (during which he was a military postman), he married and emigrated to South Africa, where his distinguished career as artist and teacher continued until his death. About 170 postcard designs have been identified.

Pub. Birn Bros. (1904)
London views, set of 6 .. .. .. 50p/**75p**/£1

Pub. Hildesheimer
See also LITERARY.
At least twenty series, including 'How Men Propose' (twelve cards), 'Months of the Year' (twelve cards), Hans Andersen Fairy Tales, sketches from Scott, Shakespeare, Thackeray. (50% premium for complete sets of twelve) .. 50p/**£1**/£1.50

Pub. Smith, W. H. and Ashton, Wm.
Ancient British Halls, set of 6 .. 50p/**75p**/£1

Pub. Tuck
The Homes of Literary Men, set of
6 .. .. 50p/**75p**/£1

CASCELLA, BASILIO (1860–1950)

Italian artist whose range covered commemorative designs with an *Art Nouveau* flavour, local 'Abruzzi' types, patriotic designs and glamour.

Price range .. .. 75p/**£3**/£7.50

CASS1ERS, HENRI (b. 1858)

Fine Belgian artist who designed for the postcard from its earliest pictorial days. His distinctive but delicate style found expression in Dutch scenes with figures, landscapes and town scenes. His series for the shipping line 'Red Star' are beautiful examples of how well the art of the poster translates to the smaller medium.

Pub. Dietrich of Brussels from 1900

Bruxelles et Anvers Pittoresque .. £3/**£4**/£5
Glasgow Exhibition (*see* EXHIBITIONS)
.. .. £2/**£3**/£5
La Hollande Pittoresque .. .. £2/**£3**/£5
Le Littoral Belge .. .. £2/**£3**/£5
London views .. .. £2/**£3**/£5
18th-century Characters .. .. £2/**£3**/£5
En Zélande .. .. £2/**£3**/£5

Pub. Moss, Henry & Co. (1903–1905)

Several series .. .. £2/**£3**/£5

Pub. Huardel, P. G. & Co. from 1900

Paris views .. .. £2/**£3**/£5

Pub. Southwood, F. C. (1901)

Several series .. .. £1/**£2**/£4

Red Star Liner Advertisements

Thirty cards have been identified .. £5/**£10**/£15

CATON WOODVILLE, RICHARD ■46c

Born of a German mother and partly educated in Germany, Caton Woodville served under Kitchener in Egypt. He covered the Boer War as a military artist and continued his military work during WW1. *See also* HISTORICAL and WAR.

■46a

Reg. Carter. Pub. Mack. Caricature of Lloyd George. Period 2 .. .. £2

■46b

Sydney Carter. Pub. Hildesheimer. Hans Andersen Fairy Tale. Period 2 .. .. £1

■46c

R. Caton-Woodville. 'Imperial Army' series. 10th Bengal Lancers (1904) £3

Early Period 2

Pub. Collectors' Pub. Co. (1901). Five sets of Boer War cards	£1/**£2**/£4
Pub. Hartmann, Fred. (1901). Famous British Battles	£1/**£1.50**/£3
Pub. 'Imperial Army Series' (1904). Military types	£1/**£1.50**/£3
Pub. Picture Postcard Co. Boer War designs	£1/**£2**/£4
Pub. Watkins & McCombie. The Gentleman in Khaki	£1/**£1.50**/£2

Period 3

Designs for St. Dunstans	75p/**£1**/£1.25
Others (tanks, etc.)	50p/**75p**/£1

CHÉRET, JULES (1836–1932) ■47a

French *Art Nouveau* artist who contributed to many of the important early French series, like the 'Job' (No. 3, 1896), Editions Cino (Nos. 1–7 and probably 27 and 34, 1898), *Les Affiches Célèbres* (French Tuck series), *La Collection des Cent* (No. 35, 1901), *Les Cartes Postales Mariani* (adverts for Mariani wine, 1910). From 1856–66 Cheret had studied colour lithography in London and on his return to Paris made a great impact on theatrical poster design (of which he is credited with designing over 1000) and hence on the postcard.

Price range .. .. £30/**£50**/£75

CHIOSTRI, CARLO

Italian *Art Deco* artist. Subjects include pierrots, fashion and lovely ladies. He was at his peak in 1925.

Price range .. .. £3/**£6**/£10

CHRISTIANSEN, HANS ■47b

Art Nouveau artist who contributed to many of the important early French and German series, e.g. 'Les Maîtres de la Carte Postale' (1898–1900) and 'Jugend' (1899).

Price range .. .. £25/**£50**/£70

CHRISTIE, GEORGE FYFFE ■48a

Scottish artist who often signed with his initials 'G.F.C.' and who worked for many Scottish as well as London companies. His work on the postcard spanned Periods 2 to 5. *See also* COMIC.

Pub. Lyon, Wm, Glasgow

Several comic series and some fine early political caricatures (Joseph Chamberlain, etc.) .. .. £1/**£1.50**/£2

Pub. Millar & Lang

Periods 2 to 4. Many series, often unsigned .. .. 50p/**75p**/£1

Pub. Misch & Co.

Addled Ads (1903) .. .. 75p/**£1**/£2

Pub. Photochrom

Several series. Periods 2, 3	50p/**75p**/£1
Home Guard Silhouettes. Period 5	50p/**75p**/£1

Pub. Ritchie, Wm. & Sons

Several series (*c.* 1907) incl. Diabolo, Our . . . (Evening at Home, Boarding House, etc.) .. ..75p/**£1**/£1.25

■47a

Jules Cheret. Period 2 reproduction of 1896 Job Calendar £40

■47b

Hans Christiansen. Design for 'Jugend' (1899) £50

47

CHRISTY, F. EARL (1883–1961)

This American artist (no relation to Howard Christy) was trained at the Pennsylvania Academy of Fine Arts. His specialised version of the American Girl was the 'College Girl' or 'Belle'. He drew for magazines and posters, and the many postcard versions of his designs were produced by a variety of publishers. *See also* GLAMOUR.

Price range .. .. £1/**£1.50**/£2

CHRISTY, HOWARD CHANDLER (1873–1952)

American exponent of a brand of the American Girl known as the 'Christy Girl'. He studied at the National Academy of Design and the Art Students League and became a successful commercial artist, working as a war illustrator in Cuba and for *Scribner's Magazine*, *Harpers*, *Colliers* and *Cosmopolitan*. During WW1 he did many patriotic designs. *See also* GLAMOUR.

Price range .. .. £1/**£2**/£3

CLAPSADDLE, ELLEN (1865–1934),
■133b

One of America's most popular artists, specialising in CHILDREN and GREETINGS (*qv*). George and Dorothy Miller credit her with three thousand signed cards. She worked for several years in Germany where she was stranded when WW1 broke out. Most of her work was published by the International Art Co.

Price range .. .. £1/**£2**/£3

CLOKE, RENE

Period 4 artist whose subjects include animals, children and fairies. Publishers include C. W. Faulkner, J. Salmon and Valentine. *See also* CHILDREN.

Price range .. ..75p/**£1**/£1.25
Period 7. Salmon designs .. .. −/**25p**/50p

COMBAZ, GISBERT ■48b

A superb Belgian artist of the *Art Nouveau* school. His 1898–1900 sets of 12 of 'The Elements', 'The Proverbs', 'The Sins' are particularly sought after. Pub. Dietrich of Brussels.

Price range .. .. £10/**£20**/£25

COMICUS

Pseudonym for Parlett, Harry (*qv*).

COPPING, HAROLD (1863–1932)

Artist who drew the famous picture 'The Hope of the World'. In his postcard work he specialised in classical and religious themes, also sentimental designs during Period 3. Pub. Degen & Co. 'England, Home and Beauty'.

Price range .. .. £1/**£2**/£4

■48a
George Fyffe Christie. Pub. Misch & Stock. 'Addled Ads.' No. 94. Period 2 .. .. .. £2

■48b
G. Combaz. 'The Elements' series—La Terre. Period 1, 2 .. ..£20

■48c
Hilda Cowham. Pub. Valentine's. 'Who'll Get the Apple?' Period 4 .. .. £1.50

CORBELLA, TITO (b. 1885) ■49a

Versatile Italian artist, who is best known in the glamour field. Like Barribal, Boileau and Kirchner he used his wife as his model. He also drew powerful propaganda designs. *See also* GLAMOUR.

Glamour designs .. .. ..   £1.50/**£2.50**/£4
Edith Cavell set. Period 3 (*see also* POLITICAL) (up to 50% premium for complete set) .. ..   £5/**£7**/£8

COWHAM, HILDA ■48c

An artist who specialised in drawing children and cats, her work is becoming increasingly popular. From 1913 to 1922 she produced 24 different designs for Inter-Art and several series for Valentine's.

Price range .. .. 75p/**£1**/£1.50

CYNICUS

See Anderson, Martin.

DANIELL, EVANGELINE MARY (1880–1902)

Although only about half a dozen postcard designs have been identified because of her tragically early death, this suberb *Art Nouveau* artist is amongst the most highly regarded exponents of the style. She is as highly esteemed on the Continent as in Britain, and even Queen Victoria chose one of her designs for the Royal New Year card in 1901.

Pub. Tuck. Modern Art series 2524/5 .. ..   £30/**£40**/£50

DAVEY, GEORGE ■49b

Period 2 comic artist whose humour often contained political overtones. *See also* POLITICAL.

Pub. Mandel, J. & Co.
'Straphangers' and others .. ..75p/**£1**/£1.50

Pub. Misch & Stock
'The Tourist series' and others .. £1/**£1.50**/£2

Pub. Valentine
Various designs .. ..75p/**£1**/£1.50

DE FEURE

Highly sought after French *Art Nouveau* artist who contributed to the rare 'Cocorico' series (*see* COLLECTIONS) .. .. £100/**£200**/£400

DEXTER, MARJORIE MAY (b. c. 1900)

Born in Wellingborough, she attended the Northampton School of Arts & Crafts. Most of her designs were for folded greetings cards and she also illustrated books. The small number of postcards so far identified by this attractive children's artist were for Salmon and Valentine's during Periods 4, 5.

Pub. Salmon. Nos. 3765, 3766, 3769, others.
Pub. Valentine's. Hand-painted effect, others.
Price range .. .. –/**50p**/75p

■49a
Tito Corbella. Published in Italy. Period 4   £2.50

■49b
Geo. Davey. Pub. Valentine. 'Suffragette' series. PU *1907. Premium because of subject matter* £4

DUDOVICH MARCELLO (1878–1962) ■31d
Italian artist whose postcard work spanned from 1900 to 1950. His subject matter ranged from commemorative (e.g. exhibitions, festivals) to adverts for theatrical productions, products like Vermouth, Tyres, Fernet-Branca, etc. to patriotic propaganda during WW1, to glamour in Period 4.
Price range .. .. £4/**£20**/£30

DUNCAN, COWAN
Specialist in comic heads and Scottish themes in Period 4.
Pub. Millar & Lang, Series 2616/7 and others .. ..75p/**£1**/£1.50

DUNCAN, JAMES ALLAN (HAMISH) ■50a
Comic artist, usually on Scottish themes, who drew under the name 'Hamish' or 'Hamish Duncan'. He used his real name for his more serious work.

Pub. Davidson Bros.
Period 2. Several series of Scottish humour (signed Hamish Duncan) .. .. 50p/**75p**/£1

Pub. Monson Bros., Glasgow
Glasgow views (1901) .. .. .. –/**25p**/50p

Pub. Tuck
Period 2. Several series of Scottish humour (signed Hamish) .. .. .. 50p/**75p**/£1

DWIGGINS, CLARE VICTOR (DWIG) (1873–1958) ■50b
Born in Wilmington, Ohio, Dwiggins became a self-taught, self-appointed professor of freehand drawing, who contributed to various newspapers and journals. His first postcard was designed in 1903 for Tuck and he went on to design well over 350 identified cards, some unsigned, for a variety of publishers. He often used his wife as his model. Even his girlie cards bear an unmistakeable touch of humour. *See also* COMIC.

Pub. Kaplan, R.
How Can You Do It? Two series.

Newspaper Cartoon Series (Period 4)
Huck Finn, Nipper & Bill's Diary, Tom Sawyer.

Pub. Rose, Charles
Baby, Frankfurter Girl, Moon, Moving, New York Series, Oyster Girl, Sandwich, Superstition, What are the Wild Waves Saying?

Pub. Tuck
Cheer Up, Everytime, Facts & Fancies, Jollies & Follies, Knocks Witty & Wise, Love Potions, Love's Reveries, Never, Pipe Dreams, School Days, Smiles, Toasts for Occasions, Toasts for Today, Zodiac.

Other Publishers include:
Anderson, W. P.; Blue, A.; Cardinell, Vincent; Gabriel, Sam; Gross, Eric.

Price range for all the above Dwiggins postcards .. .. £1/**£2**/£3

■50a
James Allan (Hamish) Duncan. Pub. Davidson Bros. PU *1903* £1

■50b
Clare ('Dwig') Dwiggins. Pub. Tuck. 'Dry Humour' School Days. Series No. 6. Period 4 £2

EARNSHAW, HAROLD (d. 1937) ■53a

Member of the London Sketch Club and Chelsea Arts Club, he married Mabel Lucie Attwell (*qv*) and they had two sons and a daughter. During WW1 he lost his right arm but he learnt to draw with his left and went on to contribute to *Punch*, illustrate books for Blackie, etc. His postcard work is mostly of a comic nature.

Pub. Gottschalk, Dreyfus & Davis
Period 2 designs, 'Star' series ..   –/**50p**/75p

Pub. Pulman, Geo. & Sons
Period 3 designs .. ..   –/**50p**/75p

Others
Price range .. ..   –/**50p**/75p

ELLAM, WILLIAM HENRY ■53b

Versatile and competent Period 2 artist, whose work includes a variety of general and humorous subjects.

Pub. Excelsior Fine Art Pub. Co.
Famous personages in their cars (e.g. Joseph Chamberlain in his Dixi, Duke of Connaught in his Daimler) .. .. 75p/**£1**/£2

Pub. Faulkner, C. W.
Several series of Teddy Bears .. 75p/**£1**/£1.25

Pub. Hildesheimer
Various designs, incl. 'Hard Workers' .. .. 50p/**75p**/£1

Pub. Stewart & Woolf
Seaside themes .. .. 50p/**75p**/£1

Pub. Tuck
Breakfast in Bed, Gentle Art of Angling and other series .. .. £1/**£1.50**/£2
'Japanese' series .. .. .. £1.50/**£2**/£2.50

ENDACOTT, LILLIE (*see* ENDACOTT SIDNEY)

ENDACOTT, SIDNEY (1873–1918)

Born the fifth of seven sons of an old Devon family, Sidney was educated at Ashburton Grammar School and the Blundell School. In 1893 he followed his brothers, William and Frank, to Kansas, USA, where he quickly established a reputation as a talented wood carver. His greatest achievement during his year in the USA was the art carving of a mansion 'The Castle' in Kansas, which is now a preserved building. Returning to Devon he worked as a sculptor and carver; his crucifixes being particularly admired. In his leisure time he joined the Ashburton band and was a competent musician. In 1903 he married Bertha Lillie Haydon ('Lily') and for a while worked as an instructor at Exeter Art School. Going freelance he worked for Worth's Gallery in Exeter, and continued to do so until his early death. Suffering from ill health, he taught his wife to paint so that she could support herself, and after his death she did indeed produce postcards for Worth in a very similar style to her husband's. Endacott's prolific output of postcards for Worth (listed below are all the titles that have been identified) were delivered as water colours, photographed and then printed by collotype. These were then hand tinted to the original colours. He also drew for Frith & Co. of Reigate and other publishers. During WW1 Sidney sketched military lorry parts for an operating manual and died just eight days before the Armistice. When Lily died in 1952 she was buried with him in Exeter Cemetery under a headstone shaped like an artist's palette.

Picturesque England Series (No Publisher named)
1. Gardener's Cottage, Stoke Canon
2. Woodman's Cottage, St. Cyres
3. Waggoner's Cottage, Kenton
4. Miller's Cottage, Lapford
5. Farm Labourer's Cottage, Cowley
6. Keeper's Cottage, Alphington

Devon Worthies Series
1. Sir Walter Raleigh
2. Sir Francis Drake
3. Sir Humphrey Gilbert
4. Sir Richard Grenville
5. Sir John Hawkins
6. Rev. Charles Kingsley

Exeter Cathedral
1. West Front, Showing 14th-century screen
2. Cathedral from Palace Garden
3. North Tower and Porch
4. Minstrel Gallery and Old Font
5. The Patterson Pulpit in Nave
6. West Front—No side building on right
7. South Tower
8. Bishop's Palace
9. Abbot's Lodge—1 figure in doorway
10. Inner Courtyard—Cleric under arch
11. Inner Courtyard—Showing Jacobean door
12. Inner Courtyard—Pump on left

13. Inner Courtyard—Pump on right, door ajar
14. Inner Courtyard—Pump on right, door open
15. Abbot's Lodge—2 figures and child in doorway
16. Cathedral Close—Through two arches
17. Cathedral Close—Door and five windows of house
18. The Quadrangle, Close
19. West Front—Coach and Horse
20. Cathedral Close—Arch, Gallery and Cleric
21. Cathedral Close—Half arch, half Jacobean door.

Buildings in and Near Exeter

1. Mol's Coffee House, dated 1596
1a. Mol's Coffee House, dated 1580
2. Mol's Coffee House—Woman and child in doorway
3. Mol's Coffee House—Side view
4. Oak Panelled Gallery interior, dated 1580
5. Oak Panelled Gallery interior, dated 1596
6. Oak Pannelled Gallery interior, Sepia
7. Old Cavalier's House, Fore Street
8. Old House, High Street (H. Stocker & Co.)
9. Old House, High Street (Pretty, Hairdresser)
10. Old Houses, High Street (Red Cross Flag and Mounting Block)
11. Old Houses, High Street (Hinton, Lake & Brown)
12. Old House, King Street
13. Old Shop facing Post Office
14. Old House, Frog Street
15. Old Houses, Fore Street
16. *Express & Echo* office
17. Bampfylde House (vertical)
18. Bampfylde House (horizontal)
19. Tudor House, Exe Island
20. The Liverydole, Heavitree
21. St. Catharine's Almshouses
22. St. Stephen's Bow
23. Old House, St. Mary Steps
24. Old Tudor House—Girl with basket in foreground
25. Old Priory of St. Nicholas in olden days
26. Old Priory of St. Nicholas (1910?)
27. Old Rougemont Castle—Man on horse
28. Old Rougemont Castle—Judge's Carriage
29. Old Watchtower, Rougemont Grounds
30. Old Guildhall exterior—Two youths
31. Old Guildhall exterior—Man with cart
32. Old Guildhall interior—One stool in foreground
33. Old Guildhall interior—Stool, settle and shaft of sunlight
34. Tucker's Hall interior
35. Hall of College of Vicars interior
36. Stepcote Hill—Men selling wares
37. Stepcote Hill—Children dancing
38. Mol's Coffee House from Cathedral
39. Old Houses in High Street
40. Old Watchtower, Rougemont (close-up-view)

Devon Cottages

1. Littleham
2. Upton Pyne
3. Countess Weir (1)—Man, children and donkey
4. Countess Weir (2)—Two women, faggots and basket
5. Countess Weir (3)—Man on horse, woman and 2 dogs
6. Cowley—Spring
7. Ide
8. Longdown in Winter
9. Killerton in Summer
10. Alphington—Man, dog and barrow
11. Alphington—Ladder against tree
12. Pinhoe—Outer chimney, two stooks or beehives
13. Alphington—Village Cross
14. Ide Brook (1)—Woman and stepping-stones
15. Ide Brook (2)—Houses and ducks
16. Near Totnes—Here Wm. of Orange held Parliament
17. Cottager working Honiton lace
18. Cottage at Cowley—Woman hanging washing
19. Cottages at Mars Hill, Lynton

Homes of Famous Devon People

1. Mile End Cottage—(Dickens vertical)
2. Mile End Cottage—(Dickens horizontal)
3. Hayes Barton—(Sir Walter Raleigh) figures and dogs
4. *as above*, No figures
5. *as above*, Kitchen interior
6. *as above*, Birthroom, showing bed
7. *as above*, Bed, window and tables
8. *as above*, Smoking Room
9. *as above*, House, large cart, four figures and dog
10. Ashe House—(Duke of Marlborough)
11. Birthplace of Sir Richard Grenville
12. Home of Rev. Baring-Gould
13. Parliament Cottages—(William of Orange)
14. 'Outlands', Devonport—(Capt. Scott)
15. Holne Parsonage, Near Totnes—(Charles Kingsley)
16. Plympton, South Devon—(Sir Joshua Reynolds)
17. Old Blundell's School, Tiverton—(Jan Ridd)

Views—Devon and Cornwall

1. Olde Street, Looe
2. Chapel Street, Looe—(Washing left, basket right)
3. Chapel Street, Looe—(Church in right background)
4. Market Street, Looe
5. Fish Street, Looe
6. Bay Street, Looe
7. Exeter Canal

Clovelly

Published by Frith's of Reigate (F) and for Worth's of Exeter (W).

1. North Hill (FW)
2. Temple Bar—Man in bottom left (F)
3. Temple Bar—Man, donkey and woman under arch (F)
4. Temple Bar—Woman pointing in doorway (F)

5. The Look-out Cottage—Man coming into view (FW)
6. Fisherman's look-out cottage—Woman in doorway (W)
7. Entrance to High Street (F)
8. At Clovelly—New Inn sign on right (F)
9. At Clovelly—As No. 8, but sign on wrong building (F)
10. At Clovelly—Man leaning on rail (F)
11. Red Lion Inn—Woman at window (FW)
12. Entrance to Village (FW)
13. Rose Cottage—Man and two donkeys (W)
14. Rose Cottage—Woman leaning over half door (W)
15. Fisherman's Cottage (F)
16. Clovelly from the Pier (W)
17. Clovelly from the Woods (W)
18. Clovelly from the Hobby Drive (F)
19. In the Hobby Drive (F)
20. Fish Street (W)
21. Crazy Kate's Cottage (W)
22. Temple Bar—Harbour on right (W)
23. Temple Bar—Harbour on left (W)
24. Temple Bar by Moonlight (W)
25. Temple Bar—Steps and donkey ascending (W)
26. North Hill—Girl at top of steps (*see* L. Endacott No. 8) (W)
27. New Inn and High Street (*see* L. Endacott No. 9) (W)
28. Red Lion Inn—Donkey by steps. Horizontal (*see* L. Endacott No. 6) (W)
29. Clovelly Harbour (W) (*see* L. Endacott No. 10) (W)
30. Temple Bar—Woman bottom left (*see* L. Endacott No. 2) (W)
31. The Red Lion Inn—similar to No. 11 but slight differences (W)
32. Rose Cottage—Man and Woman in doorway (W)

Cards by Lillie Endacott
1. Look-out Cottage—Woman in doorway
2. Temple Bar—Woman descending left
3. Temple Bar—Steps, donkey appearing right
4. Temple Bar—By Moonlight
5. Red Lion Inn—Woman at Window
6. Red Lion Inn—Donkey by steps
7. Clovelly High Street—Donkey ascending
8. North Hill—Girl at top of steps
9. High Street—Donkey descending
10. Clovelly Harbour
11. Shelley's Cottage, Lynmouth
12. Castle Rock, Lynton
13. Crazy Kate's Cottage and the Beach
14. Temple Bar, Clovelly (*see* No. 22, S. Endacott)
15. At Lynmouth.

Pub. Frith's of Reigate	£1/**£1.50**/£1.75	
Pub. Worth & Co.		
'Devon Worthies' series	£1.50/**£2**/£3	
Others	£1/**£1.75**/£2	
Pub. Unknown	£1/**£1.50**/£1.75	

■53a

Harold Earnshaw. Pub. Gottschalk, Dreyfus & Davis. PU *1907* 75p

■53b

William Henry Ellam. Pub. Tuck. 'Japanese'. No. 6717. Chromolithograph. PU *1905* .. £2.50

■53c

Sydney Endacott. Pub. Frith. Clovelly. Period 2 .. ..75p

ENGLISH, ARCHIBALD (also 'A.E.') ■54a

Prolific comic artist of Periods 2 and 3 whose work was usually signed with his initials only. Publishers include: Mitchell & Watkins, William Ritchie & Sons, Thridgould & Co.

Price range .. .. 50p/**75p**/£1

F.S.

Pseudonym for Spurgin, Fred (*qv*).

FELLER, FRANK

An illustrator for journals like *Boys Own Paper*, Feller produced some of the most thrilling action scenes reproduced on the postcard. Several series were published in the Tuck 'Oilette' range and those that have been identified are listed below.

Series 9255. 'In the Alps' (Climbing, daring rescues . . .)
Series 9263. 'Life in Russia'. Series 1 (Hunts, raids . . .)
Series 9296. 'Life in Russia'. Series 2 (Hunts, raids . . .)
Series 9312. 'In the Tyrol' (Avalanches, etc . . .)
Series 9324. 'Life in China' (Devils and Pirates . . .)
Series 9363. 'Life in Spain' (Gypsies and Smugglers . . .)
Price range .. .. £1/**£1.50**/£2

FERNAND, FERNEL 193a

French artist, best known for his racing car series (*see also* ROAD TRANSPORT) with black background and manic-looking drivers. A regular contributor to the satirical magazine, *Le Rire*, from 1898 to 1908, and to the 'Collection des Cent' (*qv*).

Courses Automobile (10 cards)
Various sporting series
Others

Price range for the above (highest valuation for the 'Cent' cards) .. .. .. £3/**£5**/£50

FISHER, HARRISON (1877–1934) ■54b

American artist born to an artistic family who, from an early age, had success as a commercial artist. He worked for the *San Francisco Call & Examiner*, and on moving to New York, for *Puck*, *Scribner's*, *Cosmopolitan*, *Life*, *The Saturday Evening Post* and *McLure's*. He drew the archetypal American Girl and many of his magazine covers and illustrations were reproduced on the postcard. *See also* GLAMOUR.

Price range .. .. £1/**£2**/£3

■54a

Archibald ('A.E.') English. Our Office Boy. PU *1907* 75p

■54b

Harrison Fisher. Pub. Reinthal & Newman. 'Princess Pat'. Period 2 .. .. £3

■54c

James Montgomery Flagg. Pub. T.P. & Co. Reprinted from Judge's. Period 2 .. .. £2

FLAGG, JAMES MONTGOMERY (1877–1960) ■54c

Best known for his poster of Uncle Sam in WW1, 'I Want You for the US Army', Flagg was born in New York. He was a member of the Arts Students League and studied in England and France. He sold work from the age of 12 and was particularly successful with his female studies. *See also* GLAMOUR.

Price range   ..   ..   75p/**£1**/£2

FLOWER, CHARLES E. (1871–1951) 217b

Watercolour artist who exhibited at the Royal Academy. Most of his postcard work was for Tuck in their Oilette series. Best known for his London series, he also drew cards from other parts of the UK, Germany, North and South America. Between 600 and 700 designs have so far been identified.

Price range   ..   ..   50p/**75p**/£1.50

FOLKARD, CHARLES (1878–1963) ■55a

Creator of the 'Teddy Tail' strip in the *Daily Mail*, Folkard was one of the best loved 'Nursery Artists' of Period 4. *See also* CHILDREN.

Pub. Black, A. C.

Series of Mother Goose Nursery Rhymes	£1.50/**£2**/£2.50
Songs from *Alice in Wonderland* (Period 4)	£1.50/**£2**/£2.50
Period 7 reprint	**50p**

FOUGASSE (Kenneth Bird) ■55b

Studied at the Percy Bradshaw Art School. During WW1 he was wounded in the spine at Gallipoli, leaving him bed-ridden for a while. Fighting back to fitness he became a contributor to *Punch*, eventually becoming art editor. His *nom de plume* comes from a small explosive mine! He is best remembered for his WW2 propaganda posters, many of which were reproduced as postcards. *See also* WAR.

Price range   ..   ..   £1/**£1.25**/£2

■55a

Charles Folkard. Pub. A. & C. Black. Songs from Alice in Wonderland. PU *1928* £2.50

■55b

Fougasse. Pub. Vase Press. Poster propaganda. 'Careless Talk Costs Lives'. Period 5   ..   ..   £2

■55c

Edmund G. Fuller. Pub. Stewart & Woolf. 'Box Cleared at Midnight'. PU *1904* £1.50

FULLER, EDMUND G. ■55c

Competent general artist, often with a touch of humour, whose best postcard work was in early Period 2.

Pub. Moss, Henry & Co. (before 1905)

Horse Racing
Hunting

Pub. Stewart & Woolf

London Types
Others
Price range for all the above Fuller cards .. .. **£1/£1.50**/£2

FULLEYLOVE, JOHN R. I. (1847–1908)

Born in Leicester, he was apprenticed to an architect. Travelling widely throughout Britain, Europe and the Near East, he drew town scenes and landscapes. As well as drawing for the postcard, he also illustrated books.
Publishers include Regal Art Co., Robert Peel, Tuck (many 'Oilette' series) .. .. **–/50p**/75p

GIBSON, CHARLES DANA ■56a

American artist now mostly remembered for his fashionable, glamorous creation, 'The Gibson Girl' (thought to be modelled on the artiste Camille Clifford, and on his wife, Irene Langhorne, sister of the future Lady Astor). He was a competent and successful artist. His well-observed b & w drawings gained him a contract in 1904 with *Collier's Weekly* for $100,000 for 100 drawings! During WW1 he was President of the Society of Illustrators and directed propaganda designs for the US war effort. After the war he became owner and editor of *Life* magazine.

Most of his postcard work is gentle, acutely observed situation humour of the mores and pastimes of the Edwardian middle classes—especially their courtship rituals. It was mainly published by James Henderson & Son, reprinted from their magazine, *Snapshots*. At least seventy-two designs have been identified and many 'Gibson type' series by other artists were also published by Henderson in their 'Pictorial Comedy' and other series. *See also* GLAMOUR.
Price range .. .. **£1/£1.50**/£2

GILBERT, CHARLES ALLAN (b. 1873)

Born in Hartford, Connecticut, USA he studied in New York and Paris. He illustrated *Women of Fiction* and *A Message from Mars* and, on the postcard, typical 'American Girls' (*see also* GLAMOUR).
Price range .. .. **75p/£1**/£2

GILL, ARTHUR ■56b

Much under-rated artist with a light comic touch. Period 2.
Pub. Tuck. Seaside Sketches. Humorous series 6077 .. .. .. **£1/£1.50**/£2.50
Pub. Tuck. Others .. .. .. **£1/£1.50**/£2.50

GODILLOT

Pseudonym for Orens (*qv*).

■56a

Charles Dana Gibson. Pub. Henderson. 'Heads'. No. 13. Col. with Art Nouveau *border. Period 2* **£2**

■56b

Arthur Gill. Pub. Tuck. Seaside Sketches. No. 6077. Chromolithograph. Period 2 .. **£2.50**

GUNN, ARCHIE (b. 1863) ■57a

Born in Taunton, Somerset, he found fame in the USA for his portrayals of 'The American Girl' (*see* GLAMOUR) and for his patriotic designs during WW1 (*see also* WAR).

Price range .. .. £1/**£1.50**/£2

GWENNET, GUNN

He produced some highly coloured, comic designs for Philco, e.g. Series 4001—'Some British Workmen', 4002—London Antiquities Up-to-Date', 4009—'Abbreviations'.

Price range .. ..75p/**£1**/£1.50

HAMISH

Pseudonym for Duncan, James Allen (*qv*).

HAMPEL, WALTER (sometimes seen as HAMPL) ■57b

Austrian artist, much of whose fine work was published by Philipp & Kramer soon after the turn of the century. Series include 'Carnaval', 'Variété' .. .. .. £15/**£25**/£35

HANSEN

Pseudonym for Nolde, Emile (*qv*).

HANSI (J. J. Waltz) ■57c

French artist famous for his Alsace/Lorraine designs. Periods 2, 3.

Price range .. .. £3/**£5**/£10

HARBOUR, JENNIE ■58a

Delicate artist of lovely ladies, etc., often in Period dress. Her main output was for Tuck (Oilette de Luxe). Some designs show an *Art Deco* flavour.

Price range .. .. £2/**£4**/£6

■57a

Archie Gunn (USA). Pub. Illus. Postal Card & Nov. Co. No. 1371. 'We Won't Come Back. . . .' Period 3 .. .. £1.50

■57b

Walter Hampel. Pub. Philipp & Kramer. Cyclist (1899) £30

■57c

Hansi (J. J. Waltz). Alsatian Girl. Period 3 .. £5

HARDY, DUDLEY (1867–1922)

Born in Sheffield, son of the marine painter, T. B. Hardy, he was sent at the age of 15 to Düsseldorf to study under Crola and Lowenstein, but irked by the constricting tuition he rebelled and was dismissed. He stayed in Düsseldorf and enjoyed some commercial success, being re-admitted to the Academy. Returning to England he studied under A. A. Calderon and then under Verlat in Antwerp and Raphael Collin in Paris. He first exhibited in the Royal Academy in 1885 at the age of 18. In 1888 he was exhibited at the Paris Salon. His humorous work (which accounts for most of his 125 postcard designs) was also published in *Punch*. He designed theatrical posters as well. Hardy was a founder member of the London Sketch Club, where he showed a well-developed talent for amateur music hall, and of which he was a president. *See also* ADVERTISING and COMIC.

Advertising work
Tuck 'Celebrated Posters' No. 1502 Liebig
The Pearl Girl
Egyptian Mail Steamship Co.
Royal Naval Tournament
Others

Price range for the above .. .. £5/**£10**/£20

Pub. Collins, William & Sons
Shakespeare characters in sepia (1903)
.. .. £1/**£2**/£3

Pub. Davidson Bros. (Period 2)
Several series of comic col. illustrated lines from songs, nursery rhymes, poems, Shakespeare quotes, etc. Nos. 3000–3013, Japanese Pictures and Russo–Japanese War series 3014/5 .. £2/**£4**/£6

Pub. Faulkner, C. W.
Series 102/3 .. .. £1.50/**£3**/£4

Pub. Hartmann
Sporting Girls .. .. £1.50/**£3**/£4

Pub. Smith, H. J.
Dancing Maiden (1902) .. .. £1.50/**£3**/£4

Pub. Tuck
A Humorist in France No. 765 (1904)	£1/**£2**/£3
Humour of Life No. 9176	£1/**£2**/£3
Oilette 9056	£1/**£2**/£3
Others	£1/**£2**/£3

Pub. Valentine
Period 2 designs .. .. £1.50/**£3**/£4

Pub. Wrench
Early Period 2 designs .. .. .. £1.50/**£3**/£4

HARDY, FLORENCE ■58b

She produced delightful studies of children, often in a Dutch setting, and attractive scenes with figures in period dress. Her main output was for C. W. Faulkner in Period 2.
Price range .. .. £1/**£2**/£3

■58a

Jennie Harbour. Pub. Tuck. 'Jennie Harbour' series. Period 2 .. .. £4

■58b

Florence Hardy, Pub. Faulkner. Series 1420. Period 2 .. .. £2.50

HARE, J. KNOWLES (b. 1882)

Born in Montclair, New Jersey, USA, he designed covers for the *Saturday Evening Post* and *American Magazine*. His postcard work was in the 'American Girl' genre (*see also* GLAMOUR). Periods 2 to 4.

Price range .. .. 75p/**£1**/£2.50

HASSALL, JOHN (1868–1948) ■59a, 111b

Hassall came from Walmer, Kent, and was educated at Newton Abbot College and Neuenheim College, Heidelberg. He also spent some years in Manitoba, Canada, before returning to Europe where he studied under Bouguereau in Paris. His association with the theatrical publisher David Allen led to the prolific commercial output that gave him the title 'The Poster King'. His postcard work is also vast and a definitive listing of his work in this medium has not yet been published. To date over 300 designs have been positively identified. A natural clown, Hassall was a leading light in the artistic and entertainment activities of the London Sketch Club. *See also* ADVERTISING and COMIC.

Advertising work (Products)

Blackpool Herald, British Vacuum Cleaner Co., Cobham, Danyoz Virol, Eastman's Cleaners, *Everybody's*, Exhibition Matches, Fry's Cocoa, Lemco, Nestlé's Milk, Sternol Oil, Sunlight Soap, Tantalum Lamps, Wright's Cookers £7/**£18**/£25

Tuck's 'Celebrated Posters' series. 1500 Colman's Mustard (2); 1501 A Country Girl; 1507 Shredded Wheat .. £15/**£20**/£30

Advertising work (Theatrical)

Pub. Allen, David. The Arcadians; Babes in the Wood; Broadway Jones; Charley's Aunt; Dear Little Denmark; The Duchess of Dantzic; The Follies; Little Red Riding Hood; Mother Goose; When Knights Were Bold .. .. £7/**£18**/£25

Pub. Unknown. Alf's Button; Daughters of Babylon; Good Morning Bill; A Runaway Girl; Sport of Kings; Tons of Money .. .. £7/**£18**/£25

Comic and General work

Pub. Davidson Bros. At least 20 series. Subjects include: Books Illustrated, Nursery Rhymes Illustrated, Poems Illustrated, Popular Songs, Proverbs and Write-Away series .. .. .. £2/**£4**/£5

Pub. Faulkner, C. W. Children's Pastimes (12), Fun & Frolic (12), Write-Away series (at least 6) .. .. .. £1/**£3**/£4

Pub. Hodgkinson, G. W. Wookey Hole Cave, Somerset series .. .. £1/**£3**/£4

Pub. Inter-Art. At least 3 series (1909) .. .. £1/**£3**/£4

Pub. Lawrence & Jellicoe. Series 5016 .. .. £1/**£3**/£4

Pub. Regent Pub. Co. 'Phone Series; Write Me Series .. .. £1/**£3**/£4

Pub. Tuck. Christmas Postcard Series; Others .. .. £2/**£4**/£5

Pub. Voisey, Charles. Pantomime series of 12 (1902); Puppy Dogs series of 12 (1903) .. .. £2/**£4**/£5

Other publishers include Alexander Baird, *Daily News*, Ettlinger, Jarrold & Sons, Knight, J. Miller, Munk, Savory. Subjects include Military and Scottish characters .. .. £2/**£4**/£5

■59a

John Hassall. Advert for Alf's Button by C. W. Darlington. Period 4 .. .. £25

HAYES, FREDERICK WILLIAM (1848–1918)

Born in Cheshire, he trained as an architect in Ipswich and studied painting in Liverpool and London. A man of many talents, he was a musician, song writer and author as well as painting well enough to be exhibited at the Royal Academy. His postcard work was of the scenic 'Oilette' variety for Meissner & Buch, Tuck and others. Period 2.

Price range .. .. –/50p/75p

HEARTFIELD, JOHN

Real name Herzfelde, brother of the writer Wieland Herzfelde, with whom he started the irreverent journal *Malik Verlag* after WW1. It was anti-Establishment, anti-Militarist. A prime mover in the creation of the Dada Movement in Berlin in 1916, he produced striking designs with the use of photomontage, many with a violent anti-National-Socialism theme. A favourite subject was strong, worker's hands, often seen in his Communist posters. Periods 3, 4.
Price range .. .. £5/**£10**/£15

HEATH-ROBINSON, WILLIAM (1872–1944)

Born to an artistic family, he left school at 15 to go to the Royal Academy and from an early age showed great artistic ability and enjoyed commercial success. He is now best remembered for his pictures of almost surrealist inventions that made him a household name.

Advertising work
Dr. Barnado's Homes. 'To the Rescue'
Ideal Home (1934) Set of 6
Izal. Pub. Newton Chambers & Co. (1920) (10)
Proctor Bros. Wireworks. Mouse Trap
Yorkshire Relish. Poster advertisement
Price range .. .. £3/**£10**/£15

Comic and General work
Pub. Harrap, J. Cherub/Cupid series
.. .. 75p/**£1**/£1.50
Pub. Valentine. The Gentle Art of Catching
Things (1909). Set of 6 .. .. £1/**£2**/£4

HOFFMAN, JOSEF (1870–1956)

Austrian artist, much of whose early work was published by Philipp and Kramer He also contributed to the 'Wiener Werkstätte' (*see* COLLECTIONS) and the 'Ver Sacrum' series.
Price range .. .. £20/**£30**/£60

HORRELL, CHARLES ■60a

Artist of sentimental glamour, mostly known for his WW1 designs for James Henderson. His wholesome pretty girls often pose with their pets.
Price range .. ..75p/**£1**/£1.50

HORSFALL, MARY ■60b

Portrayer of delicate female beauties in glowing colours, also children and the occasional women's suffrage theme. Publishers include Carlton Publishing Co., Wm. Ritchie and Tuck. Periods 2, 3.
Price range .. .. £1/**£1.50**/£2

■60a
Charles Horrell. Pub. Henderson. Period 3 .. £1

■60b
Mary Horsfall. Pub. Tuck. 'Maidens Fair. Rosy Days'. No. 2733. Period 2 .. .. .. £1.50

■60c
G. Huber. Pub. Max Ettlinger. 'Honeymoon' series 4762 'In the Railway' £1

HOWARD, FRED, S.

His postcard work includes Irish subjects in a comic vein and horse racing. Publishers include Misch and Pictorial Stationery Co. (Peacock). Period 2.

Price range .. .. 50p/**75p**/£1

HUBER, G. ■60c

Continental comic artist, with a most distinctive style. He specialised in caricatures of rotund, earthy, peasant types, often in courting scenes. Different language versions appear of many of his designs—English, French and German—with continental style backs. The letter 'S' precedes the serial number and the numbering indicates that most designs were drawn in sets of 6. The majority were postally used in 1906/1907. Pale, poor quality reprints with English backs were produced bearing the later series numbers. So far identified are:

285/I	His Enjoyment. Her Pleasure
320/III	Beauty at the Bath
323/II	*No caption*
323/III	Break away, that's my bit
323/V	Le gout
340	Sommer
341/IV	His Little Splash
344	*No caption*
344/I	*No caption*
344/II	The Stowaways/Beim Diner
344/IV	A Friend in Need
344/V	*No caption*
344/VI	Romeo et Juliette/Romeo und Julia
353	*No caption*
353/VI	Das Betreten des Rasen ist Verboten
359/–	*No caption*
359/–	*No caption*
371/–	*No caption*
371/II	*No caption*
375/IV	*No caption*
387/I	*No caption*
387/II	Oh la belle pièce
387/V	*No caption*
387/VI	Viens poupole
387/VI	Their First Sunday Out
388/IV	The Sunshine at Paradise Alley
388/VI	The Political Beershifters/The Three Graces
389/I	Voyage de Noces (Honeymoon) Im Theater
389/II	*as above* In the Café/Au Restaurant
389/III	*as above* Enfin Seuls
389/IV	*as above* La Promenade en Ville
389/V	*as above* Au Musée des Beaux Arts
389/VI	*as above* En Wagen—O Schoking
390/IV	*as above* On the Boulevard
404/III	Looking for Lodgings in London
411/–	Country couples. 5 different designs with no captions
411/II	And his days work was done
415/IV	Bathing scenes with quotes. 'Abashed the devil stood . . .'
415/V	*as above* 'In fullblown flower of glorious beauty . . .'
415/VI	*as above* 'Squat like a toad . . .'
466/I	Marche conclu
466/IV	Cocquin de Printemps

English backs, poor reproduction

533G	Come and have a drop of gin old dear
553d	Behind with the rent (several versions)
553J	Everything in the garden is lover'ly (*sic*)
604	Where have I seen that face before
607	Just like the ivy I'll cling to you
639	Domestic Discomforts
649	We won't get home till morning
669	The good old anual (*sic*)
1030	A doubtful bargain
1032	The smile that won't come off
—	The sleeping beauty
—	Oh my
—	Oh what a smart leg
376	Toto au telephone (with *appliqued* fish)

The compilers would appreciate any help in expanding this check list.

Price range .. .. 50p/**£1**/£1.50

■61a

Ivy Millicent James. Pub. C. W. Faulkner. Series No. 382A. Period 2 .. .. £2

IBBETSON, ERNEST ■138b
Best known for his Military work (*see also*
HISTORICAL), he also drew general subjects for
Faulkner, showing a light and humorous touch.

Pub. Faulkner, C. W.
Several fine sets, including Always Merry &
  Bright, The Lilliputian Coronation, The
  London Police, The Simple Life 75p/**£1**/£1.50
Several series with Military and Naval
  themes, e.g. The Boy Army, The Boy
  Navy .. .. £1/**£1.50**/£2

Pub. Gale & Polden
Periods 2, 3. He was the main artist for their
  famous 'History & Tradition'
  series .. .. £1/**£2**/£3
Period 5. Commandos in Action. 14th Army
  in Burma (1945), etc. .. .. £1/**£2**/£3

INNES, JOHN (1864–1941)
Canadian artist famous for his drawings of
  Red Indians, Mounties, the Prairies, etc.
  Most of his designs were published by
  W. G. MacFarlane, Toronto .. £1/**£1.50**/£2

JACOBS, HELEN (1888–1970)
Sister of author W. W. Jacobs. Subjects of
  her postcard work include elves and fairies
  and most of her output was published by
  C. W. Faulkner. *See also* CHILDREN.
Price range .. .. £2/**£3**/£4

JAMES, IVY MILLICENT (1879–1965)
■61a
Born in Weston-super-Mare, she studied at the
Weston School of Art and had additional art
tuition in London. Both Ivy and her sister Maud
drew greetings cards and calendars for Delgado,
Faulkner, Hills, Tuck and Valentine's from 1901
to 1904. Faulkner alone published her postcard
work, from 1907 to 1919. 19 sets have been
identified by the Woodspring Museum, Weston-
super-Mare, which houses the 'I.M.J.' collection,
all signed with her distinctive initials. The designs
are mostly of appealing children in the style of
Florence Hardy and Ethel Parkinson, many in the
popular 'Dutch' style.

Pub. C. W. Faulkner
  Sets of 6. Periods 2, 3. Early Period
  4 .. .. £1/**£2**/£3
  Perforated Painting Books of 12 cards
    Per card .. ..75p/**£1**/£1.50

JOSSOT ■62a
One of the group of sought-after early French
postcard artists who contributed to many of the
great series (*see also* COLLECTIONS) like the
Collection des Cent, Maîtres de la Carte Postale.
He also drew advertisements and political designs.
Price range .. .. £50/**£70**/£100

JOTTER
Pseudonym for Young, Walter Hayward (*qv*).

JOZSA, KARL
Sought after artist of the Vienna Secessionist
School. His famous series include 'Heart Ladies',
Sirens and Circes', 'Smoke Rings' and 'World of
Fairy Tales'
Price range .. .. £15/**£25**/£40

KIERNECK, GIORGIO (1869–1948) ■63a
Powerful Italian artist, best known for his
  portrayals of Dante's *Divine Comedy*.
  Period 2 .. .. £5/**£15**/£30

■62a

Jossot. From Les Maîtres de la Carte Postale
series (1899) £75

KIMBALL, ALONZO MYRON (1874–1923)

Born in Green Bay, Wisconsin, USA, he studied in New York and Paris (under Lefebre and Whistler). He was a member of the Society of Illustrators and is best known on the postcard for his 'American Girls' (*see also* GLAMOUR).

Price range .. .. £1/**£1.50**/£2

■63a

Giorgio Kierneck. Pub. Alinari. 'Inferno' from The Divine Comedy *by Dante. Period 2* £12

KING, HAMILTON (b. 1871)

Born in Lewiston, Maine, USA, he studied in Paris and was a member of the Society of Illustrators. He is best known in the postcard world for his female studies.

Price range .. .. £2/**£3**/£4

■63b

Edward Patrick Kinsella. Pub. Langsdorff & Co. Series No. 695. PU *1907* 75p

KING, JESSIE M.

One of the most prized of the children's artists, who produced beautiful nursery rhyme illustrations in the *Art Nouveau* style, but with strong hints of the *Art Deco* style to come. Publishers include Millar & Lang.

Price range .. .. £10/**£20**/£30

KINSELLA, EDWARD PATRICK ■63b

Irish artist, usually known as Pat, he specialised in sporting children and theatre posters.

Pub. David Allen (Theatre Poster Ads.)

Blue Moon
A Chinese Honeymoon
The Duchess of Dantzic
The Female Swindler (2)
Wildflower
The Worst Women in London (9)
Price range for the above .. .. £5/**£8**/£10

Pub. Langsdorff & Co. (1905)

Sporting series featuring children playing
cricket, tennis, etc. .. .. 50p/**75p**/£1.50

■63c

Raphael Kirchner. 'The Drug' (his wife Nina, his model, died an addict) (c. 1910) £15

KIRCHNER, RAPHAEL (1876–1917)
■63c

Born in Vienna, Kirchner moved to Paris in 1905 following his enormous early success in the postcard field. He also became well known in the fields of magazine illustration, portrait painting and theatrical design. Of all the *Art Nouveau/Glamour* artists he is probably the best known and the most prolific (the 1980 *Neudin Argus*, in the first comprehensive checklist of his postcard work, lists 630 cards). Kirchner's designs enjoyed fantastic success, becoming the subject of poems, sketches in stage revues, etc. They were avidly collected by young officers during WW1 and pinned up in the trenches. His girls were all based on his wife, Nina. After her husband's tragic early death of appendicitis while on a trip to New York, Nina took to drugs and died in a mental hospital.

Kirchner's work divides into three sections:

Period 1
The rare pre-1900 designs (many published by Philipp & Kramer) including the 'Leda' series of 10 .. .. .. £25/**£40**/£50

Early Period 2 (1900–1903)
Beautiful chromo-litho UB's with a strong *Art Nouveau* flavour. The designs published on the Continent by J. Gerson (Paris), Meissner & Buch (Leipzig), M. Munk (Vienna), Emile Storch (Vienna), Theo Stroefer (Nuremburg) and other fine publishers were then re-issued in Britain by Henry Moss, Pascalis Moss, H. J. Smith, Edward Taylor, Tuck and others. Famous Series include: The Japanese designs—San Toy, The Geisha, The Mikado. Les Parfums, Les Cigarettes du Monde, Fruits Doux (or Douces), Vitraux (Stained Glass Windows), Roma, Les Enfants de la Mer, Sunray, Fleurs d'Amour, etc. Also the membership card for the Union Cartophile Universelle; fifth prize winner, *Concours Byrrh*; Tuck Proof Limited Edition—three maidens.
Price range .. .. £15/**£25**/£50

Later Period 2 and Period 3
Many cards in this period were published by Leroy et Cremieu (L et C) (Paris), the Libraire de l'Estampe (LE) and 'R. et Cie' (Paris) in France and were promoted in Britain by Mr. Boss of the Bruton Gallery (some printed by the Delta Fine Art Co., some reproduced by *The Sketch*, some printed by Alphalsa). These later designs move away from the *Art Nouveau* style and into the 'Glamour' category. *See also* WAR and GLAMOUR. Designs include The 'Maude' series, the 'Riquette series, the 'Montmartre' series, Les Zeppelins à Paris, Peinte par elle-même, Lolotte, etc.
Price range .. .. £8/**£12**/£15
Many unsigned designs were printed by M. Munk, Pascalis Moss, 'BRW' and others. Even more designs, accepted without question as Kirchners, exist unsigned.
Price range .. .. £5/**£10**/£12

KLEE, PAUL (1879–1940)
Born in Munchenbuchsee bei Bern, Switzerland, Klee studied art in Munich. He travelled extensively in Italy and Tunisia and served in the Great War from 1916–1918. In 1920 he joined the Bauhaus group of Walter Gropius in Weimar, becoming an instructor. In 1931 he moved to the Dusseldorf Academy, but was dismissed in 1933 by the Nazis. He died in Locarno.
Bauhaus Postcards Nos. 4 and 5 (only 25 examples of each are thought to have been printed) .. .. £250/**£400**/£550

KLEIN, CHRISTINA ■64a
Flower and still life artist *par excellence*. Many beautiful chromo-litho series by Tuck and other publishers. Period 2.
Price range .. ..75p/**£1.50**/£3

■64a

C.Klein. Pub. Tuck. Art series 6118. Peaches. PU. *1907* 75p

KOEHLER, MELA ■65a
Elegant designs for the Wiener Werkstätte (*see also* COLLECTIONS) for which she designed about 90 cards and other fashion and glamour designs with an *Art Deco* flavour.
Wiener Werkstätte .. .. .. £40/**£50**/£70
Others .. .. £10/**£15**/£20

KOKOSCHKA, OSKAR (1886–1980)
■65b

The son of a goldsmith, the young Oskar wanted to become a chemist. But as he was entitled to a grant, he studied at the School of Arts and Crafts in Vienna, intending to become a teacher. Impressed by painters as contrasting as Klimt and Van Gogh, he drifted into art. In 1907 he worked with the Wiener Werkstatte (*see also* COLLECTIONS) drawing 13 designs for a series of postcards. These are amongst the most highly prized—and priced—of all postcards. After this initial success, Kokoschka left the Workshop to become a portrait painter, but his distorted, tormented style found little acclaim. Gradually he won renown as an Expressionist, and member of the Vienna Secession. Volunteering for military service in 1914, he was badly wounded, which left him profoundly affected both mentally and physically. He gained recognition for his original and powerful style between the wars, but it was condemned as 'decadent' by the National Socialist regime, who destroyed 400 of his works during the late 1930s.

Price range   ..   ..   £50/**£150**/£500

KYD (J. Clayton Clark) ■139a
See also LITERARY. Famous for his representations of characters from Dickens.

Pub. Faulkner, C. W.
Characters from Dickens. Series 497/8/9

Pub. Hildesheimer
'Heads—And the Tales They Tell' (1903)

Pub. Pictorial Stationery Co.

Pub. Tuck
Characters from Dickens

Pub. Welch, J. & Sons (1905)
Studies from Life by Charles Dickens

Pub. Wrench
About 50 Dickens characters

Others
Price range for the above   ..   ..   £1/**£2**/£4

LEETE, ALFRED (b. 1882)
Most famous for his WW1 recruiting poster, 'Your King and Country Need You', he contributed to *The Passing Show* and other magazines and was President of the London Sketch Club in 1925. His postcard work includes several comic designs.
Price range   ..   ..   £1/**£1.50**/£2

LELEE, LEOPOLD (b. 1872)
French artist of the *Art Nouveau* school who studied at the School of Decorative Arts in Paris but who settled in Arles in Provence, which had a local influence on his work. Some of his work contained elements of surrealism.

Girls' Eyes (10)	£10/**£15**/£30
Mid-day and Midnight	£10/**£15**/£30
Others	£5/**£10**/£15

■65a

Mela Koehler. Design for the Wiener Werkstätte *'The Park in Vienna'* (1909) £45

■65b

Oskar Kokoschka. Design for the Wiener Werkstätte. *'The Shepherds'* (1909) £150

LOIR, LUIGI ■66a

French artist who did many fine UB chromo-litho scenes and town types, notably Paris. His work was published in Britain by P. G. Huardel 1900–1904.

Price range   ..   ..   £1/**£3**/£5

LUDOVICI, ANTHONY

An accomplished general and comic artist, he is best known for his satirical political caricatures of Joseph Chamberlain, Roseberry, etc. *See also* COMIC, POLITICAL.

Pub. Davidson Bros. (Period 2)

Series 6054	'Mrs. Caudle' types, signed 'AL'
Series 6087	Mr. Chamberlain at Glasgow
Series 6089	as 6054
Series 6093	Female occupations
Series 6098	Political Dances
Series 6100	Home Comforts
Series 6102	London Life
Series 6103	Fiscal Games
Series 6104	Boys' School
Series 6105	Girls' School

Others ..   ..   £2/**£3**/£4

Pub. Valentine's

'Write Away' series, signed 'AL'   £2/**£3**/£4
Others ..   ..   £1/**£2**/£3

Other Publishers

Various   ..   ..   £1/**£1.50**/£2

LYNEN, AMEDEE

Belgian artist, sought after for his delightful studies of town life and occupations in Brussels and Brabant, *De-ci, de-la* (Here and There). Period 2.

Price range   ..   ..   £4/**£6**/£7.50

MACDONALD, A. K. ■66b

An elegant artist, about whom little seems known.

Various Publishers (Early Period 2)

Coloured *Art Nouveau* designs   ..   £10/**£25**/£30

Pub. Henderson, James (1909)

Gibson-like pen and ink designs   ..   £1/**£2**/£3

Pub. Valentine (1908–1910)

Designs for Franco–British and Japanese–British exhibitions (more for signed examples)   ..   ..   £5/**£10**/£15

■66a

Loir Luigi. Pub. Huardel. Tour St. Jacques, Paris. UB. *Period 2* £5

■66b

A. K. Macdonald. Pub. Valentine. Japan–British Exhibition. PU *1910 from the Exhibition*   .. £10

■66c

A. Mailick. Pub. Giesen Bros. 'Purity' in the same series as 'Faith, Hope, Charity', etc. PU *1906* £2

MAILICK, A. ■66c

Versatile German artist whose work includes charming views/Faith, Hope, Charity, etc. and other greetings, WW1 sentiment and propaganda.
Early Period 2 and Period 3 .. .. £1/**£2**/£3

MARTY, ANDRÉ

French artist of the *Art Deco* school, he trained at the Paris Ecole des Beaux Arts. He had a witty and highly original approach and was well known for his fashion illustrations in magazines such as the *Gazette du Bon Ton, Modes et Manières d'Aujourd'hui* etc. Period 4.
Price range .. .. £5/**£10**/£15

MATANIA, FORTUNINO (1881–1963) ■67a

A child prodigy born in Naples, he first exhibited at the Naples Academy in 1892. His news pictures for *L'Illustrazione* led to an invitation to come to London to cover the coronation of Edward VII for *The Graphic*. He settled near London and, working mainly for *The Sphere* covered every royal event thereafter until the coronation of Elizabeth II, working with lightning speed. During WW1 he was appointed an official war artist and drew his most famous postcard design 'Goodbye Old Man' (*see* WAR). He was also famous for his religious paintings and drew scenes for de Mille's *Ten Commandments*.
Pub. *The Sphere*. Reproductions of his illustrations for the magazine. Periods 2 to 4
Others, including advertising cards, WW1 themes (incl. Italian military scenes/War Bond issues)
Price range .. .. 75p/**£1**/£1.50

MATTHISON, WILLIAM

A landscape and coastal painter, he lived in Oxford and Banbury. He painted views from around the British Isles and exhibited in Birmingham from 1874 to 1910. His 'Oilette' type postcard views were printed by Robert Peel of Oxford and by Tuck. Period 2.
Price range .. .. –/**50p**/£1

MAY, PHIL (1864–1903) ■111c, 157a

Born near Leeds, Phil May soon gravitated to London. He had a well-developed sense of humour that led him easily into the company of Whistler, Wilde and, inevitably, the other founder members of the London Sketch Club. He lived for 3 years in Australia and worked on the *Sydney Bulletin*.

Back in London he worked for *Punch, The Graphic* and joined the Chelsea Arts Club. His tragically early death curtailed a prolific output of brilliantly observed sketches of London Life and other types. Ninety postcard designs have been identified to date. *See also* COMIC.

Advertising work
Dewar's Whisky .. .. £15/**£20**/£25
Tuck's Celebrated Posters 1506.
   Appolinaris .. .. £15/**£20**/£25

Comic and General work
Pub. Davidson Bros. Nos. 6073–6 (1904/ 5). Several series of 'Write-Aways', Humour of Life Series .. .. £1/**£3**/£5
Pub. Landerer & Brown (Ellanbee) (1904/5). Phil May Aquasimile. Series 106–7 .. .. £1/**£3**/£5
Pub. Tuck. Humour of Life 9266 £2/**£4**/£6
Pub. Tuck. Medieval Characters 1258–9, 5259 .. .. £1/**£3**/£5
Pub. Tuck. Newspaper Headlines 764 .. .. £1/**£3**/£5
Pub. Tuck. Oilette series 1771–8 .. £1/**£3**/£5
Pub. Tuck. Phil May series 1294–6 .. .. £1/**£3**/£5
Pub. Tuck. 'Proof' sets (*qv*) Nos. 1008, 1294–6 .. .. £4/**£6**/£8
Pub. Tuck. Write-Away series .. £2/**£4**/£6
Pub. Valentine. Comic Sketches (1903). No. 1903 .. .. £1/**£3**/£5
Pub. Wrench. Cartoons from *Punch* UB (20+); Humour of Life; Newspaper Headings .. .. £2/**£4**/£6

■67a

Fortunino Matania. Reproduced from The Sphere *for the Blue Cross Fund. 'Goodbye Old Man'. Period 3* £1

MARTINI, ALBERTO (1876–1954)

Italian artist who drew some powerful propaganda surrealist designs during WW1, also adverts and pretty girls, e.g. 'Venetia Antiqua'—medieval maidens (1903).

Price range .. .. £5/**£15**/£30

McGILL, DONALD (1875–1962) ■112a, 212c

Donald McGill started designing postcards in 1904 for a sick nephew. He continued pouring out designs for most of the rest of his long life and is, without doubt, Britain's most prolific postcard artist. McGill himself claimed 10,000 designs and experts believe this cannot be too inaccurate a figure (nearly 9000 have been positively identified). Known to collectors and the general public alike for his rumbustious, often vulgar, seaside comics.

McGill also drew pungent social and political comments during both World Wars, as well as many well-drawn samples of military humour and patriotic designs. McGill's output is usually classified into 4 periods and, generally speaking, the earlier the card, the higher the value.

McGill's seaside humour was the subject of an essay by George Orwell in the magazine *Horizon* in 1941 entitled 'The Art of Donald McGill'.

Early Period (1904–1906)

About 650 designs. Publishers include Eyre & Spottiswoode, Hudson Bros. and Pictorial P.C. Co. .. .. £1/**£2**/£3

Second Period (1907–1914)

About 1750 designs. Publishers include Joseph Asher, Thridgould & Co., Woolstone Bros. and others .. .. 75p/**£1**/£1.50

Inter-Art Period (1914–1935)

About 3500 designs. The most prolific period of all, which included some designs for Woolstone Bros. and for Thridgould & Co. .. .. 50p/**75p**/£1

Modern Period (1935–1952)

About 2500 designs. Asher now formed a new company under the name of D. Constance Ltd. which produced the 'New Donald McGill Comics'—greatly inferior printing on poor quality board. Nevertheless the WW2 designs have some interest—*see also* WAR. At the beginning of this period McGill also drew for Birn Bros. and McCrum (Inter-Art) –/**50p**/75p

MENPES, MORTIMER ■68a

Water-colorist who is best remembered for his Boer War sketches of Churchill, Conan Doyle, Kipling, Rhodes, Roberts, etc. and scenes at Ladysmith, Modder River, etc. His postcard work includes a delightful series of 'The World's Children' published by Wrench from A. & C. Black's book of the same name.

Price range .. .. 50p/**75p**/£1

MERCER, JOYCE (1896–1965)

One of the 'Nursery Artists' (*see also* CHILDREN) whose subjects include children, fairy stories and nursery rhymes, with an *Art Deco* flavour. Most of her work was published by C. W. Faulkner.

Price range .. .. £2/**£3**/£4

MEUNIER, HENRI (1873–1922) ■32b

Belgian artist, many of whose early restrained *Art Nouveau* designs were published by Dietrich of Brussels. He contributed to the famous 'Editions Cinos' series and the Collection Job (*see also* COLLECTIONS). His beautiful series of girls, (1900), is particularly sought after.

Price range .. .. £30/**£50**/£60

■68a

Mortimer Menpes. Pub. Wrench from A. & C. Black's book, World's Children'. PU *1905* .. 75p

MILLIÈRE, MAURICE (b. 1871) ■69a

Born in Le Havre, Millière studied under Bonnat at L'Ecole des Beaux Arts. He contributed to *La Vie Parisienne* and was exhibited in Paris, London and New York. His postcard work is mainly known for 'glamour' subjects during WW1, although there are fine examples of his work during Period 2. *See also* WAR.

Early Period 2
M. Munk Vienna series .. .. £3/**£5**/£10

Period 3
La Vie dans La Campe Indienne à Rouen

.. .. £2/**£3**/£5
Petites Femmes de Paris .. .. £2/**£3**/£5
Others .. .. £2/**£3**/£5

MIGNOT, VICTOR

Belgian *Art Nouveau* artist, best known for his beautiful series of 'Sports' (Bicycling, Horse Racing, Ice Skating, Mountaineering, etc.) Pub. Dietrich.
Price range .. .. £5/**£12**/£15

MORELAND, ARTHUR ■69b

One of Britain's most under-estimated comic artists, who was also capable of making political comments (*see* POLITICAL). Over 160 designs have been identified from early Period 2. The 'Humours of History' series were originally published in *The Morning Leader* and also appeared in book form.

Pub. Faulkner, C. W.

Series No. 233	Write Away
234	Motoring Themes
235	Book Titles
237	Write Away
238	Play Titles
239	Small 'ads'
240	Humours of History
245	Occupations
246	Quotations
248	John Bull (*Political*)
255	Songs and Singers (*bordered*)
257	Chamberlain (*unsigned. Political*)
258	Songs and their Singers
259	Town Life
260	John Bull (*Political. Free Trade*)
270	Humours of History
271	Humours of History
290	The Electionist Series
314	Extracts from Fiscal Speeches (*Political*)
322	Motor Mania
459	Humours of History
588	Political (*signed AM*)
590	Chamberlain (*Political*: Morning Leader. *Signed 'AM'*)
591	Chamberlain (*Political*: Morning Leader. *Signed 'AM'*)
777	Sufragettes

Price range .. .. £1/**£2**/£3

Pub. Eyre & Spottiswoode: Woodbury Series

Series No. 545	Humours of History from *The Morning Leader* in chronological order from 100 B.C.
548	*as above*
557	*as above*
563	*as above*

Price range .. .. £1/**£2**/£3
Publisher Unknown. Boer War (1904)
.. .. £3/**£4**/£5
Others .. .. £1/**£2**/£4

■69a

Maurice Millière. Pub. 'C.C.M.', Italy. Period 3 .. .. £5

■69b

Arthur Moreland. Pub. Faulkner. John Bull reacts to Free Trade. PU *1903* £3

MOSER, KOLOMAN (1868–1918) ■195a

Austrian artist, co-founder of the Secessionist Movement in Vienna and a member of the Wiener Werkstätte (though none of his postcards appeared in that collection). His best postcard work was published by Philipp & Kramer and is in a restrained *Art Nouveau* style. He also contributed to the great German series 'Meggendorfer Blätter'.

Price range .. .. £15/**£30**/£50

MUCHA, ALPHONSE (1860–1939)

Czech artist who came to Paris at the age of 26 in 1887. His first success, which assured his future career, was with a poster of Sarah Bernhardt in 1894. His poster work was published by M. Champenois of Paris, who reproduced the designs on postcards. The most reproduced of all the *Art Nouveau* artists, Mucha contributed to many of the important early French series (*see also* COLLECTIONS). Mucha returned to his native Czechoslovakia for the last years of his life and died in Prague. His work falls into four categories:

Period 1

The glorious pre-1900 era. Sarah Bernhardt Posters (1898): Dame aux Camélias, Gismonda, Lorenzaccio, La Samaritaine; Cocorico (1899)
.. .. £50/**£70**/£100

Early Period 2

Collection des Cent (2 designs); Champenois series, incl. The Four Seasons, The Months of the Year, Precious Stones; Moet et Chandon (10 designs) £40/**£60**/£75

Later Period 2

Postcard reproductions of 1897, 1898 Job Calendars in 1911; Album Mariani; Others .. .. £20/**£30**/£50
Nearly 110 cards have been identified for these three 'French' periods.

Late Period 2/Periods 3, 4 (The Czechoslovakian Period)

Mucha's output from about 1909 until he died in Prague in 1939 was mostly produced in Prague, often with Czech themes, moving away from the stylised *Art Nouveau* influence of the French period. Nearly 60 designs have been identified for this period .. .. £15/**£20**/£30

The Champenois designs were republished in Britain by Huardel, Pascalis Moss, Henry Moss, H. J. Smith and F. C. Southwood from 1900 to about 1905. Dietrich of Belgium also published many early Period 2 designs .. .. £10/**£20**/£40

Period 4

Advertisements for the YWCA .. £10/**£15**/£25

MUTTER, K. ■70a

German landscape artist. Publishers include Schmidt, Staub & Co., with many fine UB chromo-litho .. .. £1/**£2**/£3

NANNI, GIOVANNI (1888–1969)

Italian artist best known for his elegant, fashionable girls, notably a superb series of behatted heads, Periods 3, 4. He also drew patriotic, propagandist designs in the 1920s and 1930s and commercial work for products like Pirelli. During this period his work was strongly influenced by the *Art Deco* style and included some beautiful film posters (*see also* CINEMA and GLAMOUR).

Price range (higher price for *Art Deco* posters) .. .. £3/**£5**/£18

NASH, ADRIENNE, A. ■71a

Subjects include children, patriotic and suffragettes etc. in Periods 2 and 3.

Pub. Henderson

Children's Birthdays (7 cards) 50p/**75p**/£1.50
Others .. .. 50p/**75p**/£2.50

Pub. Inter-Art

25 series between 1913–1918 (*see also* PUBLISHERS, Inter-Art) .. 50p/**75p**/£2.50

■70a

K. Mutter. Pub. Nister. Roederthor. UB *chromolithograph. Early Period 2* £3

NIXON, KATHLEEN (b. 1895)

Children's artist (*see also* CHILDREN). To date 18 postcards only have been recognised, published by C. W. Faulkner, including animals and *Alice in Wonderland* series .. .. £1/**£2**/£3

■71a

Adrienne A. Nash. Pub. Inter-Art. 'Artistique' series. No. 1939. PU *1919 to the BEF in France* £1

NOLDE, EMILE (HANSEN) ■71b

Christened Emil Hansen, he changed his name to Nolde after his birthplace. Brought up on his father's farm, he became a wood carver and in 1890 moved to Berlin as a furniture designer. By 1892 he was teaching industrial and ornamental design in the Industrial Museum at St. Gallen. In 1894 he drew the personifications of the Swiss mountains which, reproduced on postcards, were such a financial success that he could become an independent painter. He studied and travelled widely—to Munich, Paris, Copenhagen, Berlin. His frenetic, excited, brightly coloured style emerged as he experimented with Impressionism. He became a member of the Dresden group, *Die Brucke* (the Bridge) from about 1905. His religiously inspired paintings were extremely controversial and he withdrew from active participation in the art world to study primitive painting. In 1918, established as an expressionist, he joined the *Novembergruppe*. Before WW2 his work was regarded as 'degenerate' by the National Socialist regime and over 1000 examples of it were destroyed during the 1930s.
Fantasy mountain designs. Pub. F. Killinger.
Period 2 .. .. £5/**£8**/£12

■71b

Emile Nolde (E. Hansen). Pub. F. Killinger. 'The Eiger, the Monk and the Jungfrau.' No. 113. Period 2 .. ..£12

NOURY, GASTON

French *Art Nouveau* artist of early Period 2 who contributed to the famous 'Editions Cinos' (*see also* COLLECTIONS) and others .. .. £8/**£15**/£50

■71c

NYSTROM, JENNY ■71c

Swedish artist, subjects include children, greetings, some in the *Art Deco* style. Periods 2/3 including some 'miniature' postcards .. .. £2/**£3**/£4

Jenny Nystrom. Pub. Eliassons, Stockholm. No. 7587. New Year miniature card £3

O'NEILL, ROSE (1874–1944)

American artist best known for her 'Kewpie' (corruption of 'Cupid') dolls and greetings cards, who also did the occasional Women's Suffrage design. Periods 2, 3 .. .. 75p/**£1.50**/£3

ORENS (DENIZARD) ■72a

French satirical caricaturist, many of whose designs were produced in small limited editions (of 75 to 250 only). He also drew under the names 'Denizard' and 'Godillot', and contributed to the 'Collection des Cent'. *See also* POLITICAL.
Price range (highest valuation for the 'Cent' cards) .. .. £5/**£10**/£40

OUTCAULT, RICHARD F. (b. 1863)

Born in Lancaster, Ohio, USA, his creation in 1896 in 'The New York World' of the 'Yellow Kid' comic strip was a sensation. He followed its success with 'Buster Brown' in *The New York Herald* in 1902. Newspapers vied for his services and many of his comical drawings appeared on postcards (*see also* CHILDREN and COMIC).
Price range .. .. 50p/**75p**/£1

OUTHWAITE, IDA RENTOUL (1889–1961)

Australian artist of the nursery genre (*see also* CHILDREN). A. & C. Black produced postcard reproductions of the illustrations she drew for their books. Period 4 .. .. £1/**£1.50**/£2

OWEN, WILL (d. 1957)

Member of the London Sketch Club, most famous for his 'Aah, Bisto' advertisement, he contributed to *Punch*, illustrated books, drew posters and also published books.

Pub. David Allen (Theatre Poster Adverts)

A Little Bit of Fluff; When Knights were Bold .. .. £3/**£7**/£10

Pub. Davidson Bros.

Illustrated Songs series .. .. .. £2/**£3**/£4

Pub. Meissner & Buch

'K-nuts' .. .. £2/**£3**/£4
Fishing series .. .. £2/**£3**/£4

Pub. Tuck

Write-Away series .. .. £2/**£3**/£4

Pub. Wrench

Illustrated Songs and other series £2/**£3**/£4

Others

Various .. .. £1/**£2**/£4

■72a

Orens. Pub. 'F.J.' Paris. Design for L'Actualité Satirique *on the situation in Russia (1905)* £15

PARKINSON, ETHEL ■72b

Several series of charming wintry scenes and children, mainly published by C. W. Faulkner.
Price range .. .. £1/**£2**/£3

■72b

Ethel Parkinson. Pub. Faulkner. Series 353 'Homeward Bound'. UB. *Early Period 2* .. £3

PARLETT, HARRY (COMICUS) ■73a

Many of Parlett's comic cards are signed by his pseudonym, 'Comicus', and others bear only his initials, 'H.P.'

Pub. Gottschalk, Dreyfus & Davis, Star series

Several series of 'How to behave . . .'
.. .. 50p/**75p**/£1

Pub. H. B. Series

Several series of comic cards .. 50p/**75p**/£1

Pub. Midland Pictorial Postcard Co.

Several series of comic cards .. 50p/**75p**/£1

Others (incl. 'Rinking' themes)

Price range .. .. 50p/**75p**/£1

PATELLA, B.

French *Art Nouveau* artist, often confused with Raphael Kirchner. His most famous series are the *Femmes Voilées* .. £5/**£10**/£15

PAYNE, ARTHUR CHARLES (1856–1933) ■73b

Brother of the more famous Harry (*qv*) with whom he occasionally did joint work. Arthur painted the background and architectural detail while Harry did the foreground figures. Although Arthur also drew many military designs, his postcard work mainly comprised cathedrals, views and river scenes.

Pub. De Little, Fenwick & Co.

Several designs .. .. 50p/**75p**/£1

Pub. Hildesheimer

Series include 15th-century London, Cathedrals, London on Thames .. 50p/**75p**/£1

Pub. Ruddock

'Artist' series .. .. 50p/**75p**/£1

Pub. Tuck

Early chromolithographed vignettes of Cathedrals .. .. £3/**£4**/£5
Various Oilette series, incl. 'English Cathedrals', interior and exterior views, churches and Thames views .. .. .. 75p/**£1**/£1.50

PAYNE, G. M.

A highly competent, somewhat under-estimated artist of comic and general subjects during Period 2.
Subjects include Bathing, 'Before our Time', sporting, etc. He did many series for Gale & Polden and other publishers, incl. Period 3 .. .. 50p/**75p**/£1.50

■73a

Harry Parlett ('Comicus'). Pub. 'H.B.' Signed 'Comicus'. Period 2 .. ..75p

■73b

Arthur Payne. Pub. Hildesheimer. London on Thames series. No. 5369. PU *1912 .. ..75p*

PAYNE, HARRY (1858–1927) ■26a, 136a

Though his drawings now seem somewhat stereotyped and wooden, Harry Payne is undoubtedly the most famous of all the military postcard artists. He had only a sketchy art training at evening school, but his splendid, colourful pictures, with an attention to detail of uniform and horses' trappings, had an early success. He and his brother Arthur (*qv*) with whom he had a long artistic collaboration, were fascinated as boys by all things military. In 1883 Harry joined the West Kent Yeomanry, serving till 1906 and attaining the rank of sergeant. He was engaged by Tuck (for whom he had been designing 'scraps' and books for several years), to design postcards for them and produced some of their earliest picture postcards. The association was to last until 1918. In the next two years Gale & Polden commissioned 67 designs, of which 22 are estimated to have been published, including his last postcard. In his biography of Payne, Michael Cane lists much of his astonishing output which probably numbers about 700 designs. *See also* HISTORICAL.

Pub. Davis, A. M. & Co.
Period 3 War Bond poster .. .. £2.50/**£4**/£6

Pub. Gale & Polden (1918/1919)
Twenty-two known military designs
.. .. £2/**£3.50**/£4.50

Pub. Hildesheimer
At least 2 Rural series .. .. .. £1.50/**£3**/£4

Pub. Stewart & Woolf
At least 4 series of military designs
.. .. £2/**£3**/£4

Pub. Tuck

Chromo-litho UBs. *Period 1/early Period 2*
British Army series Nos. 100–124; Empire series (Baden-Powell, CIV's, Wiping Something off the Slate, etc.); Animal Life series; Types of the British Army
.. .. £8/**£10**/£12

Military Oilettes. Periods 2/3
About 40 sets and many single designs on Ceremonial, Regimental, Uniforms, etc.
.. .. £2/**£3**/£4
Badges and their Wearers (30 identified)
.. .. £3/**£5**/£8

Boy Scouts/Red Cross/US Army .. £2/**£4**/£6
Defenders of the Empire. Period 3 £1/**£3**/£5
Defenders of the Empire with whisky advert (1924) .. .. £3/**£5**/£7
King George V series 9877 .. .. £2/**£4**/£6
Period 3 Patriotics incl. 'Wake up England'
.. .. £2/**£3**/£5

Rural Oilettes
About 40 series, including 'County' series, Country Life, Man's Best Friend, Seasonal .. .. £1/**£2**/£4

Wild West, USA (1907)
Two series and single designs .. £2/**£4**/£6

> *The Stanley Gibbons Postcard Department is at 391 Strand London WC2. Open Mon.–Fri. 9 a.m.–5.30 p.m.; Sat. 9.30 a.m.–12.30 p.m.*

PHILLIMORE, REGINALD (1855–1941) ■75a

Born the son of a doctor at Nottingham Asylum, Reginald graduated from Oxford with a B.A. degree in the early 1870s. He went on to teach at a private school in Eccles, Lancashire. Over the next twenty years he enjoyed sketching in the Manchester area and his interest in history grew. When the new art form, the picture postcard, became popular in the 1890s, this shy, reserved artist saw a way of combining his two interests commercially. The idea coincided with a legacy from two maiden aunts—a large house in North Berwick. In 1894 Phillimore went into the business of designing, printing and publishing postcards, many of them being hand tinted by his 14-year-old assistant, Mary Pearson. Phillimore postcards are characterised by their fascinating historical and architectural detail, often combining several designs on a single card. Typical, too, are the small pictures which continue the story on the reverse. Peak production was from 1900 to 1910. Nearly 700 different designs have so far been identified, a list of known titles appears on pp. 75–81.
Pub. Phillimore. Periods 1, 2 .. £1/**£2**/£3

Key to Symbols/Abbreviations

N.B. = North Berwick
Italic figs means two or more cards show the same number.
/ Oblique means separate picture shown—but many cards also have insets which are not described on this short list.
H = Horizontal format.
V = Vertical format.

1. Fidra (N.B.) showing 4 sailing boats (H)
2. Bass Rock (N.B.) (Storm) (to the Bass) (H)
3. Bass Rock at Sunset (H)
4. Herring Boats off the Craig, N.B. (V)
5.
6. Bass Rock Sunrise/Entrance to Great Cave (V)
7.
8. Berwick Law from East Links, N.B. (H)
9. Solan Geese, Bass Rock (V)
9. Bombardment of Tantallon by Gen. Monk (1651) (H)
10. Whitekirk, near N.B. (H)
10. The Gardens, Dirleton Castle, near N.B. (H)
11. Dirleton Castle (N.B.) (H)
12.
13.
14. Coastguard Station and Auld Kirk, N.B. (H)
15.
16. Storm, at N.B., Lifeboat to the rescue (H)
16. *Norman Clark* to the rescue, ship in distress off N.B. (H)
17.
18. Edinburgh Castle/Capture in 1313 (*cf.* No. 154) (V)
19. Canty Bay, near N.B., showing sheep, primroses and boat (H)
20.
21.
22. A Corner of Dirleton Village, near N.B. (H)
23. Town Hall, N.B./Old Stocks in the Town Hall (V)
24. Tantallon Castle/Marmion's escape/Marmion's defiance (H)
24(a) As No. 24—Note. Brackets on card
25. The Harbour, N.B., showing 9 boats and entrance (H)
26.
27. The Law, Harvest Time, N.B./Whale Bone Arch (V)
28. Dr. Johnson's House, Lichfield
29.
30. The Glen (Ladies Walk), N.B. (V)
31.
32. Dirleton Castle, N.B. (H)
33. Smugglers at Tantallon (Castle), N.B. (H)
34. Courtyard, Tantallon Castle, N.B. (H)
35.
36. Scene of Battle of Dunbar (H)
37.
38. Bass Rock, the last fortress, etc. (H)
39. Phoenix Tower, Chester (V)
40.
41.
42.
43. Pease Glen, Berwickshire (H)
44. Ruins of the Abbey, N.B. (H)
45. Saltcoats Castle, near Gullane (V)

46. West Links, N.B. (H)
47. Priory Church, Malvern (H)
48. Rothesay Castle, Bute (H)
49.
50.
51. Inchcolme Monastery, near Aberdour (H)
52. West Bay, N.B. (A Good Catch) (H)
53. Knaresborough Castle (H)
54. Bury St. Edmunds, The Abbey Gate, etc. (H)
55.
56. Roslin Castle and its Legend (H)
57. Bell Tower, Berwick on Tweed, etc. (V)
57. Rothesay Castle, Bute—as No. 48 (H)
58. New Light House, Isle of May (H)
58. Hailes Castle, near East Linton (H)
59.
60.
61. West Door, Holyrood Chapel (V)
62.
63. Castle Rising, Norfolk (H)
64.
65. A Nautical Argument at N.B. Harbour (H)
66. Culloden (H)
67.
68.
69.
70. Stratford-on-Avon, Tomb on which Longfellow wrote these lines . . . (H)
71.
72. Shakespeare Hotel, Stratford (H)
73. The Two Bridges, Stratford (H)
74. Interior, Holy Trinity Church, Stratford (V)
75. Braemar Castle (V)
75. Birthroom Shakespeare's House, Stratford (H)
76. Interior Ann Hathaways Cottage, Stratford (H)
77. Stratford from Memorial Tower (H)
78. Harvard House, Stratford (V)
79.

■75a

Reginald Phillimore. Pub. Phillimore. Holyrood Chapel. No. 61. Period 2 .. .. .. £1.50

80. Holy Trinity Church, Stratford (H)
81. Holy Trinity Church, Stratford, The Avenue
82. Rhodes Links, N.B. (H)
83. Guild Chapel and School, Stratford (H)
84. The Greenland Fishery, Kings Lynn (H)
85. Roslin Chapel (H)
86. Shakespeare's House, Stratford/Coat of Arms on right (H)
86. Shakespeare's House, Stratford/Coat of Arms on left (H)
87. Ripon Cathedral (V)
88. Ann Hathaway's Cottage, Stratford (H)
89. Fountains Abbey (V)
90. Tudor House, Stratford (V)
91. Dryden, near Roslin (H)
92. Fidra, N.B., showing dog, fishermen with boat (H)
93. Bridge of Clunie, Pitlochrie (H)
94. Threave Castle, Castle Douglas (V)
95. Rhuddlan Castle, North Wales (H)
95. The Castle Gate, Nottingham (V)
96.
97. Bonewaldsthorne's Tower, Chester (V)
97. Memorial Theatre, Stratford (H)
98. Tantallon Castle (V)
98. Tantallon Castle near N.B./Earl of Bothwell, etc. (V)
99. Blair Castle, Perthshire (H)
100. Stannal's Bank, near Stratford (H)
101. The Prentice Pillar, Roslin Chapel (V)
102. Chapel of Our Lady of the Mount, Kings Lynn (V)
102. Bass Rock Lighthouse, Ruins of Covenanters Prison etc. (V)
102. The Cloisters, Gloucester Cathedral (H)
103. Melrose Abbey (South Window) (V)
104. East Linton, The Old Bridge (H)
105.
106. Little Wamphray near N.B. A shepherd's care (H)
107. Old Blair Church, Blair Atholl (H)
108. Burns' Cottage (H)
109. Lancaster Castle (V)
110. Chapter House, Gloucester Cathedral (H)
111. Queen Mary's Bath (House) Edinburgh (V)
111. Gloucester Cath., Pilgrims at Shrine of Edward II—(as No. 264) (H)
112. Davaar Island & McCrimmon's Point (H)
113. Gloucester Cathedral, Nave (H)
113. Davaar Island, Campbeltown Loch (H)
114. The Village Green, Dirleton, near N.B. (H)
115. (Wreck at) Tantallon (H)
115. Bodiam Castle, Sussex (H)
116. Natural Arch, Fidra Island, N.B./The Mysterious Monk etc. (V)
117. Canterbury, West Gate/Canterbury Pilgrims/Chaucer (V)
118. Berkeley Castle (H)
119. Conway Castle (H)
120. Llanberis Castle, N. Wales (V)
121. Castle Bridgnorth/1649 Siege (V)
122. Village Green and Church, Dirleton, near N.B. (H)
123.
124. Swimming Pond, N.B. (H)
125. The Castle, St. Andrews (H)
126. Chepstow Castle (H)
127. Norham Castle (V)
128. Carnarvon Castle (H)
129. Pevensey Castle (H)
130. Richmond Castle, Yorkshire (H)
131. Old Inverlochy (H)
132. Ravenscraig Castle, Fife (V)
133. Lewes Castle, Sussex (V)
134.
135. Cirencester (V)
136. St. Hilda's Abbey, Whitby (V)
137. The Golf Links, N.B., Invereil (H)
138.
139. Hawthornden (H)
140.
141. Old Bridge, Stirling (H)
142. Tobermory/Searching for Spanish Treature in Bay (V)
143. Tattershall Castle, Lincolnshire (V)
143. Canty Bay Inn, near N.B./Life on the Bass Rock etc. (V)
144. Whittingham Tower, Haddingtonshire (V)
145.
146.
147. Mason Croft, Stratford, Residence of Marie Corelli (H)
148. Goodrich Castle, Ross (H)
149.
150. William Shakespeare
151. Rothesay Castle (H)
151. Window in the Chapel Royal, Holyrood (V)
152.
153. Battle Abbey/Battle of Hastings A.D. 1066 (V)
153. Sanctuary Knocker, Durham Cathedral/Fugitive seeking sanctuary (V)
154. Edinburgh Catle from the Grassmarket (similar to No. 18) (V)
155.
156. Quality Street, N.B. The Lodge (H)
157.
158.
159. Tom Tower, Christ Church, Oxford (V)
160. Chester Cathedral (H)
161.
162. Iona Cathedral/St. Columba preaching (V)
163. Old St. Pauls Cathedral from the East (V)
164. St. Peter's, Mother Church of Wolverhampton (H)
165. Durham Cathedral (V)
166. Altar Screen of Winchester Cathedral (V)
167. Old Seven Stars Inn, Manchester (H)
168. Old King's Head Inn, Chester (V)
169.
170.
171.
172.
173.
174.
175. Gamull House, Chester (V)
176. Bishop Lloyd's House, Chester (V)
177. Raglan Castle (H)
178.

179. Abbots Bridge, Bury St. Edmunds (H)
180. Dunbar Town Hall (V)
181. The Law, N.B., showing cattle and cattleman (H)
182. Wolvesey Castle, Winchester/King Alfred (H)
183. Wolvesey Castle, Winchester/King Egbert (H)
184.
185. Winchester Cathedral, N.E. (H)
186. St. Nicholas Cathedral, Newcastle-on-Tyne (V)
187. Blackgate and Castle, Newcastle-on-Tyne (H)
188. The Old Walls, Southampton (H)
188. West Gate, Winchester (V)
189. Winchester College From Warden's Garden (H)
190. Rufus Stone, New Forest (H)
191.
192. Bargate, Southampton (V)
193. Henry VIII's Palace, Southampton (H)
194. West Gate, Southampton (V)
195.
196. Netley Abbey, Southampton (H)
197.
198. Bury St. Edmunds. Remains of High Altar (V)
199.
200.
201. Exeter Cathedral, West front (H)
202.
203. Mol's Coffee House, Exeter (V)
204. Choir, Looking East, Exeter Cathedral (V)
205. Exeter Cathedral, S.E. (H)
206. Rougemont Castle, Exeter (H)
207. Guildhall, Exeter (V)
208. Tiverton Church (H)
209. Bristol Cathedral from S.E. (H)
209. Bristol Cathedral, Colston and Butler Towers (V)
210.
211. Bristol Cathedral, Norman Arch from the South (V)
212. Cabot Tower, Bristol (V)
213.
214. St. Peter's Hospital, Bristol (V)
215.
216.
217. York Minster from S.E. (H)
218. York Minster, West Front (H)
219. St. Mary's Abbey, York (H)
220. Micklegate Bar, York (V)
221. Dunbar Castle (H)
222. East Bay, N.B./View from East Bay (H)
223. Church of St. Cross, Winchester (V)
224. Bolton Abbey, Yorkshire (H)
225. Old Cheesemill Rectory House, Winchester (H)
226. St. Cross Hospital, Winchester (H)
227. Gardiner's Monument, Prestonpans (V)
228. Wolsey's Kitchen, Christchurch, Oxford (H)
229.
230. The Deanery, Winchester (H)
231. Winchester Cathedral—Shrine of English Nation (H)
232. Charles Dickens at The King's Head, Chigwell (H)
233.
234. Wolvesey Castle, Winchester (H)
235. Ruins of the Cathedral, St. Andrews, West Front (H)
236.

237. Alloway Kirk, Ayr (V)
238. Fair Maid's House, Perth (H)
239.
240. Peterborough Cathedral
241. Ruins of St. Andrews, N.B. (H)
242. Fenton Tower, Kingston/Kingston Village (V)
243.
244. Old White Horse Inn, Canongate, Edinburgh (*cf.* 535) (H)
245. Dr. Johnson's House, Lichfield (V)
246.
247. Lichfield Cathedral, West Front (V)
248.
249.
250. St Giles Cathedral, Edinburgh (V)
251. Tolbooth, Canongate, Edinburgh (V)
252.
253. Abbey Gateway, Great Malvern (H)
254. High Whitbys cloistered pile showing Abbey (H)
255. East Bay, N.B./View from East Bay (different to No. 222) (H)
256.
257. Pembroke Castle (H)
258. Carew Castle, Pembrokeshire (H)
259. Manorbier Castle, Pembrokeshire (H)
260. Gloucester Cathedral. From the S.W. (H)
261. New Inn, Gloucester (H)
262. The Deanery, Gloucester Cathedral (H)
263. Gloucester Cathedral, The Choir (V)
264. Gloucester Cathedral/Pilgrims at Shrine of Edward II (as No. 111) (H)
265.
266.
267. Clifton Suspension Bridge (H)
268. Chapter Room, Bristol Cathedral (V)
269. Muniment Room, St. Mary Redcliff, Bristol (H)
270. Bristol Cathedral, West Front and Gateway
271. Bristol Cathedral and College Green (H)
272. St. Mary Redcliff, Bristol (H)
273. North Porch, St. Mary Redcliff, Bristol (V)
274.
275. Off the Lamb, N.B.
276. Cottage by the Glen, near N.B. (H)
277. Abbey Ruins, Dunbar (H)
278. Craigmillar Castle (H)
279. Promenade, Dunbar/View from the Promenade (H)
279. Innerwick Castle, Dunbar (V)
280.
281. Luffness Mill, Gullane (H)
282. Cleikam Toll, Dunbar (H)
283. Old Toll Cottage, Dirleton (H)
284.
285. Village of Spott, near Dunbar (H)
286.
287. Haddington, Birth Place of John Knox (H)
288. Aberlady Church and Loupin'-on-Stane (H)
289. Luffness Mill, Harvest Time (H)
290. Cat's Row, Dunbar (H)
291. Gullane (H)
292. Village Green and Ruined Church, Gullane (H)

293. The Old Smithy, Gullane (H)
294. Luffness House, near Gullane/Aberlady Bay (V)
295. Dirleton 'Sweet Auburn Loveliest Village of the Plain' (H)
295. Dirleton Village 'When the kye come hame' (H)
296.
297.
298. Cockburnspath Tower/Ravenswood's fatal gallop (V)
299.
300. Rosyth Castle and Forth Bridge (H)
301. Sir Walter Scott's Cottage, Lasswade (H)
302.
303. Duddingston (V)
304. Queen Mary's Tree, Little France, Craigmillar (V)
305. Aberlady (H)
306.
307. Through Binning Woods to Tynninghame (V)
308. Cottage in Binning Wood, near Whitekirk (H)
309.
310. Aberdour Castle (H)
311.
312. May Island, Firth of Forth—A Storm coming on (H)
312. Crichton Castle, Midlothian (V)
313. Cove Harbour, Cockburnspath, Storm Coming In.
314.
315. Dunbar Harbour (H)
316.
317.
318. St Margaret's Chapel, Edinburgh Castle, etc. (V)
319.
320. Pease Bridge (H)
321. Tantallon/(Walter Douglas) Consulting the Wizard, etc (V)
322. Inchkeith, Firth of Forth (H)
323.
324. Crossroads, Top of Malvern Hills (H)
325.
326. North Gate, Bridgnorth/At the seige (V)
326. A Stormy Sea at Dunbar (H)
327. Carisbrooke Castle (H)
328. Road through the Village, Dirleton (H)
329.
330. Dr. Samuel Johnson/Birthroom (V)
331. The Towers, Broxmouth, Dunbar (H)
332.
333. Dirleton, Haddingtonshire, Old Post Office (H)
334. Gullane, West End (H)
335. A gallop by the Sea, N.B. (H)
336. Corbies, Craig, Gullane (H)
337. East Links and Tantallon Hotel N.B. (H)
338. Whittinghame, Haddingtonshire (H)
339. Ladies Tower, Elie, Fife (H)
340. Cliffs, Earlsferry, Fife (H)
341. Banqueting Hall, Dirleton Catle (V)
342. Established Church, St. Monans, Fife etc. (V)
343. Newark Castle, St. Monans, Fife (H)
344.
345. Roman Bath, Behind the Pump Room, Bath (V)
346. Sham Castle, Bath/Prior Park (H)
347. Richmond Castle, Yorks. The Keep/King John Besieged (V)

348. Greyfriars Tower, Richmond, Yorks. (V)
349.
350. Grand Pump Room, Bath (H)
351. Royal Crescent, Bath (H)
352. Bath Abbey, Lantern of England (V)
353. Mineral Water Fountain, Bath—Legend of Bath Waters (V)
354. Bass Rock Lighthouse and Ruins of Fortress (V)
355. Carlisle Cathedral/Some Famous Bishops (V)
356. Theatre Close, Edinburgh (V)
357. Reid's Close, Edinburgh (V)
358. High School Wynd, and Cardinal Beaton's House (V)
359. Plainstanes Close, Edinburgh (V)
360.
361. Lady Stairs Close, Edinburgh (V)
362. Bakehouse Close, Edinburgh/Crest of Sir Archibald Acheson (V)
362. Bakehouse Close, Edinburgh/Robert Burns (V)
363.
364.
365. Chalmers Lighthouse, Anstruther, Fife
366. Courtyard, Tantallon Castle/Escape of Earl of Angus (V)
367. Elie Ness Lighthouse/Ships that pass in the Night (V)
368. Smolletts House, Edinburgh (V)
369. Flodden Wall, The Vennel, Edinburgh (V)
370.
371. Martyr's Monument, Greyfriars Churchyard, Edinburgh (V)
372. Moray House, Canongate, Edinburgh (H)
373. Sir Walter Scott's House, Castle Street, Edinburgh (V)
374. Moot Hall, Hexham/Execution of Duke of Somerset (V)
375. Jeanie Deans Cottage, St. Leonards Hill, Edinburgh (H)
376.
377.
378.
379.
380. Advocates' Close, Edinburgh (V)
381. Bass Rock at Dawn ('Mild rides the morn . . .') (H)
382. Cintra, Portugal—drawn by Cordelia Phillimore (V)
383. Auld Robin Grays Cottage, near Elie, Fife (H)
384.
385.
386. The Sands, Elie (H)
387.
388. Kilconquhar Church, Fife (V)
388. Bass Rock (H)
389. West Bow, Edinburgh (V)
390. Fast Castle/Ravenswood Leaving (V)
390. The Marquis of Huntly's House, Canongate, Edinburgh (V)
391.
392. John Knox's House, Edinburgh (V)
393. Glasgow Cathedral/St. Mungo, etc. (V)
394. Moubray House, High Street, Edinburgh (V)
395. Argyll Tower, Edinburgh Castle (V)
396. Holyrood Abbey Court House, Edinburgh (V)
397. Riddle's Close, Lawnmarket, Edinburgh (V)
398.
399.

400. Tower Bridge, Cockermouth
401.
402. St. Abbs Head, Lighthouse and Fog Horn (H)
403.
404.
405. The Priory, Coldingham/Princess Ebba (V)
406. Grey Walls, Gullane (H)
407. Barns Nest Lighthouse, Dunbar (V)
408. Old Parish Church Manse, Gullane (H)
409.
410. Tantallon Entrance Gate and Barbican (H)
410. Grey Walls, Gullane, South Front (H)
411. The Goose Green, Gullane (H)
412. Macduff's Cave, Earlsferry (V)
413. Tantallon Castle (from the East)/Dungeon (V)
414. Saltcoates Castle and Farm, Gullane (H)
415. The Old Gateway, Luffness, Gullane (H)
416. Cottage of John Todd, Roaring Shepherd, Swanston (H)
417. Queen Mary's Bedroom, Holyrood Palace (H)
418. Milton's House, Chalfont St. Giles (H)
418. Lord Danley's Room, Holyrood Palace (H)
419. De Quincey' Cottage, Lasswade (H)
420.
421. Advocates Close, High Street, Edinburgh (V)
422. Chessel's Court, Canongate, Edinburgh (V)
423.
424. Palace Courtyard, Edinburgh Castle (V)
424. Jordans Meeting House, Beaconsfield, Bucks (H)
425.
426. Room in Edinburgh Castle in which James VI was born/dungeon (V)
427. Red House Castle, Longniddry (V)
428. Edinburgh Castle (H)
429.
430.
431.
432. Brown's Court, Canongate, Edinburgh (V)
432. Ruins of Lindisfarne Abbey (H)
433. St. Anthony's Chapel, Edinburgh (H)
434.
435.
436.
437. Banqueting Hall. Edinburgh Castle (H)
438. Greyfriars Church, Edinburgh (H)
439.
440.
441. Fishing Fleet off Fidra, Firth of Forth (H)
442. Dryburgh Abbey—From East/Preaching friars (V)
443.
444.
445. St. Abbs from the West (H)
446.
447. Melrose, East Window (V)
447. Chancel, Melrose Abbey (V)
448. Dryburgh Abbey, St. Marys Aisle (V)
449. Darnick Tower (V)
450. Bishop Paterson's House, White Horse Close, Edinburgh (V)
451.
452.

453.
454. Warkworth Castle, Northumberland (V)
455. A Brigantine off the Bass (H)
456. A Topsail Schooner off the Bass (H)
457. Twizel Castle, Northumberland (H)
458. Old Cowport Gate, Berwick (H)
458. Mons Meg, Edinburgh Castle (H)
459. Battle Ships off Bass Rock (H)
460.
461. Cannon Ball House, Castle Hill, Edinburgh (V)
462. Golfer's Land, Canongate, Edinburgh (V)
462. Carlton Hill, Edinburgh, Royal Observatory, etc. (H)
463. Mercat Cross and City Chambers, Edinburgh (V)
463. Holyrood Palace—A House of many memories (H)
464. Bishop Percy's House, Bridgnorth (V)
465. Bridgnorth (H)
465. Stoneway Steps, Bridgnorth (V)
466.
467. Entrance Gateway, Bamburgh Castle (V)
468.
469. James' Court, Edinburgh (V)
470. Thistle Chapel—St. Giles Cathedral, Edinburgh (V)
471. Monument to Greyfriars Bobby, Edinburgh (V)
472.
473. Statue of St. Bridget in Melrose Abbey (V)
474. Dunstanburgh Castle, Northumberland (V)
474. Edinburgh Castle from Esplanade etc. (as No. 617) (V)
475. Liberton Tower, Midlothian (V)
476. S. W. Corner of Greyfriars Churchyard (V)
477. Melrose Abbey. Tomb of Michael Scott—The Wizard (V)
478 Town Hall, Bridgnorth, Market Day (V)
479. Interior of Parliament Hall, Edinburgh
480.
481. Canongate Church, Edinburgh
482. Lady Stair's House, Edinburgh (V)
483. Conspirator's Doorway, Holyrood Palace (V)
484. Statue to Wallace on Hill above Dryburgh (V)
485. Bothwell's House, Byer's Close, Edinburgh (V)
486.
487. Lindisfarne Castle (V)
488. The Keep, Bamburgh Castle (V)
489.
490.
491.
492.
493. West Bay, N.B., A Good Catch (similar to No. 52) (H)
494. Barnbougle Castle (V)
495. Shoemaker's Land, Canongate, Edinburgh (V)
495. Queen Mary's Audience Chamber, Holyrood Palace (H)
496. Queen Mary's Oratory, Holyrood (V)
497. Town Hall, Musselburgh (V)
498. Allan Ramsay's Shop, High Street, Edinburgh (V)
499. Ruins of Whitekirk Church (H)
500. Lighthouse Inchkeith/Inchkeith, Firth of Forth (V)
501. Edinburgh Castle and Ross Fountain (V)
502. Heriot's Hospital, Edinburgh (V)
503.
504. The Study, John Knox's House, Edinburgh (V)
505. Gladstone Lane, Lawn Market, Edinburgh (V)

506. Queen Mary's Supper Room, Holyrood/Private staircase (V)
507. Bridgnorth, Low Town, from Castle Hill (H)
508.
509. Haverfordwest Castle, Pembrokeshire (V)
510.
511. The High Rock, Bridgnorth (H)
512. Bridgnorth from Knowle Sands (H)
513. Cirencester, Hospital Gate, Abbey St. Mary (V)
514. Easby Abbey, Richmond, Yorks (H)
515.
516. Bath Abbey (V)
517.
518. Richmond Castle, 'The Font of Beauty, . . .' (H)
519. Cirencester Church from the Abbey Grounds (H)
520. Easby Abbey
521. Cirencester, Capital of the Cotswolds, etc. (H)
522. St. Margaret's Chapel, Edinburgh Castle etc. (V)
522. St Leonard's, Bridgnorth, from Oldbury (V)
523.
524. Hermitage Rock, Bridgnorth (V)
525. Beach and Sand Dunes, Gullane (H)
526. The Rows, Water Gate, Chester (H)
527.
528.
529.
530.
531.
532.
533.
534.
535. Old White Horse Inn, Canongate, Edinburgh (as No. 244)
536.
537. Stoke Poges Church (V)
538. Coleshill Village, Amersham (H)
539.
540. Old Houses, Amersham (H)
541.
542.
543.
544.
545.
546.
547.
548.
549.
550. Chester Castle (H)
551. Bamburgh Castle and Village (H)
551. Eastgate Street, Chester (H)
552.
553.
554. Lasswade/Legend of Lasswade (V)
555. Circular Roman Bath, Bath/Bladud Banished (V)
556. Royal Crescent, Bath/Queen of the West (V)
557.
558. Stoke Poges (V)
559. Punch Bowl, Braemar (H)
560.
561.

562.
563.
564. Castle Hill and Ancient Rock Dwellings, Bridgnorth (V)
565.
566. Bass Rock from Canty Bay/Entrance to Natural Tunnel etc. (V)
567. Wood House/St. John's Hospital, Cirencester (V)
568. Airship scouting somewhere off the east coast (V)
569.
570. Flight of aircraft over the sea (V)
571.
572. The Bridge, Lasswade/Legend of Lasswade (V)
572. Bowden Church, One of Oldest Churches in Scotland (H)
573. Sir Walter Scott's Cottage, Lasswade (V)
573. Old Toll, Gosford (H)
574.
575.
576. Lindisfarne Priory (V)
577.
578.
579. Across the Sands to Holy Island (H)
580.
581. Newbridge, Gardens and Pier, Clacton (H)
582.
583. The Fountain, Bowden near Melrose (H)
584.
585.
586.
587.
588.
589.
590. Ye Olde Hostel of God-Begot, Winchester (V)
591. Ye Olde Hostel of God-Begot, Winchester (Side View)
592. Dirleton—Where Peace and Calm Contentment dwell Serene (H)
593. Crab Fishing off the Bass (V)
594.
595.
596. Bass Rock Siege 1694/A Row to the Bass (V)
597.
598.
599.
600. Interior of Queen Margaret's Chapel, Edinburgh Castle (V)
600. Edinburgh Castle at Sunset (V)
601. The University of Edinburgh (V)
602. Off Inchkeith (H)
602. Bridgnorth from the Railway Station (V)
603.
604. Bridgnorth—Aeroplane Flight over Castle Hill (V)
605. High Street, Bridgnorth (H)
606.
607.
608. George Hotel, Crawley (H)
609. Ship Inn, Alveston (H)
610. Crown Hotel, Amersham (H)
611.
612.
613.

614. Tantallon Castle from the Air (V)
615.
616. Heriot's Hospital, Edinburgh
617. Edinburgh Castle from Esplanade/etc. (as No. 474) (V)
618.
619. Homeward Bound—Schooner Off Bass Rock (H)
620. A Ketch Off The Bass (H)
621.
622. Great Airship R34 passing the Law, N.B. (H)
623.
624. Post Office, Bridgnorth (H)
625. Whitby Harbour, Low Tide (assumed as card shows No. 925) (H)
626.
627.
628.
629.
630.
631. Tantallon Castle, Courtyard (H)
632. St Aidan's Church, Bamburgh/Grace Darling (V)
633.
634. Picture Gallery, Holyrood (H)
635.
636. Canty Bay, N.B.—showing sheep and boat (H)
637. Chapel Royal, Holyrood (V)
638. Old King's Head Inn/Ye Olde Yatch Inn (V)
639. Bamburgh. Memorial to Grace Darling (V)
640. Lord Darnley's Dressing Room, Holyrood (H)
641.
642.
643. Baillie John Macmorran's House, Edinburgh (V)
644. Ballantine's Close, Grassmarket, Edinburgh (V)
645.
646. Old Houses in Cowgate, Edinburgh (H)
647.
648. Jenny Geddes' Stool (V)
649. Trunk Close, Edinburgh (V)
650. Tailors Hall, Cowgate, Edinburgh (V)
651. Chapel of St. Mary Magdalene, Edinburgh (V)
652. Carrubber's Close, Edinburgh (V)
653.
654.
655.
656.
657.
658. Solan Geese on Bass Rock—Homecoming (V)

Cards Unidentified by Number
Dirleton Castle—cannon in left hand corner (H)
Kenilworth Castle
Neidpath Castle, near Peebles (V)
Stirling Castle/Battle of Bannockburn (H)
Scarborough Castle (V)
Dunolly Castle, Oban (H)
Olde Rover's Return Inn, Manchester (H)
Poets Corner, Manchester (V)
Bull's Head Inn, Manchester (H)
Olde Fyshing Tackle Shoppe Wellington Inn, Manchester (V)
Chetham Hospital, Manchester (H)
Moulin and Black Castle, Pitlochry (H)

St. Mary's Church, Haddington (H)
Dunottar Castle (V)
Barnard's Inn, Fetter Lane (H)
Soldier's Leap, Pass of Killiecrankie (H)
Links, Gullane (H)
St. Baldred's Church, N.B. (H)
Golf Links, N.B. (H)
Whitekirk near N.B. Binning Wood in distance (H)
Tantallon Castle/Lord Marmion' Defiance (H)
The Harbour, N.B., boats and warehouses (H)
Lincoln Cathedral (H)
Bruce's Resting Place, near Pitlochry (V)
The Fort, Tenby (H)
Dirleton Castle, N.B., Entrance Gateway (V)
Dawn breaking over Bridgnorth (H)
The Bass Rock—showing moonlit scene (H)
The Law (Harvest Time) N.B.—sheep, men and horse (H)
Dirleton Road, N.B. (H)
Longstone Lighthouse/Grace Darling (V)
David Garrick (V)
High Street, N.B. (H)
Herring Fleet in the Forth (V)
N.B. from Point Garry (H)
Ruins of the Cathedral, St. Andrews (V)
St. Baldred preaching at Canty Bay (H)
Evesham/De Montfort/Battle/Henry III (V)
Bass Rock, Sunrise (H)
Shakespeare's House, Stratford
Fruit Seller in Portugal—Cordella Phillimore
Whitekirk and Binning Wood.

■81a

Reginald Phillimore. Pub. Phillimore. Lord Darnley's Room, Holyrood Palace. Period 2   £1.50

■81b

Reginald Phillimore. Pub. Phillimore. Reverse of card No. 300, Rosyth Castle and Firth Bridge. Period 2 .. ..   £1.50

PINKAWA, ANTON
Art Nouveau artist, particularly highly regarded for his delicate 'Seasons' Series. Early Period 2.
Price range .. .. £5/**£10**/£15

PIRKIS, ALBERT GEORGE ■82a
Amusing and skilful artist, best known for his series showing accident-prone cyclists and motor-ists for Hildesheimer, many of them 'Write-Aways'. He also did views and London scenes.
Price range .. ..75p/**£1.50**/£3

POULBOT, FRANCISQUE ■82b
French artist who came to the public eye in WW1 with his pitiful but spirited urchins ('gosses') orphaned and made homeless by the horror of war. C. B. Cochran introduced a Poulbot sketch into his Bairnsfather 'Better 'Ole' play. Poulbot also drew advertisements and political cards, notably of the famous 'Landru' trial. *See also* POLITICS.
Price range (highest valuation for the 'Landru') .. .. 50p/**£1.50**/£10

'PYP'
Comic artist of Period 2, many of whose designs were published by Davidson Bros., e.g. UB Illustrated Songs, credited as 'Originals by PYP'.
Price range .. ..75p/**£1.50**/£3

QUINTON, ALFRED ROBERT (1853–1934) ■82c
Born in Peckham and educated at Hornsey School and Heatherley Arts School, he excelled in oils, exhibiting at the Royal Academy, the Royal Society of British Artists and many other exhi-bitions. He travelled extensively through the British Isles on his bicycle, sketching, and illustrated several books with his watercolours. His most productive association was with J. Salmon, the postcard publishers of Sevenoaks, and he worked for the firm from 1911 until his death.

Pub. Faulkner, C. W.
Several series of views.

Pub. McKenzie, W. & Co.
Artistic series.

Pub. Tuck
Picturesque Coaching Inns and other Town series.

Pub. Salmon, J.
Many series of village, small town, country views. Periods 2 to 4, some signed 'A.R.Q.'
Price range for all above .. .. 50p/**75p**/£1

■82a
Pirkis. Pub. Hildesheimer. Motoring Write-Away. Early Period 2 .. .. £3

■82b
F. Poulbot. Comment on the infamous Landru trial (c. 1920) £10

■82c
Alfred Robert Quinton. Pub. McKenzie. 'Old London' signed 'A.R.Q.' PU *1905* 75p

RAEMAEKERS, LOUIS (1869–1956)

Dutch artist whose bitter, anti-German cartoons, published as 'Drawings of a Neutral' did much for the Allied Propaganda machine in WW1 (*see also* WAR). They were published for the Amsterdam paper *De Telegraaf* and reprinted in booklet form in aid of British and French wounded and published by Geo. Pulman & Sons.

Price range   .. ..75p/**£1**/£2.50

REYNOLDS, FRANK (b.1876)

Art editor of *Punch* for 10 years, he also worked for *The Sketch* and was a member of the London Sketch Club of which he was President in 1909 and 1922. His 'Characters from Dickens' were reproduced as postcards by A. V. N. Jones & Co.

Price range   .. .. £1/**£1.50**/£2

RICHARDSON, AGNES (1885–1951)

■83a

Popular artist, whose postcard work spanned Periods 2 to 4. Subjects include children and patriotic designs.

    Publishers include: Birn Bros. Davidson Bros. Faulkner, C. W., Geographia Ltd., Hauff, Charles, Inter-Art., Millar & Lang, Photochrom, Regent Pub. Co., Tuck, Valentine's, Vivian Mansell.

Price range   .. ..75p/**£1.50**/£2

ROBIDA, A.

French artist who did many charming landscapes and town scenes in early Period 2 and who contributed to many of the important French series, e.g. *Collection des Cent*, *The Gala Henri Monnier*, Album Mariani (*see also* COLLECTIONS).

Price range (highest valuation for the 'Monnier') .. .. .. £2/**£5**/£50+

ROBINSON, ROBERT (1886–1952)

American artist in the genre of Norman Rockwell, who drew covers for *Saturday Evening Post* and illustrations for *Colliers*, *Harpers*, etc. His postcards depict ordinary Americans and ordinary American life for Edmund Gross. Period 4.

Price range   .. .. £1/**£2.50**/£4

RUBINO, ANTONIO (1880–1964)

Italian artist who drew some fine Period 3 caricatures, also advertisements.

Price range   .. .. £3/**£5**/£8

■83a

Agnes Richardson. Pub. Inter-Art. 'Back To The Land'. Period 3 .. .. £1.25

■83b

Xavier Sager. Pub. Solomon Bros. No. 8020. Hand coloured. 'The Merry Widow'. Period 2 £6

SAGER, XAVIER ■83b

Most prolific of all French postcard artists (Neudin has identified 3000 designs), Sager is best known for his risqué glamour designs. He also produced commercial work and during WW1 his designs had a distinct propaganda message. Sager drew under several pseudonyms, including 'Leger' and 'Salt Lake'. All his work shows a light and humorous touch.

Early Period 2 from 1900	£3/**£6**/£10
Mid Period 2	£2/**£3**/£5
Period 3 (*see also* WAR)	£2/**£4**/£6
Period 4	£2/**£3**/£5
Ads for 'Welcome' heels/chocolate	£3/**£5**/£8
Pseudonyms/Kirchner copies ..	£6/**£8**/£10

SAUBER, ROBERT (1865–1936)

One of the founder members of the London Sketch Club in 1898, Sauber spent much of his working life in Northampton. He is chiefly known for his 'London Types' series.

Pub. Pictorial Stationery Co. (from 1901)

Set of 12 'Familiar Figures of London' (*see also* SOCIAL HISTORY). At least four different printings have been identified, some with white borders and some without. The borderless cards are UB   £4/**£5**/£6

Complete set   ..   ..   £50/**£65**/£80

Pub. Tuck

Series in 1900 of works of literary figures
..   .. £4/**£5**/£6

Tuck Celebrated Posters

No. 1502 Tatcho   ..   ..   .. £15/**£20**/£25

SCHIELE, EGON (1890–1918)

Recognising his talent while at secondary school, his teachers, against his family's wishes, sent him to study at the Vienna Academy in 1906. The following year he set up his own studio and developed his harsh, disturbing, expressionist style. The erotic element in some of his drawings led to his detention for indecency. Schiele became part of the Vienna Secessionist Group and also worked with the group 'Sema' (with Klee and Kubin) in Munich. He also worked for the Wiener Werkstatte, designing some fine postcards in a gentler style, including several striking studies of red-heads in large hats. Called up for military service in 1915 he continued working and in 1916 contributed a special issue of the political Berlin review *Aktion*. His brilliant career was tragically cut short in 1918 when both he and his wife died in the great influenza epidemic.

Aktion/Wiene Werkstatte   £75/**£250**/£500

SCHÖNPFLUG, FRITZ (1873–1951) ■84a

Born in Vienna, son of a prosperous solicitor, Schönpflug was a 'natural', untaught artist, with a sharply observant eye. He recorded with benign accuracy the life and leisure pursuits of fashionable Austrian society and the Austrian army—from personal experience gained during his military service. He had a distinctly humorous touch and his work could as well have been described under COMIC. His output was prolific, well over 500 designs are estimated and the majority of his postcards were published by Brüder Köhn.

Pub. Köhn, Brüder (Periods 2 to 4)

Many sets of 6   ..   .. £2/**£3**/£5

Pub. Munk, M. (Period 2)

Glamour and caricatures   ..   .. £2.50/**£4**/£6

Period 5

Designs with Nazi interest, e.g. *Tag der Wehrmacht fur das K.W.H.W.* (Winter Relief Campaign. Army Day) ..   £3/**£5**/£10

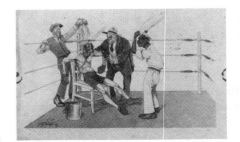

■84a

Fritz Schönpflug. Pub. Brüder Köhn, Vienna. The Boxing Match. PU *1922* £4

■84b

G. E. Shepheard. Pub. Tuck. 'Egg-cellent' series. No. 9344. PU *1919* £1

SEVERN, WALTER (1830–1904)

Born in Rome, he was educated at Westminister. After a short spell as a civil servant he became a landscape artist and designer, founding the Dudley Art Gallery.

Pub. Tuck ('Oilette') and others

Price range .. .. –/**50p**/75p

SHEPHEARD, GEORGE EDWARD ■84b

Talented caricaturist, many of whose designs were reproduced on, or drawn for, the postcard. He is perhaps most famous for his caricature of Rudyard Kipling.

Pub. Avenue Pub. Co. (1906)

Doctor set .. .. 75p/**£1**/£2

Pub. Faulkner, C. W.

Several sets, of which many 'horsy' designs
have been remaindered .. .. –/**50p**/75p

Pub. Photochrom Co. (Period 3)

Silhouette series .. ..75p/**£1**/£1.50

Pub. Tuck

Cricket, Dutch and Seaside themes
.. ..75p/**£1**/£1.50
'Egg-cellent' series (1918) .. ..75p/**£1**/£1.50

SMITH, JESSIE WILLCOX (1863–1935)

Born in Philadelphia, Jessie trained as a teacher before she discovered her drawing ability. After studying at the Pennsylvania Academy of Fine Arts, she went on to become one of America's most successful women artists of Periods 2, 3. During her distinguished career she won many awards, including the Silver Medal for Watercolours at the Panama Pacific Exposition, San Francisco 1915. She illustrated books, magazines, and did many advertisements. Children are her favourite subjects and her work often shows a strong, and beautiful *Art Deco* influence. Much of her postcard work was published by Reinthal & Newman.

Price range .. ..£3/**£5.50**/£15

SOWERBY, MILLICENT (1878–1907)

Now much in vogue for her *Art Deco* designs, her main subjects were children, flowers and nursery rhymes. Publishers of her postcard work include: C. W. Faulkner, Hodder & Stoughton, Misch & Co. during Periods 2 to 4 .. .. £3/**£4**/£5

SPURGIN, FRED (also 'F.S.') (1882–1968) ■166a

Of Latvian origin, born Izydor Spungin, Fred Spurgin came to Britain with his parents at the turn of the century and became a naturalised British subject in 1925. Success came soon, with postcard designs, magazine and book illustrations and advertisements (notably for Rothmans—he married Lilly Rothman). One of the postcard's most versatile artists, he drew humour (from the vulgar seaside type to the political), glamour and many patriotic designs during WW1. Though his work was promoted by a multitude of publishers, his greatest partnership was with the Art & Humour Pub. Co. with which he had family connections. His output was enormous, over 2000 designs have been identified, through Periods 2 to 4. In his twilight years he did many 'hack' designs for folded greetings cards. He used many pseudonyms, 'F.S.', collected by many, being the most famous.

Pub. Anon (many printed in Germany)
.. ..75p/**£1**/£1.50
Pub. Art & Humour/Inter-Art. The bulk of
the Spurgin designs. Comic/glamour/
patriotic .. .. 50p/**£1**/£2
Pub. Bamforth. Rare fantasy design
.. .. £1/**£2**/£4
Pub. Blum & Degen. Signed 'F.S.' 75p/**£1**/£1.50
Pub. Ettlinger. Signed 'F.S.' ..75p/**£1**/£1.50
Pub. Gale & Polden. Signed 'F.S.' 75p/**£1**/£1.50
Pub. Garner, H. Signed 'F.S.' ..75p/**£1**/£1.50
Pub. J.W.A. & Co. Signed 'F.S.' ..75p/**£1**/£1.50
Pub. London View Card Co. Various
designs .. .. 50p/**75p**/£1
Pub. Paternoster. Some of the finest Spurgin
designs, incl. 'Japanese–British Exhi-
bition', 'Tramps', etc. .. .. £1/**£1.50**/£2
Pub. Regent Pub. Co. Signed 'F.S.'
.. ..75p/**£1**/£1.50
Pub. Tuck. Various designs .. ..75p/**£1**/£1.50
Pub. Vertigen. Signed 'F.S.' ..75p/**£1**/£1.50
Pub. Wildt & Kray. Various designs
.. .. 50p/**75p**/£1

Theatre advertisements

Princess Charming; Take your Girl Friend to
   See the Girl Friend .. .. ..   £3/**£5**/£10

Best known Series

'Khaki' (12 cards) per set .. .. £15/**£20**/£30
'Leap Year' (12 cards) per set .. £15/**£20**/£30

STANNARD, HENRY JOHN SYLVESTER (1870–1951)

Born in London, the son of the sporting painter, Henry Stannard, he studied at South Kensington and painted rustic and garden studies. In 1922 he held a joint exhibition with his daughter Theresa in the Brook Street Galleries. Publishers of his postcard work include Boots and Tuck ('Oilettes')
Price range .. .. 50p/**75p**/£1

STARR-WOOD, H. ('S.W.') ■86a

A self-taught artist, his first exhibition was in 1903. He was a member of the London Sketch Club, where he played an active role in the clowning escapades. He produced few postcards, mainly for Valentine, during Period 2.
Price range .. .. £1/**£1.50**/£2

STEINLEN, ALEXANDRE THEOPHILE (1859–1923) ■87a

A Swiss artist who became one of the brilliant group working in Paris around the turn of the century. He was a contributor to many of the important early French series (*see also* COLLECTIONS) and to magazines and poster designs. His inspiration was the theatre/music hall and 'Bal Tabarin'. Many of his designs show the *Art Nouveau* influence. Most of his turn of the century work was published by M. F. Champenois. Neudin 1980 identifies 50 postcard designs.
Price range .. .. .. £25/**£50**/£100+

STUDDY, GEORGE (1878–1948)

Born in Devonshire, educated at Newton and Dulwich and Heatherley Art School, Studdy contributed to *The Sketch*, *Titbits* and other publications and became a member of the Savage, the Chelsea Arts Club and the London Sketch Club of which he was President in 1921. His most famous creation was 'Bonzo', a cheeky, cuddly puppy with a distinct personality. Bonzo emerged in the 1920s and like 'Old Bill' appeared on all manner of toys, pottery items, car mascots, etc.

Advertising work

Excelsior Reisen. Ger. .. .. £3/**£8**/£15
Pascall Butter Almonds .. £7.50/**£15**/£20
Sandeman, Stanley. Cotton Belting Co.
  .. .. £3/**£8**/£15
Wolseley 10 Motor .. .. £7.50/**£15**/£20

Pub. Deans

Various designs .. .. .. £2/**£3**/£4

Pub. Inter-Art

12 different designs. Early Period 4
  .. .. £2/**£3**/£4

Pub. Photochrom

Celesque Series. Pre-Bonzo WW1
  Patriotics .. .. .. £2/**£3**/£4

Pub. 'R.P.S.'

Period 4. Nos. 1002–1072, possibly
  more .. .. £2/**£3**/£4

Pub. Valentine

Period 4. The Bonzo Series .. £2/**£3**/£4
Period 5. Anti-Hitler designs .. £3/**£4**/£5

Pub. Warne

Various designs .. .. .. £2/**£3**/£4

■86a

H. Starr Wood. Pub. Valentine. 'Situations Vacant'. PU *1904* £1.50

TARRANT, MARGARET (1888–1959)
■87b

Artist who specialised in children and flower designs during Periods 2 to 4. Publishers include C. W. Faulkner, Humphrey Milford, The Medici Society and Ward Lock. *See also* CHILDREN.

Price range .. .. 50p/**75p**/£1

TEMPEST, MARGARET (b. 1892)

After studying at art school in Ipswich, Westminster and Chelsea, she became a founder member of the Chelsea Illustrators' Club. She was most famous for her illustrations of Alison Uttley's *Little Grey Rabbit* books. The Medici Society published postcards of some of her animal designs.

Price range .. .. 50p/**75p**/£1

■87a

Alexandre Théophile Steinlen. Pub. E.G. Paris. Collection des Cent. Period 2 .. .. .. £50

■87b

Margaret Tarrant. Pub. Medici Society. 'Fairy Secrets'. PU *1939* £1

THACKERAY, LANCE (d. 1916)

Born in Yorkshire, Lance Thackeray was another of that élite band of founder members of the London Sketch Club in 1898. As Tom Browne accounted for an important percentage of Davidson Bros.' comic output, so Thackeray was Tuck's leading comic artist, and the grand master of the 'Write-Away' genre. He worked for Tuck from 1900 to his death in 1916. He produced nearly 1000 postcard designs. A great traveller, Thackeray's Egyptian scenes and types are comparable to Tom Browne's Dutch work. Where Browne portrayed the working classes in a multiplicity of social situations, Thackeray's types were generally middle to upper class. Another Thackeray trademark was the small sketch in the border of the design that was a continuation of the main joke. Most of his work was comic in nature, but a couple of advertising cards have been identified.

Pub. David Allen. Theatre Poster Adverts
The Earl and the Girl .. .. .. £5/**£8**/£10

Pub. Black, A. & C.
People of Egypt. Series 12/13 .. £2/**£3**/£4

Pub. Faulkner, C. W.
Series 181 .. .. £3/**£5**/£8

Pub. Hills
'For the Empire' horse pictures .. £2/**£3**/£4

Pub. Nestlé's
Advert for Swiss Milk .. .. .. £5/**£8**/£10

Pub. Tuck
Early chromographed series (over 30). Subjects include Cricket, Golf, Journals Illustrated, Motoring, Popular Plays, Greetings cards (re-issues—over 30), Write-Away designs, incl. Boer War .. £1.50/**£4**/£8

Oilette series. Subjects include Bridge, Golf, Egypt, Leap Year, Motoring, Roller Skating, Sea & Riverside, Varsity .. £1.50/**£3**/£5

Proof Limited Editions. Series 955, 983, 984 .. .. £3/**£5**/£8

THIELE, ARTHUR ■88a

Much confusion surrounds this increasingly popular artist. It is now felt by several researchers that recently published biographical information about Thiele refers to another, earlier artist of the same name. Thiele's signed production spans the years 1899–1930s—clearly impossible for an artist thought to have died in 1919. There is also doubt as to his nationality. One school of thought is that he was Belgian, not German. Any authoritative information on this artist would be welcome. Whatever his history, Thiele is an artist whose work becomes increasingly appreciated as even more and varied examples are discovered; prices for good Thiele cards are rising fast. More confusion arises in cataloguing his output. As he was collected throughout Europe, Britain and the USA, many series were reproduced by several publishers in a variety of qualities. Few of his many series are named, another source of difficulty in identifying and listing his work. As research is still continuing and no definitive check list has appeared we will name here only the most important series or famous sets and list the main publishers of them. *See also* ANIMALS/CATS.

Animals

Cats—*see* ANIMALS. ■23b	
Chicken/cockerels/hens	£2/**£4**/£5
Chimpanzees	£4/**£6**/£8
Dogs' heads	£4/**£5**/£7
Dogs—Others	£3/**£4**/£5
Monkeys (in school etc.)	£3/**£5**/£7

Dusky Belles/Braves .. ..£4/**£6**/£8

Motoring

'Horse Power Series'—Rare ..	£6/**£8**/£10
Others	£3/**£5**/£7

Period 1

Gruss aus Moorbad (Mudbath) Chromo-litho vignettes 1899	£6/**£8**/£10
Others	£4/**£6**/£8

Period 4

Poorer quality designs, e.g. bathing scenes, cats	£1/**£2**/£3

Propaganda (*see also* WARS)

Anti-British—Boer War	£6/**£10**/£15
Anti-British—WW1 (incl. Zeppelin Kommt)	£4/**£6**/£8
Hamster Erlebnisse (post-War Black Market)	£3/**£5**/£7
Red Cross	£4/**£5**/£6
Wir Barbaren (WW1)	£3/**£4**/£5

Romantic Scenes

Couples, dancing, etc.	£3/**£4**/£5

Sporting Scenes

Billiards, bowling, football, horseracing, hunting, roller-skating, tennis, and tobaganing	£3/**£5**/£7

Topical Themes

Komet Kommt (Halley's Comet, 1910)	£6/**£8**/£10
Zeppelin Kommt (Peacetime) ..	£4/**£6**/£8

Others .. .. £2/**£5**/£12

Publishers of the Above

Bürger, Bruno & Ottillie, Leipzig
Faulkner, C. W.
'F.E.D.'
Gebrüder Dietrich, Leipzig.
Klaus, Adolf & Co., Leipzig.
Kunzli, Carl, Zurich
Stroefer.
'T.S.N.'
Tuck.
Zieher, Ottmar, Munich.

■88a

Arthur Thiele [*Ger.*]. *Pub. Bruno Bürger & Ottillile, Leipzig. 'Gruss' from the Mudbaths.* PU 1899 .. .. £8

THOMAS, BERT ■89a, 233a

Born in Newport, Wales, the son of a sculptor, he came to London to work, his first job being as Art Director for a small advertising agency. He also contributed to comics and magazines like *London Opinion* and *Punch*. During WW1 he served as a private in the Artists' Rifles and during the War did the picture that was to bring him fame—''Arf A Mo, Kaiser!', for the *Weekly Despatch* Tobacco Fund for Troops (Pub. Gale & Polden)—which earned £250,000. After the War he continued to contribute to magazines and newspapers (like the *Evening News*) and re-emerged mainly for Tuck in WW2 with ITMA jokes and other timely humour. Mainly comic, his work also includes some striking caricatures between the Wars (Pub. Odhams). *See also* COMIC and WAR.

Price range .. ..75p/**£1.50**/£4

TWELVETREES, CHARLES H.

Prolific American artist of babies and cute kids, crosspatches and comic animals, fatties and teddy bears. His work spanned from about 1907 until well into the 1930s. Many cards are signed with the initials 'C.T.' only, some are unsigned but instantly recognisable (although many attempts were made to fake his popular style). The snappy captions are an integral part of the design.

Twelvetrees also drew some glamour, seasonal greetings and WW1 patriotics. In the USA the majority of his work was published by Edward Gross, the House of Art and Reinthal and Newman. In the UK his cards were published by Alfred Stiebel as 'Alpha Smile Messengers'.

U.S. Publishers

Edward Gross, N.Y.	..75p/**£1**/£1.50
House of Art, N.Y.	50p/**75p**/£1
Illustrated Postal Card & Nov. Co.	50p/**75p**/£1
Reinthal & Newman	50p/**75p**/£1

Cards Distributed in UK

Alfred Stiebel, still with the Gross imprint/ Alpha Pub. Co. (mainly as Smile Messengers, the series running into several hundreds) .. ..75p/**£1**/£1.50
The 'Wedding' series .. .. .. £1/**£1.50**/£2

UPTON, FLORENCE (1873–1922) ■89b

Creator of the golliwog in 1893, Florence Upton illustrated a children's book using her original character called *The Adventures of Two Dutch Dolls*; it was an instant success. In 1903 Tuck bought the rights to the book and reproduced the 'llustrations as postcards. Sadly Florence Upton was too naïve about business to profit much from the international success of her creation.

Pub. Tuck (from 1903). About 15 sets of 6, many overprinted with Christmas Greetings .. .. £5/**£6**/£7

VILLON, JACQUES (Gaston Duchamp) (1875–1963) ■90a

French artist who contributed to many satirical publications, like *Le Rire*, *L'Assiette au Beurre*, etc. His postcard output was small and therefore much sought after. First and foremost a poster artist he contributed 7 cards to the Gala Henri Monnier series and his design for the 'Collection des Cent' (*see also* COLLECTIONS) is the most highly rated of all.

Price range .. .. £50/**£100**/£250

■89a

Bert Thomas. Pub. Odhams. Le Tigre (Clemenceau). Period 4 .. .. £4

■89b

Florence Upton. Pub. Tuck (with permission of Longmans, Green & Co.). Golliwogg comes to Grief on the Ice. Chromolithograph. PU *1905* £6

WAIN, LOUIS (1860–1939)

Louis Wain is known as 'The Cat Man' *par excellence*. His cats remain typically feline while displaying uncannily human characteristics. They first brought fame to their creator as illustrations for children's books—for which Wain is mostly remembered. He also drew dogs, birds and other animals with equal competence, and his postcard output, for a variety of publishers, was large—500–600 designs have been identified. His most successful association was with Tuck, especially in the 'Amewsing Write-Away' series. Wain's preoccupation with cats was obsessive, and sadly he spent his last 15 years in a mental hospital (where he still continued to work). He died there, too, at the age of 79. Most of his work bears at least a trace of almost zany humour and his cards are popular with collectors in several fields—animals, humour, or themes like diabolo, ping-pong, etc. After an unrealistically high boom in 1977/78, his cards have now settled down. *See* ANIMALS: Cats for a detailed listing of his work.

Price range .. .. £4/**£8**/£20

WARD, SIR LESLIE (SPY)

Pub. Stewart & Woolf (1902). Four series of
12 cartoons from *Vanity Fair* .. £2/**£3**/£4

WENNERBURG, BRYNOLF ■90b

Versatile German artist, whose work ranged from early UB chromo-litho bathing beauties (*see also* BATHING) through comic tennis players to sentimental WW1 scenes of lovers/nurses (*see also* WAR). He also contributed to the famous 'Lustigen Blätter' series.

Price range .. ..£1.50/**£8**/£15

WHEELER, DOROTHY (1891–1966)

From an artistic family and trained at Blackheath Art School, Dorothy was a successful illustrator of magazines and books (incl. Enid Blyton stories).

Pub. Black, A. & C. (*c.* 1926). English
Nursery Rhymes .. .. .. £1/**£1.50**/£3
Pub. Milford, Humphrey. Day at the Fair
series .. .. £1/**£1.50**/£3
Pub. Salmon, J. Several series .. 75p/**£1**/£1.50

WHITE, FLORA

Best known for her patriotic children designs during WW1 (*see also* WAR) mostly published by Photochrom.

Price range .. .. –/**50p**/75p

WIEDERSEIM, GRACE (1877–1936)

American artist best known for her chubby, pop-eyed children. She also signed cards by her married name, Grace Drayton. Most of her designs were published by Reinthal & Newman and Tuck in Period 2. She was also famous for being the creator of the 'Campbell's Kids'.

Comic children, general .. .. ..75p/**£1**/£1.50
Campbell's soup ads. .. .. .. £1/**£2**/£4

■90a

Jacques Villon. Pub. E.G., Paris. Collection des Cent. Period 2 .. .. £150

■90b

Brynolf Wennerburg. Bathing Beauty. UB. PU *1905* £8

WIELANDT, MANUEL (1863–1922)

German artist who studied at Karlsruhe and Stuttgart. His love of travel (to Capri, France, Italy, Malta, etc.), resulted in some fine watercolour views. Over 100 designs have now been identified of the French and Italian Rivieras, Lakes, Gulf of Venice, Germany and Switzerland, many UB. Publishers include Moser, Nister, Schmidt-Staub and Velten.

Price range .. .. £2/**£3**/£4

WILLEBEEK le MAIR, HENRIETTE (1889–1966)

Dutch-born artist of a wealthy family. She enjoyed a privileged upbringing but found her own commerical success at an early age. Augener Ltd., the music publishers, soon recognised her talents and published her drawings to illustrate a series of children's books, reproducing some of them as postcards.

Price range .. .. £1.50/**£2**/£3

WILLRICH, WOLF ■91a

In Hitler's campaign against 'degenerate art', Willrich was one of the few artists approved by the National Socialist Regime. He was one of the team of four appointed delegates who, in the 1930s, visited galleries and museums throughout Germany to root out all 'unapproved' art. Literally thousands of priceless and irreplaceable works of art were destroyed as a result. Willrich's own work depicted idealistic, sturdy, Aryan, thoroughly approved, Germanic characters—soldiers, sailors, airmen, mothers, fathers, Hitler Youth types, etc. His fine line-drawing portraits are reminiscent of the work of Albrecht Durer—Germany's greatest Renaissance engraver and artist—as is his spindly, distinctive signature, a 'W' interspersed with the date of the drawing. Major series (all o/s) include:

Deutscher Blutadel in Aller Welt (German Aristocracy of Blood Throughout the World) incl. 'Carinthian Farmer's Wife; Lower Saxony Maiden; Old Bavarian Countryman; Westphalian Country Girl. Periods 4, 5.

  b & w .. .. £1.50/**£2**/£2.50
  col. .. .. £2/**£2.50**/£3

Fallschirmjager (Parachutists). Fine col. series, incl. Sgt. Arpke, Col. Brauer, Capt. Delicia, Maj. Koch. Period 5

.. .. £6/**£8**/£15

Fundraising cards for National Socialist causes, e.g. V.D.A.— Volksbund fur das Deutschtum in Ausland (League of Expatriate Germans). Subjects similar to 'Deutscher Blutadel. Periods 4, 5. b &

w .. .. £1.50/**£2**/£2.50
col. .. .. £2/**£2.50**/£3

Heer und Panzer (Army annd Tanks) Period 5. Fine series of portraits, incl. Oberst Brauer, Obltn. Brenner, Dietl, Fulda, Goricke, Guderian, von Lutzow, Rommel, von Rundstedt .. .. .. £5/**£8**/£15

Luftwaffe (Airforce) Period 5. Airborne personalities, incl. Graf Kageneck, Hanna Reitsch. .. .. £6/**£9**/£14

Marine (Navy) Period 5. Similar series of naval portraits incl. Donitz, Endrass, Kretschmer, Prien, Raeder, Schepke, Schuhart .. .. £6/**£9**/£11

WIMBUSH, HENRY B.

An accomplished landscape artist, his most productive period was from 1881 to 1908. He painted views of the British Isles and the Channel Isles, illustrating books as well as designing postcards. Most of his postcard work was reproduced by Tuck in the 'Oilette' range and by A. & C. Black. Period 2

Price range .. .. .50p/**75p**/£1.50

■91a

Wolf Willrich. 'Volksbund fur das Deutschtum im Ausland'. 'Madchen aus Bessarabian'. Period 4 .. .. £2.50

WOOD, CLARENCE LAWSON (1878–1957)

Coming from a distinguished artistic family, his talent for drawing showed at an early age. He studied at the Slade School of Fine Art and Calderon's School of Animal Painting. He was a member of the London Sketch Club and a friend of Tom Browne. He served with gallantry in the Royal Flying Corps in WW1 and drew a series of patriotic designs during the war. His postcard production spanned from Period 2 to Period 4. The early work is characterised by 'stock' characters—the cheeky boy, the rotund policeman, etc. Also famous were his 'Prehistoric' series. After the war his greatest success came with the creation of 'Gran'pop', an engaging chimpanzee. Parrots were another favourite theme.

Pub. Allen, David. Theatre Poster Advert
   (1903). Beauty and the Barge   £3/**£6**/£8
Pub. Brown & Bigelow (B & B), USA.
   Period 4, 'Gran'pop' Calendar cards for
   the J. E. Fricke Co.   ..   ..   ..   £2/**£3**/£4
Pub. Carlton Pub. Co. Period 2 Comics
   ..   .. 75p/**£1**/£1.50
Pub. Davidson Bros. Period 2. 'Prehistoric'
   series   ..   .. 75p/**£1**/£1.50
Pub. Dobson, Molle & Co. Period 3.
   Patriotics   ..   .. £1/**£1.50**/£2
Pub. Henderson. Weather Forecasts
   ..   .. 75p/**£1**/£1.50
Pub. Inter-Art. 'Artistique' series/'Comique'
   series (children) ..   .. 50p/**75p**/£1
Pub. Lawrence & Jellicoe. Period 2. London
   Opinion series   ..   .. £1/**£1.50**/£2
Pub. Pictorial Stationery Co. 'Prehistoric'
   series   ..   .. 75p/**£1**/£1.50
Pub. Salmon, J. Period 3 designs   75p/**£1**/£1.50
Pub. Stiebel, Alfred. Modern Humour
   series   ..   .. 75p/**£1**/£1.50
Pub. Valentine. Periods 2, 3. Several series;
   Period 4. Gran'pop/Parrots   .. 75p/**£1**/£1.50

WOOD, STANLEY L. (1866–1928)

Best known for his WW1, dashing military pictures (*see also* WAR) he exhibited at the Royal Academy and his paintings fetched £100 in his heyday.
Price range   ..   .. 50p/**£1**/£1.50

YOUNG, WALTER HAYWARD ('JOTTER') (1869–1920) ■92a

Prolific water colour artist of views of landscapes, towns and villages—usually under his pseudonym, 'Jotter'. His drawings, which also include coastal views, often incorporate some figures. He was a founder member of the Aldwych Club and a member of the Savage Club, the theatre being his second love. Under his real name he drew posters and also some postcards, including Period 3 patriotics and humour (*see also* WAR). As 'Jotter' he toured the British Isles, often with his daughter Gwendoline (who also designed postcards), and the great bulk of his work is reproduced in the Tuck Oilette series. Other publishers include: Boots, Ettlinger, Frith, Hartmann, Jarrolds, Charles Martin, Misch & Co., Robert Peel, Pictorial Stationery Co., Gordon Smith, Wildt & Kray and Woolstone Bros.
Price range   ..   .. 50p/**75p**/£1

ZILLE, H.

The Berlin artist *par excellence*, whose output includes finely observed Berlin types—prostitutes, traders, urchins, etc. A member of the Berlin Academy, he was described by the right-wing newspaper *Fridericus* as 'The Berlin portrayer of toilets and pregnancy'. He contributed to the famous German series, 'Lustigen Blätter'. His designs continued to be produced during WW1 and show women doing men's jobs, soldiers on leave, etc.
Price range   ..   .. £3/**£5**/£8

■92a

Walter Hayward Young ('Jotter'). Pub. Tuck. Picturesque Counties No. 7115—Northbourne, Kent. Period 2 ..   .. 75p

AUTOGRAPH CARDS

Value according to fame of personality.

Bray Collection

Known as 'The Autograph King', Reginald Bray sent thousands of postcards to contemporary celebrities (some printed with his message) asking them to sign and return the cards. Period 2.

Famous personalities .. .. .. £3/**£5**/£10
Lesser known personalities ■93b £2/**£4**/£8

Cards Signed by the Artist

Famous or sought after artist ■93a
.. .. £2/**£8**/£20
By minor artist .. .. £1/**£3**/£5

Cards Signed on Reverse by Celebrity

With picture related to subject .. £1/**£3**/£5
With picture not related to subject 50p/**£1**/£3

Signed Photographic Cards ■93c

Real signatures .. .. 50p/**£2**/£5
Facsimile signatures .. .. .. –/**50p**/75p

■93b

UB *Chromolitho card of HM Torpedo Gunboat* Rattlesnake *with victorian stamp from Reginald Bray to the Paymaster of the ship.* PU *1 April 1901* £8

■93c

Pub. J. Beagles & Co. Mr. (later Sir) Seymour Hicks. Autographed card. Period 2 .. .. £2

■93a

Pub. Ettlinger. Artist Hassall. Signed Hassall. Period 4 .. .. £8

■93d

Period 2. Accident in 1911. Aeroplane belonging to Morison £7

AVIATION

This section is one in which card values will be greatly enhanced by postal history features such as time and place of posting, cancellations used and the messages written on the back. These valuations do not allow for such special features unless stated. The aeroplane came into being when the postcard was at the peak of its popularity, and thus there were many aviation meetings to go to and daring personalities, first flights and crashes to see and picture. There were also opportunities to carry postcards from place to place by air, and such flights frequently employed special postmarks.

Probably the earliest aviation postcards are those sent out of Paris by balloon during the seige of 1870, while the latest collectables are the cards flown in Concorde. There is a great deal in between, and generally speaking real photographic cards with clear detail are most highly valued. However, cards flown by balloons or airships are amongst the most highly priced cards too, probably because of their relative scarcity, and in this highly specialised field, postal history attributes can raise card values way beyond the ranges given here. Because association with a balloon or airship flight seems currently to overwhelm other features of a card, we also list under the heading *Flown* examples of such cards, although their obvious thematic classification might be quite different, e.g. a Tuck Edward VII Coronation card overprinted for celebrations at Beckenham and then dropped from a balloon. Such a card fetched £1050 in auction at Phillips in 1980. But what would it fetch next time?

The two great wars spurred flight development and their cards (Periods 3 and 5) are listed under WAR. Because much of the early aeroplane flying activity was by Frenchmen in French machines, French cards feature prominently in Period 2, but British publishers such as Beagles, W. H. Smith, Millar & Lang, Rotary and Valentine, plus many local firms, can be found. Airship cards are predominantly German, however, and fine German cards show LZ (Luftschiff Zeppelin) airships from 1900 onwards.

Accidents

Aircraft. Blackpool, 7 September 1935	£5/**£6**/£10
Aircraft. Period 2. ■93d	£4/**£7**/£12
Aircraft. Others	£1/**£2**/£4
Airships	£6/**£8**/£10

Aircraft (Photographic Types)

Period 2	£2/**£4**/£6
LL 'Nos Aeroplanes' series	£2/**£4**/£4.50
Period 4	£1/**£2**/£3
Periods 6, 7	**50p**

Airfields (Photographic Types)

Period 2. General views	£1/**£1.50**/£2
Period 2. With aircraft	£3/**£4**/£7

Airships (Photographic Types)

British. Period 2	£3/**£6**/£8
British. Period 4	£6/**£8**/£10
British. Other periods	£1/**£2**/£3
Foreign. Period 2. ■94a	£2/**£4**/£6
Foreign. Other periods	£1/**£2**/£4

Balloons (Photographic Types)

Period 1	£3/**£5**/£7
Period 2	£2/**£4**/£6
Other periods	£1/**£2**/£3

Artist Drawn

Bannister, Derek
Pub. J. Salmon. Faithful drawings of contemporary aircraft. (*See* WAR for Periods 3, 5.) Periods 2, 4 .. .. .. 50p/**£1**/£2
Oilette. Pub. Tuck. 'Famous Aeroplanes' series .. .. £2/**£3**/£4
'In the Air' series .. .. .. £1/**£1.50**/£2

■94a

Pub. G. Scriba, Metz. Period 2. Zeppelin 1 landing (1909) £4

■94b

Period 2. 9 Sept. 1911. First UK aerial post. Green printing. Flown London to Windsor .. £12

Handville, R.
US National Air & Space Museum Series. Pub. Dexter. Subjects Amelia Earhart, Charles Lindbergh, Wright Brothers, etc.
.. .. **50p**

Commemorative/First Flights/Meetings
(in chronological order)
Manchester & Salford 1903. Lifeboat Saturday. Unflown (See also *Flown*)
.. .. £30/**£50**/£75
Australia. First Aerial Post. Melbourne to Sydney. Pilot Maurice Guillaux, 16 July 1909 .. .. £5/**£7**/£10
Doncaster, 1909 .. .. .. £10/**£12**/£14
Paris, 1909. Aviation Exhibition £2.50/**£3**/£4
First cross-channel flight. Blériot, 25 July 1909 .. .. £1/**£2**/£3
Blackpool Meeting, 1910 .. .. £6/**£10**/£15
Bournemouth Meeting, 1910 .. £4/**£8**/£12
Endurance Flights. Paris to Brussels. Pub. ELD. Aviators and their machines. Photo-origin, 1910 .. .. .. £4/**£5**/£6
Lyon, 1910. Map of course. Pub. Farges
.. .. £6/**£10**/£11
Nice, 1910. Aviators and their machines
.. .. £2/**£2.50**/£3
Rouen, 1910. *Grande Semaine D'Aviation.* 19–26 June. Poster Competition cards
.. .. £8/**£15**/£25
Circuit Européen, 1911. Inset portraits of Garros, etc. Pautauberge ad. backs
.. .. £2/**£4**/£5
First UK Aerial Post (1911). London to Windsor. ■94b .. .. .. £10/**£12**/£15
First UK Aerial Post (1911). Windsor to London .. .. £15/**£25**/£50
Daily Mail circuit. Pictures of competitors with their machines plus facsimile signatures of Salmet, etc. 1912 .. £4/**£5**/£6
Daily Mail. Multi-portrait cards. Artist Henry Laussucq .. .. £10/**£12**/£18
Kiel Flying Week, 1912 .. .. £4/**£5**/£6
Stüttgart, 1912. Gordon Bennet event, Col. litho. .. .. £10/**£25**/£30
Circuit de L'Est, 1913 .. .. £8/**£10**/£12
Paris to Bordeaux. Aviators and their machines. Photo-origin, 1913. ■95a
.. .. £6/**£8**/£10
Staffordshire Aerial Post. Stone to Stafford, 1913 .. .. £7/**£8**/£9
Sheffield, 1914. Aviation week. Pub. Hawley, R.P. .. .. .. £6/**£10**/£12
Alcock & Brown. First non-stop cross Atlantic flight. June 1919. ■95b .. £3/**£4**/£5

Geneva, 1922. Gordon Bennet event. Col. litho. .. .. £10/**£15**/£19
Schneider Trophy, 1927. Supermarine S5, S6, R.P. .. .. £2/**£2.50**/£3

■95a
Period 2. 1913. Paris to Bordeaux race. Aviator Bielovucie £10

■95b
Pub. Beagles. Period 4. Captain Alcock & Lt. Brown. No. 168J £4

■95c
Period 7. Concorde card. Produced in Berlin with printed stamp. Flown Paris–Berlin–Paris on 17 January 1976. Flight map on reverse £6

■95d
Period 4. Luxemburg. Flown by balloon on the last day of the International Stamp Exhibition. 8 September 1927 .. .. £25

Schneider Trophy, 1929. Supermarine S6, R.P. .. .. £2/**£4**/£4.50

Johannesburg World Exhibition series, 1936 .. .. £5/**£6**/£7

Hanover, 1938. *Flugtag* (Flying Day). Artist drawn. Official card o/s .. .. £3/**£4**/£7

50th Anniversary First UK Aerial Post. Oversize card with facsimile of the original. Flown BEA from Hendon to Windsor, 1961 .. .. .. £2/**£3**/£4

Manchester & Salford, 1903
Life-Boat Saturday. Card carried by Balloon Post during fund raising for the Lifeboat Service. Valuation very subject to condition, 29 August 1903 .. .. £350/**£500**/£650

Zeppelin Centenary, 1938. LZ129 Hindenburg. Flight from Frankfurt to Denmark, 8 July 1938 .. .. £8/**£9**/£12

Concorde

The advent of commercial supersonic passenger flight brought a rash of first day stationery. On some flights postcards were carried. The cards listed here are those flown on commercial flights, including special, schedule and charter. Values can fluctuate widely owing to the large variety of handstamps used.

Air France Charter, Paris–Berlin–Paris. German card, 17 Jan. 1976. ■95c .. .. £2/**£4**/£6

Air France Charter, Frankfurt–Hamburg–Paris. German card, 24/25 April 1976 .. .. £2/**£4**/£6

British Airways. London–Washington inaugural flight, 24 May 1976. Concorde on ground at night .. .. .. 50p/**£1**/£2

Ditto. Concorde in flight .. .. 75p/**£1**/£2

Air France, Paris–Buenos Aires. First flight. World Cup, 24 May 1978 .. £2/**£4**/£6

Fantasy/Photo-Montage

Artist drawn visions of future air transport .. .. 75p/**£1**/£1.50

People photographed in 'Flying Machines' .. .. 75p/**£1**/£1.50

Photographic scenes with superimposed aircraft .. .. 50p/**75p**/£1

Flown

Beckenham, 1902. Pub. Tuck. Edward VII Coronation. Overprinted, 'Despatched from the Clouds', 9 August 1902 (see above) .. .. **P/A**

Friedrichshafen, 1931. Official card. Printed 8pfg stamp. Centenary of the airfield. Flown in the L.S. Graf Zeppelin, 27 August 1931 .. .. .. £35/**£40**/£50

Luxembourg, 1927. International Stamp Exhibition Commemorative. U/S. Flown by balloon, 8 September 1927. ■95d .. .. £18/**£20**/£25

Personalities

R.P. cards tend to be most highly valued, particularly if both aviator and aeroplane are featured in close-up. Most cards are Period 2.

Alcock & Brown, Period 4	£2/**£4**/£6
Aubrun	£3/**£4**/£5
Audemars	£5/**£7**/£8
Barnes	£3/**£5**/£6
Bielovucie	£3/**£4**/£5
Blackburn, Harold	£3.50/**£4**/£5
Blériot, Louis	
Pub. 'LL'. Landing at Dover ..	£2/**£3**/£3.50
Others	£2/**£6**/£8
Breguet	£2.50/**£3**/£4
Cody, Col.	£2/**£5**/£6
Drexel	£3/**£5**/£6
Dubonnet	£4/**£7**/£8
Dumont, Santos	£4/**£6**/£9
Earhart, Amelia (Period 4) ..	£3/**£4**/£5
Farman	£3/**£7**/£9
Ferber	£2/**£4**/£5
Gilmour	£4/**£5**/£6
Godden	£2.50/**£3**/£4
Grace	£1.50/**£2**/£3
Grahame-White	£2/**£3**/£5
Hamel, Gustav	£2/**£4**/£5
Hawker, H. G.	£1.50/**£2**/£3
Hucks, B. C.	£1/**£2.50**/£5
Latham	£2/**£6**/£7
Lindbergh, Charles A. ..	£1.50/**£2**/£3
McArdle	£3/**£5**/£6
Pegoud	£3/**£4**/£5
Prosser	75p/**£1**/£2
Reitsch, Hanna (Period 4) ..	£5/**£7**/£8
Roe, A. V.	£5/**£7**/£9
Rolls	£2/**£3**/£5
Rougier	£1/**£1.50**/£2
Salmet, H.	£2/**£6**/£7
Sopwith	£2/**£4**/£5
Valentine	£1/**£1.50**/£2
Wright Bros.	75p/**£1.50**/£3
Zeppelin, Count von ..	£2/**£2.50**/£5

BATHING/THE BEACH

High quality Real Photogrpahic (R.P.) cards attract higher valuations than a general photographic origin postcard.

BATHING BEAUTIES

Pub. Editions du Panorama de Paris. Series of coloured cards of photographic origin,
UB   ..   ..   £1/**£2**/£4

Artists
Abeille, Jack. Period 1. ■97a   .. £10/**£15**/£20
Wennerburg, B. Period 2 UB   ..   £2/**£4**/£8
Other signed artists. Period 1   ..   £3/**£5**/£10
Other signed artists. Periods 2, 3   £1/**£2**/£3
Other signed artists. Periods 4, 5   50p/**75p**/£1
Unsigned artist drawn. Period 1 ..   £1/**£2**/£3
Unsigned artist drawn. Periods 2, 3
  ..   ..   75p/**£1**/£2

BATHING MACHINES

Photographic Origin/R.P. Periods 1 to 3
Close-up, sharp picture with detail of people
  ..   ..   £1/**£2**/£4
In distance, but with detail of people
  ..   ..   50p/**£1**/£2

COMIC BATHING SCENES

Most of the humorous postcard artists did seaside postcards (*see also* ARTISTS for details), e.g. Browne, 'FS', McGill, Thackeray, as well as many unknown, unsigned artists.
Periods 2 to 4 ..   .. 75p/**£1.50**/£3
Periods 5 to 7. ■97b   ..   ..   ..   −/**25p**/50p

CONCERT PARTIES on beach, pier. *See also* THEATRE/WIRELESS

Photographic Origin/R.P. Periods 2 to 4
Pierrots
Close up, sharp detail with people   £2/**£4**/£6
As part of general beach scene   .. £1/**£1.50**/£3
Other Players
Close up as above. ..   .. £1.50/**£3**/£5
General scene as above ..   ..   .. 75p/**£1**/£2.50

DONKEYS

Artist Drawn. Periods 2 to 4
Signed   ..   .. 50p/**75p**/£1
Unsigned ..   ..   −/**50p**/75p

Photographic Origin/R.P. Periods 2 to 4
Close up, sharp detail with people. ■97c
  ..   ..   75p/**£1.50**/£3
As part of general beach scene   .. 50p/**£1**/£2

GENERAL BEACH SCENES

Photographic Origin/R.P. Periods 2 to 4
LL, with plenty of activity/people   £1/**£1.50**/£2
Others, with plenty of activity/people
  ..   ..   50p/**£1**/£1.50

Photographic Origin/R.P. Periods 5 to 7
Various   ..   ..   −/**50p**/£1

PADDLING

Artist Drawn. Periods 2 to 4
Signed   ..   .. 50p/**75p**/£1
Unsigned ..   ..   −/**50p**/75p

Photographic Origin/R.P. Periods 2 to 4
LL, with sharp detail of people.
  ..   ..   £1/**£2**/£3
Others, with sharp detail of people 75p/**£1.50**/£2

■97a
Artist Jack Abeille. UB. *1898* £20

■97b
Pub. Bamforth. Comic series 438. PU *1938 but foreshadowing WW2* 50p

■97c
Pub. R. Briaut, Burgess, Bognor, Sussex. 'Donkeys at Bognor' with goat cart. PU *1907*   ..   £1

BICYCLING

Bicycling flourished in Victorian and Edwardian times, as well as being a viable means of transport. Advanced young ladies shocked society with their bicycling bloomers; cycling clubs sprang up around the country, rallies, gymkhanas and races regularly took place.

See ADVERTISING for advertisements for bicycles.

High quality Real Photographic (R.P.) cards attract higher valuations than general photographic origin postcards.

Artist Drawn
Pub. Pascalis Moss & Co. (1901/1902). Cyclists of All Nations. Series of 12 col. caricatures .. .. £1.50/**£2.50**/£4
Pub. Tuck. Period 2. ■98a. Artist. Leslie Willson. 'The Scorcher's Progress'. Set of 6 witty cycling jokes .. .. .. £1/**£1.50**/£2

Most of the well-known comic postcard artists of Period 2 designed series of postcards on cycling themes, notably Browne, F.S., Pirkis—*see also* ARTISTS for details.

Signed artists .. .. 75p/**£1**/£4
Unsigned artist drawn. ■98b 50p/**75p**/£1.50

Cycling Champions
Periods 2, 3 .. .. 75p/**£1.50**/£2.50
Periods 4 to 6 .. ..50p/**£1**/£1.50

Cycling Clubs
Photographic origin/RP Periods. 2 to 4.
■98c .. .. 75p/**£1**/£2

Cycling Gymkhanas
Photographic origin/RP Periods. Periods 2 to 4. ■98d .. .. 75p/**£1**/£2

Cycling Races/Rallies
Artist drawn. Period 2 souvenir cards (notably Italian, like Bologna 1902)
.. .. £2/**£4**/£6
Artist drawn. Others .. .. .. £1/**£2**/£4
Milk Race. Periods 6, 7 .. .. –/**50p**/75p
Tour de France. Periods 2, 3 .. £2/**£4**/£6
Tour de France. Periods 4, 6 .. £1/**£2**/£3
Photographic. Others .. .. ..50p/**£1.50**/£3

Photographs of Edwardian cyclists (*see also* SOCIAL HISTORY). Many fascinating photographic cards, often anonymous, exist of cyclists, from posed portraits to street scenes. .. .. ..75p/**£1.50**/£3

■98a

Pub. Tuck. 'The Scorcher's Progress'. Artist Leslie Willson. PU *1913* £2

■98b

Pub. Stewart & Woolf. Shakespeare quote applied to cycling. UB £1.50

■98c

Pub. Anon. Local Cycling Club. PU *1905* .. £1

■98d

Pub. H. H. Hole, Williton. Local Gymkhana £1

CHILDREN/TOYS

Dutch dolls, golliwogs and teddy bears are much collected. The most important series in this section is Tuck's 'The Queen's Dolls' House'.

ARTISTS

American Artists (Periods 2, 3)
Mainly 'Cute Kids', often chubby and wide-eyed (even 'pop'-eyed), 'Kewpie' dolls (a corruption of 'Cupid') and 'Sunbonnet' children. The most brilliant exception is the superb work of Jessie Willcox Smith.

† = *see also* ARTISTS for more details.

Anderson, V. C.†	50p/**£1**/£1.50
Brundage, Frances† ■42a	£1/**£3**/£5
Clapsaddle, Ellen†	75p/**£1.50**/£2
Corbett, Bertha (Sunbonnets) ..	£1/**£2**/£3
Drayton, Grace (*see* Wiederseim, **below**)	
Dixon, Dorothy (Sunbonnets)	£1/**£2**/£3
Dwiggins, C. W.† ('Dwig') ..	75p/**£1**/£1.50
Gassaway, Kate	50p/**75p**/£1
Griggs, H. B. (signed also 'H.B.G.')	
.. ..	50p/**75p**/£1
O'Neill, Rose† (Kewpies) ..	75p/**£1.50**/£3
Outcault, Richard Felton ..	50p/**75p**/£1
Smith, Jessie Willcox† (incl. *Art Deco*)	
	£2/**£8**/£15
Twelvetrees, Charles†	75p/**£1**/£2
Wall, Bernhardt (incl. Sunbonnets)	
.. ..	£1/**£2**/£3
Weiderseim, Grace†	£1/**£1.50**/£2

Publishers of the above include Gabriel, Sam; Gross, Edward (New York); House of Art (New York); Reinthal & Newman; Rose, Chas.; Rotograph; Tuck; Ullman.

European Artists (Periods 2, 3)
Many of these well-known artists did general designs as well.

† = *see also* ARTISTS for more details.

Barber, C. W.	–/**50p**/75p
Barribal, W.†	£1/**£1.50**/£2
Bertiglia, A.† (It.)	£1/**£2**/£4
Butcher, Arthur (*see also* WAR) ..	50p/**75p**/£1
Caldecott, R.† ■44a	50p/**75p**/£1
Dexter, Marjorie	–/**50p**/75p
Ebner, Pauli ■100a	£1/**£2**/£4
Gilson, T. (*see also* WAR) ..	50p/**75p**/£1
Goodman, Maude	50p/**£1**/£3
Hardy, Florence† ■58b	£1/**£2**/£4

Hassall, John† (Nursery Rhymes).	£1/**£2**/£4
King, Jessie, M.† (incl. *Art Deco*)	£5/**£15**/£40
Kinsella, P.† (cricket/tennis).	■63b
.. ..	£1/**£1.50**/£2
Mallet, Beatrice	50p/**75p**/£1
Nash, A. A.† ■71a	£1/**£1.50**/£2
Parkinson, Ethel. ■72b	£2/**£3**/£4
Poulbot, F.† (*see also* WAR).	■82b
.. ..	75p/**£1.50**/£2
Richardson, Agnes† (*see also* WAR).	■83a
.. ..	75p/**£1**/£1.50
White, Flora† (*see also* WAR). ..	75p/**£1**/£1.50

Publishers of the above include Davidson Bros.; Faulkner, C. W.; Hildesheimer; Inter-Art; Millar & Lang; Tuck.

Unsigned European Artists (Early Period 2)
Many delightful and beautifully produced early chromo-litho studies (some embossed or silvered) were produced by publishers like Meissner & Buch; M. Munk (Vienna); Nister; Stewart & Woolf; Tuck and many foreign unnamed publishers.

Price range	£1/**£2**/£4

'Nursery' Artists (Period 4)
Just beginning to come into vogue (now that more is known about them since the Cope's book, *Illustrators of Postcards from the Nursery*) are the children's cards of the 1920s and 1930s. The children depicted are more ephemeral creations than the robust American children and they often feature elves, fairies, nursery rhymes and whimsical animals. The best illustrators of the genre show a distinct *Art Deco* flavour.

† = *see also* ARTISTS for more details.

Barker, Cecily Mary	50p/**75p**/£1
Bowden, Doris	50p/**75p**/£1
Brett, Molly†	50p/**75p**/£1
Cloke, Rene†	50p/**75p**/£1
Cooper, Phyllis (incl. *Art Deco*). ..	75p/**£1**/£1.50
Folkard, Charles† ■55a	£1/**£2**/£3
Jacobs, Helen†	£1/**£2**/£3
Mercer, Joyce†	£1/**£2**/£3
Nixon, Kathleen†	£1/**£2**/£3
Outhwaite, Ida Rentoul† ..	75p/**£1**/£1.50
Pearse, Susan BB.	£1/**£1.50**/£2
Shand, C. E. (*Art Deco*)	£2/**£4**/£6
Sowerby, Millicent†	£1/**£2**/£4
Tarrant, Margaret† ■87b ..	50p/**75p**/£1.50
Tempest, Margaret†	50p/**75p**/£1
Wheeler, Dorothy†	£1/**£1.50**/£2

Publishers of the above include Augener Ltd.; Black, A. & C.; Faulkner, C. W.; Liberty & Co.; Medici Society; Milford, Humphrey; Millar & Lang; Tuck; Valentine; Vivian Mansell.

European Artists (Periods 4, 5) (*see also* WAR)

† = *see also* ARTISTS for more details.

Attwell, Mabel Lucie† ■36c (also Periods 2 to 4)	£1/**£1.50**/£2
Birch, Norah Annie	–/**50p**/75p
Broo, Piet (Dutch)	£1/**£2**/£4
Comicus (Harry Parlett) ■73a ..	–/**50p**/£75p
Cooper, Phyllis	50p/**75p**/£1
Dean, Dora	50p/**75p**/£1
'Dinah' ■251a	50p/**75p**/£2
Forres, Kit	50p/**75p**/£1
'Henry' (Belg)	75p/**£1**/£1.50
Mallet, Beatrice	50p/**75p**/£1
Patterson, Vera	50p/**75p**/£1
Richardson, Agnes	75p/**£1**/£1.50
Taylor, Arnold	50p/**75p**/£1
Tempest, D.	50p/**75p**/£1
White, Brian ('Nipper')	50p/**75p**/£1
Williams, Madge	50p/**75p**/£1
Also many unsigned Belgian, British, Dutch, French and Italian artists ..	50p/**£1**/£3

Publishers of the above include Bamforth; Lychgate Ltd. (Worthing); Millar & Lang; Photochrom; Regent Pub. Co.; Salmon; Tuck; Valentine.

COONS

A popular theme during Period 2. Artists include († = *see also* ARTISTS for more details):

Burbrook (Coon series)	50p/**75p**/£1
Gilson, T.† (Pub. Hey, E. J.)	75p/**£1**/£1.50
Hyde, Graham (Pub. Tuck. 1906)	75p/**£1**/£1.50
Sandford, H. Dix (Pub. Tuck 'Happy Little Coons', etc.).	75p/**£1.50**/£2
Twelvetrees, C. (Pub. Reinthal & Newman).	75p/**£1**/£1.50
Wood, Lawson (Pub. Valentine). ..	£1/**£1.50**/£2
Unsigned artists	50p/**£1**/£1.50
Pub. Coe–Collotype, Bradford ..	–/**50p**/75p
Pub. Davis, A. M. ('Little Darkies')	–/**50p**/75p
Pub. Ettlinger (various 'Coon' designs)	50p/**75p**/£1
Pub. Inter-Art (Quaint Kids, etc.)	–/**50p**/75p

Pub. Tuck ('Coon Town Kids', etc.)	75p/**£1**/£1.50
Pub. Watkins & McCombie (Coon series)	50p/**75p**/£1
Other pubs.	50p/**75p**/£1

American 'Coon' Postcards. Countless American series by a variety of artists and publishers .. .. 50p/**75p**/£2

DOLLS/GOLLIWOGS/TEDDY BEARS/ OTHER TOYS

Artist drawn. Periods 2 to 4. Value according to calibre of artist and date.

Mirror Grange Miniature house in the tradition of the Queen's Dolls House and Titania's Palace, constructed by *The Daily Mirror* for their cartoon characters, *Pip, Squeak and Wilfred,* drawn by A. B. Payne.

Pub. Tuck. Period 4. sepia ..	75p/**£1**/£1.50
col.	£1/**£1.50**/£2
Nudekins. British version of the 'Kewpie' doll. Pub. Tuck. Periods 2, 3 ..	50p/**75p**/£1
Posed Photographic. Periods 2 to 4. ■100b	50p/**75p**/1.50

■100a

Pub. Anon. Artist Pauli Ebner. 'Dance Music on the Radio' Period 4 .. .. £4

■100b

Pub Anon. Foreign photographic card, hand-tinted, of child with dolls £1.50

PHOTOGRAPHIC PORTRAITS OF CHILDREN

Thousands of posed portraits of children, ranging from the very appealing to the coyly sentimental, were produced in Periods 2 to 4. Publishers include Birn Bros.; Carlton Pub. Co.; Davidson Bros.; Ettlinger; Hildesheimer; Knight Bros.; Rotary; Schwerdtfeger; Tuck; Wildt & Kray; as well as foreign and other British publishers.

Price range   ..   ..   –/**50p**/£1

POSTCARD TOYS

Pub. Faulkner. Perforated postcard painting booklets by Ivy Millicent James and Agnes Richardson

Pub. Hall, B. P. & Co. (1905). Horticultural series. At least 12 flowers.

Pub. Oates, S. (1905). Art Amateur series

Pub. Ruskin Studio Art Press. Period 4. Outline painting postcards

Pub. Tuck. Period 2. Postcard painting books (*see also* COMPETITIONS). Artists include Frances Brundage, Helena Maguire and Christina Klein.

Pub. Tuck. Period 4. Various cut-out models (incl. dressing doll series)

Others

Pub. in USA. Series of fairy stories with tiny books that pull out.

Price range all above   ..   ..   ..   50p/**75p**/£2

QUEEN'S DOLLS' HOUSE

This famous dolls' house, designed by Sir Edward Lutyens, portrays a typical British home in the reign of George V. It was presented to Queen Mary and was on view at the Wembley Exhibition 1924. It is now to be seen at Windsor Castle. It took $2\frac{1}{2}$ years to complete and over 1000 firms contributed to it. Tuck produced 6 sets of 8 cards. Nos. 4500–4505, which were sold to benefit Queen Mary's favourite charities. Period 4.

Tuck Oilette series. ■101a
1. The house, hall and dining room
   ..   ..75p/**£1**/£1.50
2. Drawing room, library (with miniature books by Kipling and pictures by Studdy, etc.)   .   ..   .75p/**£1**/£1.50
3. The Royal Bedrooms   ..   ..75p/**£1**/£1.50
4. The Queen's Private Apartments
   ..   ..75p/**£1**/£1.50
5. Nursery and Kitchen   ..   ..75p/**£1**/£1.50
6. Round about the house (garage, games room, electrical system, etc.)   ..75p/**£1**/£1.50

Tuck also produced special albums to hold the series, with a description of the house, which came in an illustrated carton.

Complete album (premium if in original carton)   ..   ..   £40/**£50**/£65

Later Tuck Photographic (2 series of 6 cards)
1. Drawing Room, Garden. Hall, King's Bedroom, Library, Regalia   ..   50p/**75p**/£1
2. Queen's Bedroom and Boudoir, Dining Room, Drawing Room, Royal Kitchen, Royal Nursery   ..   ..   50p/**75p**/£1

■101a

Pub. Tuck. Queen's Dolls' House. Oilette 4503
..   ..   £1.50

TITANIA'S PALACE (Period 4)

Designed by Sir Neville Wilkinson for his daughter (to attract fairy folk to stay) this 16-room palace is 9ft by 6ft and took over 15 years to construct. It was opened by Queen Mary at the Women's Exhibition, Olympia 1922. In 1978, after being exhibited around the world to raise money for needy children, it was sold by auction at Christie's for £135,000 to the Danish firm of toymakers, Lego.

Pub. Dixon, J. Arthur   ..   ..   ..   £1/**£1.50**/£2

Readers are cordially invited to send in details to Mr. and Mrs. Holt of cards, series, publishers, artists ... indeed any relevant information which they may have upon any postcard topic which adds to what appears in this edition. All correspondence addressed to them at the publishers will be answered and all contributions will be formally acknowledged in the next edition.

CINEMA

CINEMA ADVERTISING

Periods 2 to 4	£1/**£2**/£3
Periods 5 to 7. ■103a	—/**£1**/£2

Italian artist Nanni. Superb *Art Deco* poster portraits of stars like Vittorio di Sica, Elsa Merlini .. .. £9/**£12**/£15

CINEMAS/BIOSCOPES (Buildings)

Periods 3 to 5. Sharp photographs £3/**£6**/£10

FILM STARS

Many durable stars' careers spanned two or three postcard periods and these are listed in brackets after their name. Those stars whose postcards command a premium (of up to £2 over their Period price) are marked *. Plain backed cards (e.g. 'Red Letter') are not postcards, and are not listed.

'Fatty' Arbuckle (4)
Fred Astaire (4, 5, 6, 7)*
Tallulah Bankhead (4)
Vilma Banky (4)
Brigitte Bardot (6, 7)
Freddie Bartholomew (4) (child star)
John Barrymore (4, 5)
Lionel Barrymore (4,5)
Wallace Beery (4)
Ingrid Bergman (5, 6, 7)
Dirk Bogarde (6, 7)
Humphrey Bogart (4, 5, 6)*
Charlès Boyer (4, 5, 6)
Marlon Brando (6, 7)
Yul Brynner (6, 7)
Jack Buchanan (4, 6)
James Cagney (4, 5, 6)*
Eddie Cantor (4, 5)
Charlie Chaplin (3, 4, 5, 6)*
    Artists Donald McGill, Louis Wain/others
    Essanay Film Mfg. Co. ■103b
    Imperial Playhouse Series
    Rotary
    Others
Maurice Chevalier (4, 5, 6)
Claudette Colbert (4, 5, 6)
Ronald Colman (4, 5, 6)
Gary Cooper (4, 5, 6)
Jackie Coogan (4) (child star)
Cecily Courtneidge (4, 5)

Buster Crabbe (4, 5)
Joan Crawford (4, 5, 6, 7)
Bing Crosby (4, 5, 6)
Tony Curtis (6, 7)
Bette Davis (4, 5, 6, 7)*
Doris Day (5, 6)
James Dean (6)*
Marlene Dietrich (4, 5, 6, 7)*
Robert Donat (4, 5, 6)
Deanna Durbin (4, 5, 6)
Nelson Eddy (4, 5)
Douglas Fairbanks Jr. (4, 5)
Gracie Fields (4, 5)*
W. C. Fields (4, 5)*
Errol Flynn (4, 5, 6)
Henry Fonda (4, 5, 6, 7)
Joan Fontaine (4, 5, 6)
Clark Gable (4, 5, 6)
Greta Garbo (4, 5)*
Ava Gardner (5, 6, 7)
Judy Garland (4, 5, 6)*
Lilian Gish (4, 5, 6)
Betty Grable (5, 6)
Stewart Grainger (5, 6)
Cary Grant (4, 5, 6)
Jean Harlow (4)*
Olivia de Haviland (4, 5, 6)
Susan Hayward (5, 6)
Audrey Hepburn (6, 7)
Katherine Hepburn (4, 5, 6, 7)
Bob Hope (5, 6)
Jack Hulbert (4, 5)
Jennifer Jones (5, 6, 7)
Boris Karloff (4, 5, 6)*
Buster Keaton (4)*
Gene Kelly (5, 6, 7)
Grace Kelly (6)
Hedy Lamarr (4, 5, 6)
Dorothy Lamour (4, 5, 6)
Laurel & Hardy (4, 5)*
Peter Lawford (6)
Vivien Leigh (4, 5, 6)*
Harold Lloyd (4)*
Margaret Lockwood (4, 5, 6)
Carole Lombard (4, 5)*
Marx Bros. (4, 5, 6)*
Jeanette MacDonald (4, 5)
James Mason (5, 6, 7)
Jessie Matthews (4, 5)*
Carmen Miranda (5, 6)
Robert Mitchum (6, 7)
Tom Mix (4)*
Marilyn Monroe (6)*
Anna Neagle (4, 5, 6)
Pola Negri (4)*

Ramon Novarro (4)*
Merle Oberon (4, 5, 6)
Laurence Olivier (4, 5, 6, 7)*
Maureen O'Sullivan (4, 5, 6)
Pavlova (3) (*see also* THEATRE)*
Mary Pickford (3, 4)*
Nova Pilbeam (4)
Tyrone Power (4, 5, 6)
George Raft (4, 5, 6)*
Ronald Reagan (5, 6)*
Rin-Tin-Tin (5, 6) (dog star)*
Edward G. Robinson (4, 5, 6)
Ginger Rogers (4, 5, 6)*
Jane Russell (5, 6)
Norma Shearer (4)
Frank Sinatra (5, 6, 7)
Eric von Stroheim (3, 4, 5, 6)*
Gloria Swanson (4, 6, 7)*
Norma Talmadge (4)*
Elizabeth Taylor (5, 6, 7)
Robert Taylor (4, 5, 6)
Shirley Temple (4, 5, 6)* (child star)
Spencer Tracey (4, 5, 6)
Rudolph Valentino (3, 4)*
John Wayne (4, 5, 6, 7)
Johnny Weismuller (4, 5)*
Orson Welles (5, 6)
Mae West (4, 5, 7)*
Pearl White (3, 4)*
Michael Wilding (5, 6)
Loretta Young (5, 6)

B & w/sepia			
Periods 2, 3	.. ..		−/**50p**/75p
Periods 4, 5	.. ..		50p/**75p**/£1
Periods 6, 7	.. ..		**50p**
Coloured			
Periods 2, 3	.. .. ..		50p/**75p**/£1
Periods 4, 5	.. .. ..		.. 75p/**£1**/£1.50
Periods 6, 7	.. ..		**50p**

Hand autographed cards will always attract a premium.

Animated Film Characters (Periods 4 to 6)
Disney/scenes/characters. .. .. £2/**£4**/£6
Felix the Cat .. .. £1/**£1.50**/£3
Others .. .. 75p/**£1**/£2

FILM STILLS (with postcard backs)
Value according to Period and stars
.. .. 50p/**£1**/£2

Publishers of Film Star Portraits
These include many of the usual portrait specialists, e.g. Beagles, Lilywhite, 'Milton', Rotary, Valentine's, etc. Movie Magazines and Studios, e.g. Biograph Essanay Film Mfg. Co., Film Kurier, *Film Weekly*, Gaumont Imperial Playhouse Series, Metro Mayer, Pathé, *Picture Magazine, Picturegoer*, Translantic Film Co., Vitagraph Players, etc.
Price range as per stars listed above.

■103a

French reproduction of cinema poster. Period 7 .. .. £1

■103b

Pub. Essanay Film Mfg. Co. Charles Chaplin. No. 1 (Postcard back) £3

CIRCUS

The Circus has its origins in the Roman amphitheatre (from which it takes its shape and hence its name) and the Greek hippodrome. The amphitheatre staged pageants and contests between men and animals, usually ending in death. The hippodromes staged equestrian events.

The modern circus has its origins in England in the late 18th-century when Philip Astley popularised trick riding. Showmen moved in from the declining fairs with their varying acts. Astley took his circus to France (in 1772), Belgrade, Brussels and Vienna. One of his original horsemen, Charles Hughes, introduced the circus to Russia. Soon circuses started in America and by the turn of the century had spread throughout Europe and the USA. Permanent buildings housed some European circuses and a theatrical element crept in, adulterating the pure skill of the acts, which were still predominantly equestrian. But the circus reverted to its true vitality and throughout the world the circus 'families' flourished, each with its own traditions and specialities, acrobats and animal acts growing in daring and skill, the clowns developing their own special brand of magic. By 1900 the circus was thriving throughout the world. Showmen like P. T. Barnum and James A. Bailey in the USA, and C. B. Cochran in Britain put the circus on a more business-like basis. During Periods 1 and 2 the popularity of the circus gave rise to some of the most fascinating and beautiful of postcards. The delicate chromo-litho drawings, the colourful poster type adverts and the intriguing photographs are all to be found in this category.

Named Circuses
Barnum & Bailey
    Illustrations by Courmont and Franzl
    .. .. £2/**£3.50**/£5
    Poster type ads. Periods 2, 3. ■104a
    .. .. £10/**£15**/£20
    Various photographic cards of acts
    .. .. £1/**£2**/£4
Buffalo Bill's Wild West Show
    Poster type ads. .. .. £6/**£8**/£10
    Various photographic cards of acts
    .. .. £2/**£4**/£6
Busch Circus
    Colourful poster type ads. Period 2
    .. .. £2/**£5**/£8
Circus Althoff
    Early Period 2. 'Gruss Aus' .. £1/**£2**/£4
Circus Cesar Sideli
    Colourful poster type ads. Period 2
    .. .. £2/**£5**/£8
Hagenbeck's Circus
    Various animal and other acts .. £1/**£1.50**/£2
Royal Netherlands Circus
    Early Period 2 vignettes .. .. £2/**£3**/£5
Zirkus Krone, Zirkus Lorch, Zirkus Semsrott
Period 2 .. .. £1.50/**£3**/£6

Sites/Tents
    Artists impressions .. .. .. 50p/**£1**/£2
    Photographs .. ..75p/**£1.50**/£3

Acts
Madame Alaska and her Performing Seals
Capt. Alphonzo, the Intrepid Lion-Tamer
The Sarrasani
Waldemeer, the Modern Hercules
Zarmah the Wild Animal Trainer
Others (incl. acrobats, animal acts, bands, clowns, jugglers, strongmen, etc.)
Period 1/Early Period 2.
    Chromo-litho drawings .. £1.50/**£3**/£7.50
    Photographs .. .. .. £1.50/**£3**/£7.50
    Poster type ads. .. .. .. £1.50/**£3**/£7.50
Periods 2 to 4 .. .. £1/**£2.50**/£5

■104a

Pub. The Springfield News Co., USA. Coloured poster type advertisement (both sides) for Duryea Automobile. Period 2 .. ..£10

COLLECTIONS: The Great Series

On the Continent there exist several well-documented, artist drawn, 'Classic Collections' of picture postcards—the most prized and sought after cards in existence. Cards from these beautiful series are collected today all over the world, although the prices they command vary from country to country. Both on the Continent and in the USA, fine examples will fetch at least 25% more than the British prices indicated in this catalogue.

The three most famous series of all—the *Collection des Cent*, *The Concours Byrrh*, and the *Wiener Werkstätte* are listed in full below. Brief details of the lesser known smaller collections (but which are in some cases even finer and rarer than the 'Big Three') are also listed.

In Britain three fine, artist drawn series were also produced—all by the great British publisher, Raphael Tuck. They are the *Celebrated Posters* series, the *Kings and Queens of England* series and the *Proof Limited Edition* series. There are also superb photographic collections in France *Les Petits Métiers Parisiens*; *Paris Vécu*; *Les P'tits Métiers de Paris*; *Paris Pittoresque* and *Les Petits Métiers de Paris* (2 series). They are early Period 2 photographs of Paris buildings, occupations, types and scenes many of which are long gone.

In Britain the Beagles and Rotary *London Life* series (*see also* SOCIAL HISTORY) offer a fascinating glimpse into British Edwardian life in the capital. The compilers would welcome any information on these British collections with a view to publishing a full listing in future editions of this catalogue.

THE THREE GREAT CONTINENTAL ARTIST DRAWN COLLECTIONS

Collection des Cent ■106a

French. Pub. Greningaire. Literally 'The Collection of the One Hundred'. Actually 99 designs have been identified. They started to appear from 1 Nov. 1901 in packaged sets of 10. It is thought that about 500 examples were printed of each of the early numbers, and less than 100 of the later series. Only one example of the Mucha horizontal design and the Vogel design are known to exist today.

Merson (1)
Louis Morin (Chaperon Rouge) (2)
Louis Morin (2)
Steinlein (3)
L. Borgex (4)
Sem (5)
L. A. Girardot (6)
Leandre (7)
Boutet (8)
Cadel Eug. (9)
L. Gregoire (10)
Mucha V. (11)
Mucha H. (11)
Caran D'Ache (12)
Lebegue (13)
Gil Baer (14)
Guy Bonnet (15)
E. Grasset (16)
F. Bac (Femme au Chapeau) (17)
F. Bac (17)
R. Ranst (18)
L. Lebegue (18)
J. Wely (Le Pecheur) (19)
J. Wely (19)
Lelee (20)
Willette A. (21)
Guillaume A. (22)
Villon (23)
A. Chapront (24)
C. Boiry (25)
Giraldon (26)
Rene Pean (27)
C. Henrida (28)
A. Le Petit (29)
Escudier (30)
A. Gorguet (31)
S. Dola (32)
G. Noury (33)
J. Jouve (34)
J. Cheret (35)
A. Cadiou (36)
Conrad (Moulin Rouge) (37)
Conrad (37)
E. Flament (38)
P. Guignebault (39)
L. Burret (40)
M. P. Verneuil (41)
Follot (42)

E. G. Le Petit (43)
G. Vare (44)
Heran (45)
C. Guerin (46)
P. Kauffmann (47)
E. Cause (48)
L. De Beauvais (49)
Jean Tild (50)
G. Auriol (50)
A. Herbinier (52)
Fernel (53)
Casse (54)
Widhoft (55)
G. Bigot (56)
L. Gambey (57)
C. Riom (58)
L. Malsteste (58)
Delau (59)
V. Chantesais (60)
A. Paris (61)
Marodon (62)
Dinet (63)
L. Vallet (63)
P. Hermann (64)
Huard (65)
R. Lewis (66)
Chivot (67)
Frog (68)
Kosa (69)
B. Naudin (70)
E. De Barberies (73)
Baschilec
Cappiello
L. Espinasse
H. Gerbault
Gose
Grün
H. Y. Ibels
Jacquier
Jossot
Lem
Le Riverand
G. Metivet
G. Meunier
H. Mirande
Orens
Robida
A. Roubille
J. Testevuide
J. Vogel
Lem Publicitaire

The numbers are those printed on the postcards.

Most examples .. .. .. £45/**£60**/P/A
Boutet, Capiello, Caran D'Ache, Grasset,
   Orens, Roubille, Steinlen .. £50/**£75**/£100
Mucha, Villon, Vogel .. .. £100/**£200**/£300

Concours Byrrh ■106b

French prize competition (1906) for advertisements for the aperitif *Byrrh*, a fortified wine with alleged tonic qualities. The competition attracted the very best artists of the day. One hundred and thirteen prizewinning designs were published as postcards. Each design had to incorporate the words, *Byrrh, Tonique, Hygiénique, à base de quinquina et de vins généraux.* Several prizewinners were announced for each prize—two 1st prizes, two 2nd, six 3rd, five 4th, thirty-one 5th and sixty-five 6th.

1. (1st prize) J. Cardona	46. J. Voloz (Rostand)
2. Mlle H. Dufau	47. (6th prize) L. André
3. (2nd prize) J. Hemard	48. P. André
4. V. Leydet	49. A. Beaune Miller
5. (3rd prize) Barlangle	50. B. de Beaupré
6. A. de Casimacker	51. E. Benedictus
7. A. Giraldon	52. J. Bezon
8. R. Huber	53. G. Boulanger
9. A. Launay	54. Mlle Briot
10. K. Spillar	55. A. Brouillet
11. (4th prize) M. Cleret	56. V. Brugairolles
12. L. Felix	57. A. Butteri
13. J. Gosé	58. A. Cadiou
14. R. Péan	59. H. Chenet
15. J. Rivière	60. E. Croize
16. (5th prize) Albertilus	61. H. Delaspre
17. L. Baeyens	62. H. Deluermoz
18. G. Bofa	63. M. Denis
19. C. Boulet	64. L. Desrousseaux
20. E. Bourgeois	65. H. Détouche
21. G. Bruyer	66. Diana
22. Carlègle	67. J. Engel
23. J. Chamson	68. P. Falke
24. P. Cauchie	69. Forestier
25. G. Debize	70. L. Gardette
26. P. Delaunay	71. R. de Gardier
27. Mlle M. Delorme	72. Gehel
28. H. Dumas	73. Glukowski
29. A. Edelmann	74. G. Gos
30. A. Foache	75. Mme M. Guyon
31. A. Gauret	76. Herbinier
32. Mlle Henning	77. B. de Jankowski
33. R. Hista	78. Jaumandrieu Bonsoms
34. R. Kirchner	79. L. Jayet
35. M. Leenhardt	80. E. Joannon
36. C. Levavasseur	81. G. Kienerk
37. L. Malespine	82. R. de Laban
38. F. de Marliave	83. L. Lackerbauer
39. H. D. Ponsam	84. Lamberton
40. F. Renard	85. M. Lançon
41. L. Ridel	86. G. Laurain
42. P. Schaan	87. Mme Laurent Nicolle
43. L. Selvès	88. J. Lehmann
44. M. de Thoren	89. G. Leroux
45. Vavasseur	90. L. Londe

91. E. Marsal	103. A. Roz
92. G. Meunier	104. H. Rudaux
93. B. Moloch	105. H. Schmidt
94. H. Mottez	106. E. de Senezcourt
95. G. Paulme	107. A. de Szekely
96. A. Le Petit Fils	108. E. Torrent
97. A. Le Petit Fils	109. G. Trilleau
98. R. Popper	110. Trinquier Trianon
99. L. Pousthomis	111. F. Valloton
100. R. Quesnel	112. E. Van Offel
101. G. Redon	113. A. Walter
102. H. Rioux	

Most examples .. .. .. £20/**£35**/£40
Denis, Kirchner, Valloton .. £50/**£100**/£150

■106a.

Collection des Cent. *French. One of the most sought after cards in the series. Artist Alphonse Mucha. Pub. E.G., Paris.* UB. *Period 2* £130

■106b

Concours Byrrh. *French. The most sought after card in the collection. 6th Prize. Artist Maurice Denis. Period 2* £200

Wiener Werkstätte ■107a

Austrian. Literally 'The Vienna Workshop'. Produced in Vienna between 1908 and 1913, this superb collection is the showcase for a style that foreshadowed *Art Deco*, Existentialism, Cubism and Surrealism. Like the famous German Bauhaus, the *Wiener Werkstätte* was a workshop with over 100 craftsmen engaged in a variety of arts and crafts—pottery, glass, furniture, architecture, fashion and metal work. The most highly priced examples were drawn by Oskar Kokoscka and Egon Schiele. The elegant ladies of Mela Koehler and Maria Likartz are extremely popular in Britain (*see* ARTISTS). Subjects include Christmas, Easter and New Year Greetings, Months of the Year (Low-Lazar) and illustrated proverbs (Luksch-Lazar). In 1925 a series of designs for silk material were printed for the *Werkstätte* by B. K. W. I. They bear Jewish greetings and were designed by Mlle Arker, Prof. C. O. Czeschka, C. Fochler, E. Hausler, W. Jonas and Pieidl. The postcards from the series can easily be recognised as they all clearly state *Wiene Werkstätte* on the reverse. Some oversize square cards were produced for the series by Mela Koehler, also several 1½ times normal postcard sized examples.

The numbers not listed below have not so far been identified, or are on postcards not signed by the artist.

Berger, Fritzi: 764, 787, 788, 789.
Bohler, Hans: 647, 648, 650, 651, 652, 653, 801.
Delavilla, Franz Karl: 19, 20, 149, 158, 517(?)
Diveky, Josef von: 7(?) 160, 162, 169, 170, 171, 172, 183, 229–234, 236, 238, 240–248, 261–267, 316, 317, 401–405, 494, 496–501.
Drexler: 207(?), 214, 219, (218).
M. Friedman: 543, 544, 545(?), 733(?), 785, 786, 800, (OTTEN).
Geyling, Remigius: 164–177, 181, 185, 187–189, 222, 283–287.
Hoffmann, Josef: 5, 75(?)
Hoppe, Emil: 1, 2, 3, 4, 46(?), 22, 23, 24, 25, 26, 47.
Janke, Urban: 18(?), 27, 29, 128 (twice), 129(?), 130, 131, 132(?), 133(?), 134(?), 135, 136(?), 137, 138, 139(?), 140(?), 145, 291, 126, 127.
Jesser, Hilda: 1007, 1008, 1011.
Jung, Moriz: 52, 54(?), 58, 62, 66(?), 81–83, 86–88, 91, 92, 93, 96, 97, 98, 339, 341–347, 358(?), 359(?), 360(?), 383(?), 406(?), 407(?), 504(?), 505(?), 506(?), 507, 508(?), 509(?), 510(?), 511(?), 512(?), 513(?), 514(?), 515(?), 516(?), 529, 530, 532, 533, 534, 600(?), 601(?), 653(?), 659(?), 661(?), 662(?), 663(?), 727(?), 728(?), 729(?), 731(?), 732(?), 802, 340, 361, 486, 534.
Jungnickl, Ludwig Heinrich: 328–333, 376–380.
Kalhammer, Gustave: 45, 51, 56, 57, 65, 408–410, 412(?), 431, 434, 435, 438, 487, 490, 502.
Kalvach, Rudolf: 15, 17, 33, 34, 49, 59, 84, 85, 89, 90, 94, 95, 99, 100, 102(?), 103(?), 105–109, 148
Koehler-Broman, Mela: 8, 9, 10, 110–115, 269, 270, 271, 272, 273, 274, 275, 276, 306, 307, 310–315, 321–326, 394–400, 413–429, 345–353, 362–375, 470–485, 518–528, 534, 551–556, 569–571, 579–593, 594 (twice), 595, 596, 597(?), 598(?), 599(?), 603–608, 638–643, 648, 649, 735, 736, 739, 740, 752, 753, 758.
Kokoschka, Oskar: 21(?), 55, 64, 72, 73, 76–80, 116, 117, 147, 152, 155, 157.

Kolbe: 32, 36(?), 39(?), 43(?), 44, 46.
Krenek, Carl: 154(?), 193, 194(?), 195(?), 196(?), 199(?), 200(?), 203(?), 204(?), 205(?), 253–255, 257, 629, 761, 762, 908, 909.
Kuhn, Franz: 69, 163, 430, 432, 435–437, 439, 440, 441, 442(?), 443–469, 815, 816, 817 (twice), 820.
Lebisch, Franz: 12(?), 118(?), 120(?), 121(?), 122(?), 123(?), 124(?).
Lendecke, Otto Friedrich Carl: 156(?), 159(?), 848–854, 856–859, 880(?), 882(?), 884(?), 885(?).
Leupold; 250.
Likarz-Strauss, Maria: 503, 557–566, 612, 613, 614, 615, 616, 645, 646, 660, 682–693, 710–714, 741(?), 742–748, 756, 765–768, 769(?), 770–781, 750, 797, 810, 811, 813, 814, 829, 831, 833, 836, 837(?), 830, 832, 835, 834, 840–846, 881–885, 860, 889, 898(?).
Loffler, Berthold: 48, 71, 167, 172, 175, 178, 179, 617, 619, 620, 621, 623, 628, 644(?), 911–920.
Low-Lazar, Fritzi: 694–709, 788, 789, 808, 809, 812, 818–828, 871–873, 839, 969, 1000–1005.
Luksch-Makowska, Elena: 384–395, 411, 412, 790.
Marisch, Gustav: 609, 610, 611, 782, 783, 784.
Nechanski, Arnold: 793 (twice), 794–796, 888(?), 890(?), 891, 892(?), 893(?), 894, 895, 896(?), 897(?).
Oswald, Wenzel: 146(?), 150(?), 213.
Peche, Dagobert: 362(?), 625, 626.
Petter, Valérie: 74(?), 143(?), 153(?), (ZEIS).
Pohl, Josef: 410.
Schiele, Egon: 288, 289, 290.
Schmal, Emil: 237, 239, 277(?), 278–282.
Schwetz, Karl: 194–228, 259, 260, 268, 292–295, 298–299, 302(?), 433, 437, 442, 493, 535–540, 587, 657, 665–674, 715–726.
Sika, Jutta: 633–635, 636(?), 692, 760.
Singer-Schinnerl, Susi: 319, 320, 631, 754–757, 804, 846, 905, 906.
Peyer, Agnès: 60.
Teschner, Richard: 318, 327, 334–338.
Velim, Anton: 874, 875, 876, 877, 878.
Wimmer, E.: 861–870.
Zemer, Fritz: 67(?), 68, 143, 144, 576, 577, 578, 488.
Zwickle, Hubert von: 178, 182.

Most examples	£20/**£30**/£50
Jung, Koehler, Likarz, Loffler	£25/**£35**/£70
Kokoshka, Schiele	£150/**£300**/£450

■107a

Wiener Werkstätte. *Austrian. Artist Maria Likartz. No. 646 (1909)* £70

OTHER IMPORTANT CONTINENTAL COLLECTIONS

Austrian

Ver Sacrum. 1898. Postcards reprinted from the journal of the same name.

Price range (10 cards) .. .. £40/**£60**/£80

Pub. Philipp & Kramer, Vienna. Over 100 series of 10 cards each have been identified, of which the first 30 are the most sought after, drawn by Hoffman, Kainradl, Kurzweil, Moser and Olbrich. Other superb artists include Gerlach, Hampel, Hedley, and Kirchner.

Early series: Price range .. .. £20/**£40**/£60

Austrian/German

Das Grosse Jahrhundert ■109a

A vast series of postcards of international literary, military, musical and political celebrities, produced in 1899/1900 to celebrate the new century. A hitherto uncatalogued collection, the total number is not known, but so far three different printings have been identified:

(a) Heading, 'Gruss aus . . ., den . . . 189 . . .'
In brackets *Oesterreichische Ausgabe* (Issued in Austria)

(b) As (a), plus *Benedict Fürth, Prag*

(c) Heading as (a), but without '189 . . .'
Credit is *Verlag u. Druck. Vereinigte Papierwaaren Fabriken, S. Krotoschin, Görlitz.*

Identified titles/numbers to date:

8	Feldmarschall Radetzky	37	Wolfgang Amadeus Mozart
39	Josef Haydn	41	Karl Goldmark
42	Franz von Suppe	43	Karl Millocker
44	Johannes Brahms	47	Kaspar Zumbusch
61	Henrik Ibsen	62	Heinrich Heine
77	Friedrich Schiller	78	Johann Wolfgang Goethe
85	Leo Graf Tolstoy	86	Ivan Turgenieff
90	George Noel Gordon, (Lord Byron)	102	Henry Morton Stanley
117	Pablo de Sarasate	132	Hellmuth Graf von Moltke
135	Walter Scott	143	Carl Maria von Weber
145	Giacomo Meyerbeer	146	Felix Mendelssohn-Bartholdy
148	Robert Schumann	150	Pietro Mascagni
151	Ruggiero Leoncavallo	152	Engelbert Humperdinck
153	Anton Rubenstein	154	Richard Wagner
161	William MacKinley	190	Arthur Schopenhauer
229	Friedrich August von Kaulbach	257	Elias Howe
344	Pius IX	414	Frederic-Francois Chopin
415	Ludwig van Beethoven	416	Charles Gounod
441	Gebhard Leberecht von Blucher	442	Gerhard David von Scharnhorst
		473	Li-Hung-Chang

The compilers would appreciate any information to help them in documenting this important, but little publicised, series.

Price range .. .. £4/**£6**/£8

A considerable premium would accrue to a large number of sequential postcards.

French

Cocorico

Probably the rarest of all the French series, only 12 cards, of which very few examples exist today. The artists are: Does; Faverot; De Feure; Kierneck; Kupka; Léandre; Michael; Mucha; Popineau; Roubille; Steinlen; Willette.

Price range .. .. £100/**£175**/£300

Editions Cinos (1898)

Reproductions of famous posters by the top artists of the day. About 35 cards have been identified. Artists include: Cheret, Grasset, Mucha, Meunier and Toulouse Lautrec.

The highest price is for the Lautrec. Price range .. .. £50/**£75**/£750

Job

Reproductions of posters/calendars by the cigarette paper manufacturer, 'Job'. Five different series were printed:

    1903 (horizontal) Beautiful series of 12 cards
    1905 (horizontal) 1 poster, 7 calendar designs
    1907 (horizontal) 8 calendar designs
    1911 (horizontal) 3 posters, 21 calendar designs
    1914 (vertical) 8 posters and 22 calendar designs.

Artists include: Asti, Cheret, Léandre, Mucha.

The highest prices are for the earliest series .. .. £10/**£25**/£35

Germany

Bauhaus

The rarest of all German collections, 20 designs, of which only 25 examples are said to have been printed.

The Bauhaus movement was started by Walter Gropius in Weimar in 1919, incorporating artists of all classes, several nationalities and varying skills and crafts in the fields of pure art, architecture, carving, furniture and interior design, metal work, pottery, etc. In 1926 the school moved to Dessau and exerted a powerful influence on art and crafts throughout the Continent until disapproved of by the Nazis; it was closed in 1933. *Bau* means construction and Gropius said, 'The final although distant goal of the Bauhaus is the unified work of art—the Great Construction—in which there is no distinction between the monumental and decorative art'.

The Bauhaus postcards were produced in 1923. The artists who designed them are: 1 & 2 Feininger; 3 Kandinsky; 4 & 5 Klee; 6 Marcks; 7 Moholynagy; 8 Schlemmer; 9 & 10 Baschant; 11

& 12 Bayer; 13 Haberer; 14 Helm; 15 & 16 Hirschfield-Mack; 17 Molnar; 18 & 19 Schmidt; 20 Teltscher.

(Highest price for Kandinsky, Klee and Moholynagy) .. .. .. £50/**£100**/£550

Jugend (1899)
Three series of 25 cards each. Artists include Bernuth, Caspari, Christiansen, Eichler, Hoess, Munzer, Seitz, Weinhold, Zumbach.
Price range .. .. £20/**£40**/£65

Lustigen Blätter
Postcards reproduced from the famous newspaper of the same name in Berlin. Artists include Wennerberg† and Zille† and many of them are anti-British, incl. *Kriegs-Karte* during WW1.
Price range .. .. £5/**£10**/£20

BRITISH COLLECTIONS

Tuck's Celebrated Posters (1903). ■109b
Over 60 postcards in this superb series have so far been identified, including 9 complete sets (some of 7 cards, others of 6). The numbers of the series and single postcards range from 1500 to 1511. Many of Britain's finest poster artists were represented, e.g. Cecil Aldin, G. Bataille, Beggarstaff Bros., George Belcher, Ernest Bertram, Frank Brangwyn, Gordon Brown, W. H. Caffyn, L. Cobrichen, Harry Furniss, William Grove, Dudley Hardy, John Hassall, Albert Hildersheimer, Charles Jupp, Phil May, Fred Mortan, M. A. Ramsay, Robert Sauber, Alfred Schwarz, G. L. Seymour, Walter West.

Prices range from £15 for the lesser known artists to £40 for the best examples.

Tuck's Kings & Queens of England (1902).
The complete portrait gallery of the Kings and Queens of England, from William I to Edward VII, in 3 series of 12 cards (Nos. 614, 615 and 616) plus the Edward VII, which has 6 variations in the quotation on the top right hand corner. Each card bears a full length portrait of the Monarch, with the dates of his or her reign, his or her seal, and a coin from his or her reign. Some curiosities occur in Series 616. Cromwell appears under the special title, 'Rulers of England', and Queen Anne was mistakenly called Anne II in the first printing. The card of Edward VII was printed for the coronation due to take place on 5 July 1902. Owing to the King's illness, it was postponed until 9 August. The incorrect data was obliterated from the shield.
Per card .. .. £4/**£6**/£8
Complete set of 42 .. .. .. £250/**£300**/£400

Tuck's Proof Limited Edition postcards (1903–1905).
About 70 designs have been identified of the sets of 4 or 6 postcards which were printed in runs limited to 1000, with gold edges and on superior board. A register was kept of all collectors of Proof postcard sets. They sold at 5s. each and were intended as investments.

Artists include Asti,† W. S. Coleman (rural scenes), Chas. E. Flower† (Inns of Court), F. Hartland (glamour), John Hassall† (18th-century caricatures), Prof. Van Hier (moonlight, river, sunset, woods, winter scenes), Graham Hyde (Village series), Raphael Kirchner† (Three Maidens), Phil May† (Write-Away series), M. Morris (fishing boats, rough seas, river scenery), Edith Salaman (national costumes), Lance Thackeray† (At the Wicket, Write-Away series), E. H. Vaughan (Turneresque), H. B. Wimbush (picturesque lakes, nooks).

Prices range from about £25 per set for the unsigned, to about £50 for the better artists, and about £120 for the Kirchner set.

■109a
Pub. Benedict Furth, Prag. das Grosse Jahrhundert. No. 102. Henry Morton Stanley. Period 1 .. .. £8

■109b
Tuck's 'Celebrated Posters' series No. 1500. Artist Cecil Aldin. UB *1903* £20

COMIC

This is the type of postcard at which the British excelled during the 'Golden Age' of collecting. It was typically British, as were *Art Nouveau* and topographical French, *Gruss Aus* German and patriotic/political Italian. No other country has such a rich vein of humour in its postcard production. No area of Edwardian life seemed immune from the humorous artist, and the wealth of comic artistic talent was extraordinary.

Cards in most collecting categories were given the humorous treatment. To list them all here would make this section unwieldy. Therefore many 'comic' cards are described under other main headings, notably:

CHILDREN (many artists who did 'general' humour also drew cards on this theme)

POLITICS (themes like Free Trade, National Insurance Stamps, Suffragettes, etc.)

SOCIAL HISTORY/TOPOGRAPHICAL (ethnic and regional humour)

WAR (for the large and important sections on the humour of WW1 and WW2)

Most comic cards, however, are collected because of their artists, and under ARTISTS can be found biographical detail, the main publishers and series of the most important comic designers and, where appropriate, cross references to other sections under which their work can be found. Many of them came to postcard design from the poster, or book and magazine illustration, and have a reputation far beyond their postcard output.

Listed in this COMIC section are many of the minor, but highly collectable, comic artists, examples of whose work can still be found for a modest price. Comic cards are also collected by virtue of their publisher, and some of the main comic publishers are listed here, as are some of the important comic series and the comic 'themes', often drawn by competent but unsigned artists.

† = *see also* ARTISTS for more details.

ARTISTS (Signed)

'A.A.'	**50p**
'A.E.' (*see* English, Archibald)	
Anderson, Martin† (Cynicus). ■36a. Highest valuation for early Period 2 (incl. 'Court' size)	£1/**£1.50**/£6
Attwell, Mabel Lucie† ■36c	75p/**£1**/£2
Bairnsfather, Bruce†	75p/**£1.50**/£2

Barnes, G. L.	.. 75p/**£1**/£1.50
Belcher, Geo.†	£3/**£4**/£5
Biggar, J. L. (*see also* WAR)	–/**50p**/75p
Bradshaw, P. V.† (also signed 'PVB')	
■110a	£3/**£4**/£6
Browne, Tom† ■110b	£2/**£2.50**/£3.50
Buchanan, Fred ■43a	50p/**75p**/£1
Bull, Rene ■43b	£1.50/**£2.50**/£3
Buxton, Dudley† ■43c	.. 75p/**£1**/£1.25
Cameron, Archie	–/**50p**/75p
Carter, Reg† ■46a	75p/**£1**/£2
Christie, G. F.† (also signed 'G.F.C.')	
■48a	50p/**75p**/£1.50
Comicus (*see* Parlett, Harry)	
Crombie, Chas.	50p/**75p**/£1
Cynicus (*see* Anderson, Martin)	
Davey, Geo. ■49b	.. 75p/**£1**/£1.50
'Dinah' (*see also* CHILDREN/WAR)	–/**50p**/75p
Duncan, J. A.† (Hamish) ■50a ..	50p/**75p**/£1
Dwiggins† (Dwig) (U.S.) ■50b ..	£1/**£2**/£3
Earnshaw, Harold† ■53a	–/**50p**/75p
Ellam, W. H.† ■53b	50p/**75p**/£1

■110a

Pub. Moss. & Co. Artist P. V. Bradshaw (signed 'P.V.B.') (1905) £5

■110b

Pub. Davidson Bros. Artist Tom Browne. 'Weary Willie & Tired Tim'. Period 2 .. .. .. £4

English, Archibald† ('A.E.') ■54a	
.. ..	50p/**75p**/£1.50
Esmond (highest value for 'Germs')	
.. ..	75p/**£1**/£4
'F.S.' (*see* Spurgin, Fred)	
Fuller, Edmund† ■55c ..	.. 75p/**£1**/£1.50
Gibson, Charles Dana† ■56a	.. 75p/**£1**/£1.50
Gill, Arthur†	£1/**£1.50**/£2.50
Gilson, T. (*see also* Children/War)	
.. ..	–/**50p**/£1
'Graeff'	50p/**75p**/£1
'Guy L.'	50p/**75p**/£1
Hardy, Dudley† ■111a	£2/**£4**/£5
Hassall, John† ■59a, 111b ..	£2/**£4**/£5
Heath Robinson, W.†	£2/**£3**/£4
Ibbetson, Ernest†	.. 75p/**£1**/£1.50
'K.S.'	50p/**75p**/£1
'Karaktus'	–/**50p**/75p
Leete, Alfred†	£1/**£1.50**/£2
Ludovici, A.† ■112c ..	£2/**£3**/£4
May, Phil† ■111c	£3/**£4**/£5
McGill, Donald† ■112a ..	.. 50p/**£1.50**/£3
Moreland, Arthur (*see also* Political)	
.. ..	£1/**£1.50**/£2
Morgan, F. E.	–/**50p**/75p
Noble, Ernest	–/**50p**/75p
Outcault, Richard (USA) ..	–/**50p**/£1
Owen, Will†	£1/**£2**/£3
Parlett, Harry† ('Comicus') ■73a	50p/**75p**/£1
Payne, G. M.† ■112b	50p/**75p**/£1
Pirkis, Albert George† ■82a ..	.. 75p/**£1.50**/£3
'PYP'	.. £1/**£1.50**/£2
Reynolds, Frank†	.. 75p/**£1.50**/£3
Rob, A.	.. 75p/**£1**/£1.50
Rowntree, Harry	£1/**£2**/£3
Schönpflug, Fritz† ■84a ..	.. £1/**£1.50**/£3
Shaw, W. Stocker	50p/**75p**/£1
Shepheard, Geo. Ed.† ■84b ..	.. 75p/**£1**/£1.50
'Spatz'	50p/**75p**/£1
Spurgin, Fred† ('F.S.')	£1/**£1.50**/£2
Starr Wood† ■86a	£1/**£1.50**/£2
Studdy, Geo.†	£1/**£1.50**/£2
Taylor, Arnold (*see also* War) ..	–/**50p**/75p
Tempest, Dan (*see also* War) ..	50p/**75p**/£1
Thackeray, Lance†	£2/**£3**/£4
Thiele, Arthur† ■88a	£2/**£3**/£5
Thomas, Bert† ■89a	.. 75p/**£1**/£1.50
Wain, Louis†	£6/**£8**/£15
Ward, Dudley	–/**50p**/75p
Wood, Lawson†	£1/**£2**/£3

ARTISTS (UNSIGNED/MINOR)

Periods 2 to 4 .. .. –/**75p**/£1.50

■111a

Pub. Davidson Bros. Artist Dudley Hardy. Illustrated Song series. Period 2 .. .. £4

■111b

Pub. Dean & Son. Artist John Hassall. 'Sunny Jane'. Period 2 .. .. £4

■111c

Pub. Davidson Bros. Artist Phil May. 'The Humour of Life' series. Period 2 .. .. .. £4

COMIC PUBLISHERS/SERIES/THEMES

Addled Ads.
Pub. Misch & Stock. Artist G. F. Christie.
■48a .. .. £1/**£1.50**/£2

Bamforth & Co.
Many posed humorous song and other series
of photographic origin. Periods 2 to 4.
Single cards and sets of 2, 3, 4   50p/**75p**/£3
Similar cards by other publishers   –/**50p**/75p

Couples, Courtship
One of the favourite butts of comic cards.
Artist drawn .. .. –/**50p**/75p
Photographic in origin (esp. by Pub.
'J.W.S.') .. .. –/**50p**/75p

'Dam' Family
Pubs. Crockers, Fraser & Jenkinson, others
.. .. –/**50p**/75p

Davidson Bros.
Undoubtedly the 'kings' of the comic card.
Periods 2, 3 .. .. 50p/**75p**/£3

Ethnic/Regional Humour (*see also* SOCIAL
HISTORY)
Irish humour ('Paddy' jokes, many local
pubs.) .. .. –/**50p**/£1
Jewish humour ('mean' jokes, etc.) 75p/**£1.50**/£3
Scottish humour (artists like 'Hamish',
pubs. like Millar & Lang) .. –/**50p**/75p
Welsh humour ('jawbreaking' placenames,
pubs. incl. Valentine) .. .. –/**50p**/75p
Others **50p**

Marriage
'Is Marriage a Failure?'. Pub. Millar &
Lang .. .. –/**50p**/75p
Mrs. Caudle's Lectures (various pubs.)
.. .. 50p/**75p**/£1.50
Others .. .. –/**50p**/75p

Military Humour
See also HISTORICAL and WAR.
Price range .. .. .. 50p/**75p**/£1.50

Punch Cartoons
Early Period 2/Period 3 (various pubs., see
also POLITICAL and WAR) .. .. £1/**£1.50**/£2

Sporting Humour
Cricket, Golf, Ping Pong, Skating, etc. (see
also ARTISTS) .. .. .. 50p/**£1.50**/£3

When Father Said Turn. ■112c
Pub. Millar & Lang. Series. Period 2
.. .. 50p/**75p**/£2

'Wordy' Humour
The pseudo 'essay' or 'poem' on humorous
topics, often in dialect. Various pubs.
.. .. –/**50p**/£1

Undivided-back Comics
Period 1/Early Period 2, often chromolithographs .. .. £2/**£3**/£4

■112a
Pub. Anon. Artist Donald McGill. PU *1913* £4

■112b
*Pub. Anon. Artist G. M. Payne. 'Before our Time'
series. Period 2* £4

■112c
*Pub. Millar & Lang. Artist Ludovici(?) 'When
Father Said Turn' with a political slant.* PU
1903 .. .. £3

COMMEMORATIVE

In its early days the picture postcard evolved to meet the needs of advertisers and to commemorate anniversaries, exhibitions and holidays. There are specialist sections in this catalogue to cover EARLY CARDS, EXHIBITIONS, HISTORICAL/ MILITARY/TRADITIONAL, ROYALTY, etc., all of which have a strong commemorative content. However, there are postcards that do not fit easily into those or any other classifications. And yet they are commemorative. This section is for them and we refer to cards commemorating events which are national rather than local. As is normally the case, Period 1 and Period 2 are the most valued, although Germany issued many interesting official and pictorial cards during Periods 4 and 5 and the USA began a fine series of official picture cards in Period 6 which continue today. For collectors seeking a field of interest in modern Period 6 and 7 postcards, the COMMEMORATIVE classification repays study. Period 7 cards are listed here, but the MODERN cards section should also be consulted, since there is a growing interest in the collection of Period 7 postcards that have a commemorative connection.

PERIOD 1

1893. Switzerland. 50th Anniversary of the Postal Service. Limited Edition of 36,000, valid from 25 June–31 December 1893 only .. .. £5/**£8**/£10

1894. Austria. Dr. Hermann pictured on card for 25th Anniversary of the First Postcard. Pub. Friedl.
Signed by Dr. Hermann .. **P/A**
Unsigned. ■114a .. .. .. £20/**£40**/£55

1894. San Marino. The Inauguration of the Palais de Conseil Souverain .. £4/**£5**/£7

1895. Italy. 25th Anniversary of the Liberation of Rome .. .. .. £5/**£6**/£10

1895. Port of Spain. 'Dez Reis' (Ten Kings) 1195–1895 .. .. £3/**£4**/£5

1897. Germany. 400th Anniversary of the Leipzig Fair .. .. £3/**£4**/£5

1897. Italy. National elections of 27 May .. .. £7/**£9**/£12

1898. Britain. Court size. 'I have done my best for the honour of our country. Goodbye.' Nile Expedition commemorative, showing Gordon & Kitchener. Fetched £85 in auction 1981 .. **P/A**

1898. Canada. USS Maine Memorial. Possibly Canada's first privately issued postcard. .. .. £10/**£15**/£25

1898. Germany. Mourning card for the death of Bismarck .. .. .. £1/**£2**/£3

1898. Portugal. Offical issues. 400th Anniversary of Vasco da Gama's discovery of the route to India .. .. .. £2/**£3**/£4

1899. Germany and others. 9.9.99 cards. Mint .. .. £1/**£1.50**/£2

Ditto. Posted with 'all 9's' cancellation .. .. £3/**£4**/£5

PERIOD 2

British

1900. Tuck. Empire series. Embossed with inset photo-origin cameos of famous people. 'Souvenir 1900' UB. ■114b £8/**£12**/£15

1901. Foundation of the Commonwealth of Australia. John Evelyn Wrench issued his first 'Links of the Empire' series to commemorate the Duke and Duchess of Cornwall and York's journey to and from the new Parliament. Subscribers to the set received cards posted en route. Twenty numbered cards as follows, all UB:

1. The Goodbye from Portsmouth
2. View of Gibralter
3. View of Malta
4. View of Port Said
5. Map of the Route
6. A Kangaroo
7. Adelaide Town Hall
8. Sydney
9. Brisbane
10. The Exhibition Buildings housing the Parliament
11. Durban
12. Capetown
13. The Ascension Isles
14. H.M.S. *Ophir*
15. Quebec
16. Montreal
17. Niagra (*sic*) Falls
18. The Parliament at Ottawa
19. St John's, Newfoundland
20. The Return to Portsmouth

Cards posted from the appropriate port command the higher prices, while a complete set must be valued P/A

Price range .. .. £9/**£12**/£15

1905. Centenary of Trafalgar. Artistic .. ..75p/**£1**/£1.50

Ditto. Photo-origin showing scenes in Trafalgar Square .. .. .. £1/**£2**/£2.50

1905. Death of Sir Henry Irving .. 75p/**£1**/£1.50
1912. Death of General Booth, founder of
the Salvation Army .. .. .. £1/**£3**/£6

Foreign
1900. German. Official card with printed
stamp welcoming the year 1900 £1/**£2**/£3
1901. Australia. Foundation of the
Commonwealth of Australia .. £4/**£5**/£6
1902. America. Visit of Prince Heinrich
.. .. £3/**£5**/£6
1904. South Africa. Funeral of ex-President
Kruger .. .. £1/**£2**/£2.50
1905. Belgium. 75th Anniversary of Belgian
Independence .. .. .. £2/**£3**/£4
1906. Norway. Amundsen and the North
West Passage .. .. .. £1/**£1.50**/£2
1906. USA. The Wedding of the Century.
Alice Roosevelt and Nicholas Longworth
.. .. £1/**£1.50**/£2
1908. Australia. Visit of American Fleet
.. .. £5/**£8**/£12
1908. Canada. Quebec Tercentenary
.. .. £2/**£2.50**/£3
1910. Argentina. Centenary of San Martin
.. .. £1/**£1.50**/£2
1910. USA. Chicago. 31st Triennial Con-
clave of Knights Templar .. .. £1/**£2**/£2.50
1911. Italy. Official issues for 50th Anniversary of Kingdom. Twenty cards in
series .. .. £1/**£2**/£2.50
1911. Portugal. First Anniversary of the new
Republic .. .. £1/**£1.50**/£2
1912. Bulgaria. Official card for Silver
Jubilee of Ferdinand the First (father of
Prince Boris, ... £1/**£1.50**/£2
1912. Germany. Official cards drawn by
Eugen Bracht to celebrate 'Postcard
Week'. Pub. L. C. Wittich of Darmstadt.
Flown and cancelled by Rhein & Main
aerial post .. .. £15/**£20**/£25
Ditto. Mint .. .. £5/**£6**/£8
1914. Switzerland. Official cards for the
Centenary of the Reunion of Geneva with
Switzerland .. .. .. £1/**£1.50**/£2
Year Cards. Period 2 only. ■114c. Mint
.. .. 50p/**75p**/£1
Ditto. Postally used with year cancellation
.. .. £2/**£3**/£4

PERIOD 4
Germany. Various official printed stamp issues
commemorating the 100th Anniversaries of the
deaths of famous men and carrying a head and

■114a

Period 1. Austrian. Dr. Hermann vignette on the 25th anniversary of the introduction of the first postcard (1894) £50

■114b

Pub. Tuck. Period 2. Empire series. Souvenir 1900. Victoria R.I. No. 383 .. ..£15

■114c

Period 2. German—typical year date card. This one PU *and cancelled Dresden, 12.12.12.12* £4

shoulders sketch, e.g. 1931 Baron Heinrich von
Stein, Prussian statesman. 1932 Goethe.
Per card .. ..75p/**£1**/£1.50

PERIOD 6
1948. USA. Lincoln card with Gettysburg
Address on 85th Anniversary of the
Address. PU. Gettysburg 19 Nov. 1948.
Limited Edition. Pub. Blocher,
Gettysburg .. .. £2/**£3**/£3.50
1952. Austria. Dr. Hermann picture. 50th
Anniversary of his death. Limited Issue of
10,000 .. .. £7/**£10**/£12

1954. France. Issues drawn by Raoul Serres for the Bayeux Philatelic Society to commemorate the 10th Anniversary of D-Day. Mint .. .. £3/**£4**/£5

Ditto. Postally used 5/6 June 1954 .. .. £7/**£10**/£15

1958. France. 40th Anniversary of the Armistice. Pub. Committee of 11 November Colmar. Thermographic .. £1/**£2**/£3

1962. Russia. 50th Anniversary of the founding of *Pravda*. Limited issue of 175,000 all numbered .. .. £2/**£3**/£5

1963. USA. Homage to President John F. Kennedy. President's seal on address side. Col. RP series. Pub. Capsco. ■115a .. .. −/**25p**/50p

1965. France. 20th Anniv. of the return of the deportees. 1 April 1965. .. 50p/**£1**/£1.50

1967. Russia. B & w cards issued in Moscow on 50th Anniv. of the Great October Socialist Revolution. Subjects include Lenin, the cruiser *Aurora*, *Isvestia* and a lorry load of armed revolutionaries .. .. 50p/**75p**/£1

1969. USA. Inauguration of Richard M. Nixon as President. 20 January 1969. ■115b .. .. £1.50/**£2**/£2.50

PERIOD 7

1970. British. Official card published by the Postcard Association of Great Britain for the postcard centenary and sold at the exhibition in Reed House, London. ■115c. Mint .. .. £1/**£1.50**/£2

Ditto. Used with centenary cancellation on 1 October .. .. £3/**£4**/£5

1973. USA. Official card for the centenary of the postcard with printed stamp. First day cancellation .. .. £1/**£1.50**/£2

Ditto. Mint .. ..50p/**£1**/£1.50

1974. France. 500th Anniversary of Copernicus's Birth (1973). Issued 1974 by French Post Office to coincide with commemorative stamp **50p**

1976. USA. Bicentennial of the American Revolution **25p**

1978. East Germany. DDR. o/s issues commemorating the first East German in Space—Sigmund Jahn—with facsimile signature. Pub. Agitations und Anschauungsmittel. Berlin **50p**

1979. Paris. The Egypt/Israel Peace Treaty of 26 March 1979. Card shows Begin, Carter and Sadat **75p**

1980. Moscow. *See* SPORT: Olympic Games

1980. Stockholm. 65th Universal Esperanto Congress **25p**

1981. Britain. Celebration of Release of US Hostages from Iran. Yellow Ribbon card. Pub. Veldale Covers SE 2/1 (*see also* MODERN) **25p**

■115a

Period 6. USA. The burial of John F. Kennedy at Arlington. Pub. Capsco. Washington (1963) 40p

■115b

Period 6. USA—commemorative for the inauguration of Richard M. Nixon as President of the United States. Posted on Inauguration Day— 20 Jan. 1969 .. .. £2.50

■115c

Period 7. Pub. Postcard Association of Great Britain. Centenary of the British Postcard .. £2

COMPETITIONS/CRAZES/ HOBBIES

The most famous competition immortalised on the postcard was the 'Concours Byrrh'. This is listed under COLLECTIONS.

BEAUTY COMPETITIONS

Daily Mirror International Beauty Competition (1908)
1500 entrants. Winner Ivy Close. Pub. C. W. Faulkner & Co.

English Beauty Series 847 (incl. paintings
by Arthur Hacker) .. .. .. 50p/**75p**/£1
Glossy photographic series .. .. 50p/**75p**/£1

Daily Mirror Beauty Competition for Women War Workers (1919)
50,000 entrants. Winner Miriam Babbage.
Pub. *Daily Mirror* and Rotary Photographic
Co. .. .. 50p/**75p**/£1

Daily Express & Seymour Hicks Beauty Competition
Pub. C. W. Faulkner .. .. .. 50p/**75p**/£1

CROSSWORD PUZZLES (Period 4, c. 1924/5)
The last of the great 'crazes' illustrated on the postcard.

'Crosswords' series. Artist Donald McGill
.. ..75p/**£1.50**/£3
Pub. Tuck. Oilette 3514. 'The Crossword
Craze' 1924, ■117a .. ..75p/**£1.50**/£2
Others .. .. 50p/**75p**/£1

DIABOLO (Period 2, from 1906)
The craze boomed from the invention of an aerodynamically efficient 'devil' (and there are many diabolo jokes which play on this word), by Gustave Phillipart in 1906.

Artist drawn
Browne, Tom. Pub. Davidson (Series 2627,
2631) .. .. £1.50/**£2.50**/£3.50

Christie, George Fyffe. Pub. Wm. Ritchie &
Sons (W. R. & S.) .. .. .. 75p/**£1**/£1.50
Cross, J. Pub. Tuck .. .. 50p/**75p**/£1.50
Kinsella, E. P. Pub. Langsdorff ..75p/**£1**/£1.50
McGill, Donald .. ..75p/**£1**/£1.50
Wain, Louis. Pub. Tuck .. .. £8/**£10**/£15
Other artists/publishers, including Birn
Bros., H. Vertigen & Co. ..50p/**£1**/£1.50

Greetings cards featuring Diabolo
Various publishers .. .. 50p/**75p**/£1.50

Photographic Diabolo cards
Various publishers .. .. 75p/**£1**/£2

LIMERICKS (Period 2, mainly 1907/8)
The craze followed the competition in *London Opinion* to complete the last line of a limerick. Soon other competitions and even specialist magazines appeared.

Comic cards
Pub. Davidson Bros. Artist Dudley Hardy.
Nos. 3008/9. 'Limericks' .. .. £2/**£4**/£6
Pub. Gottschalk, Dreyfus & Davis (G. D. &
D.). Artist 'KS' (c. 1906) .. .. 50p/**75p**/£1
Pub. Hildesheimer. Artist 'Kyd' (1905)
.. .. £1/**£2**/£4
Pub. W. & A. K. Johnston. Series 112, 119
(1905) .. .. 50p/**75p**/£1
Knight Series. Jingle Cards (1905)
.. ..75p/**£1**/£1.50
Pub. Millar & Lang. 'The Limerick Craze'
(1907) .. ..75p/**£1**/£1.50
Pub. Shamrock & Co. The Limerick Lunatic
with appliqué 'noose' .. .. 50p/**75p**/£1.50
Pub. Tuck. Limerick postcards with appli-
qué cheque material. Nos. 9568, 9596/
7 .. ..50p/**75p**/1.50
Pub. J. Welch & Co. (1907) .. ..75p/**£1**/£1.50
Other pubs. .. .. 50p/**75p**/£1

Competition cards
Palantine Limerick Postcard .. £1/**£1.50**/£2
Valentine & Sons (1907) .. .. £1/**£1.50**/£2

Novelty cards
Artist Ralph Ruttley. Pub. Shamrock & Co. (Set of 5 views and 1 Limerick card with last line to complete.)
Per set .. .. £3/**£5**/£7.50

POSTCARD COLLECTING

The greatest hobby-cum-craze of the Golden Age of the postcard was, of course, collecting postcards! Many cards alluding to postcard collecting can be found spanning the 7 Periods.

Postcard 'Inventors'

Besnardeau (now hotly disputed 'inventor' of
    the picture card) cards from 1870/71
    .. .. £60/**£85**/£100
Besnardeau reprints (1903) .. .. £20/**£25**/£30
Dr. Hermann (instigator of the postcard).
    See COMMEMORATIVE.
1939. 70 years of the postcard. German
    official card with printed stamp of Hitler's
    head .. .. £8/**£10**/£12

Postcard Exhibitions (*see also* EXHIBITIONS)

Period 1
Venice 1894, Berlin 1896, Leipzig, Munich,
    Zürich 1898, Nice, Berlin & others
    1899 .. .. £15/**£20**/£50

Period 2
Paris 1900, Paris 1904, Nuremberg 1907
    .. .. £5/**£10**/£25
Others .. .. £5/**£10**/£15

Period 7
Century of British Postcards 1970. ■115c.
    With Exhibition Postmark .. £3/**£4**/£5
Ditto. Mint .. .. .. £1/**£1.50**/£2

Postcard Clubs (*usually limited editions*)
Period 1. International Poste Carte Club
    (IPCC). Series of 12 cards by artists like
    Jossot .. .. £50/**£100**/£200
Period 1. Other early clubs .. £5/**£10**/£20
Period 7 .. .. −/**50p**/£1

Postcard Fairs (Period 7)

Hotel George V, Paris (1975–1978).
    ■117b .. .. £2/**£3**/£5
Park Lane, London (1976) .. ..75p/**£1**/£1.50

Miscellaneous Cards with References to Postcard Collecting

Artist drawn (value according to artist,
    Period, etc.). Putting cards in albums,
    posting/receiving cards, etc. .. 75p/**£1**/£2
Photographic (value according to sharpness
    of picture, Period, etc.). Cards showing
    collecting, albums, postcard vendors,
    shops, displays, etc. .. .. £1/**£2**/£5

■117a

Pub. Tuck. Oilette No. 3514. PU *9 Feb. 1925* £2

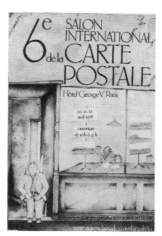

■117b

1978 Paris Salon Internationale de la Carte Postale. *Artist Anne Nogard* £2

POSTCARD COMPETITIONS

C. W. Faulkner (Period 2)

611 prizes from 10*s*. 6*d*. to £100 for putting in order the best 6 cards from a packet of 12.
Postcards advertising the competition
  .. .. £1/**£2**/£3

St. Paul's Hospital Competition (1924)

To raise funds for a new hospital. Set of 12 sepia view cards of London.
Per set of 12 .. .. 50p/**£1**/£2
Per set of 12 complete with detachable entry
    coupons .. .. £2/**£4**/£5

Shurey's Great Prize Competition (Period 2)

Delittle Fenwick & Co. per 6 cards 50p/**£1.25**/£2

Raphael Tuck & Sons

Postcards advertising Tucks' competitions are popular. The following competitions are known:

1. July 1900. £100 for largest collections of Tuck postcards. Winner 20,364 cards.
2. 1902. £2000 prizes. Winner 25,239 cards.
3. 1 Aug. 1904–31 July 1905. £3000 for placing 300 cards in order of merit.
4. 1909 in 2 parts, each with 1st prize £100.
5. 1914. 'The Fourth Competition' for the largest collection of Tuck cards posted after 1 Jan. 1914.
6. 'Father Tuck's Painting Book Competition' Children's colouring cards in the Postcard Painting Book.

By well-known artists. ■118a	..	£1.50/**£3**/£5
Unsigned artist drawn ..	..	£1/**£1.50**/£3
Advertising on reverse only ..	..	75p/**£1**/£2
Sheffield Weekly Telegraph (Kodak DIY postcard competition. Prizes in Tuck postcards)	..	75p/**£1.50**/£3
Other Competitions ..	..	50p/**£1**/£2

RINKING (Period 2)

The great roller skating craze (which reached its zenith in 1909 as far as postcard production was concerned) swept the United States, Britain and Europe. The great entrepreneur C. B. Cochran opened rinks in Olympia, throughout the UK, in Paris, Berlin, Hanover, Hamburg, Antwerp and Nice. Magazines like *The World on Wheels*, *Roller Skating Record* and *The Rinking World* were published.

Artist drawn cards

Browne, Tom. Pub. Davidson. Series 2623/1 .. .. £4/**£5**/£6	
Carter, Reg. Pub. Verdier	£1/**£1.50**/£2
'F.S.'	75p/**£1**/£1.50
Thackeray, Lance. Pub. Tuck. Set No. 9919	£2/**£3**/£5
Wiederseim, Grace	£1/**£1.50**/£3
Other signed artists	75p/**£1**/£1.50

Publishers of comic 'Rinking' cards

Artist drawn. Davidson Bros., Inter-Art, local publishers, McGlennon, Millar & Lang, Wm. Ritchie & Sons, Philco, Tuck	50p/**75p**/£1.50
Photographic. Bamforth & Co. (premium for complete set)	50p/**75p**/£1

Skating Rinks

Photographic. Various publishers 75p/**£1**/£2

Skating Rink Managers

Reprinted from *Rinking World*, Artist T. H. Smith. ■118b .. .. £1/**£2**/£3

Skating Champions

Photographic. Various publishers £1/**£2**/£3

■118a
Pub. Tuck. Artist Lance Thackeray. With details of competition on reverse. Period 2 .. .. £4

■118b
Reprinted from The Rinking World. *Artist T. H. Smith. 'Mr. Alec Flood', Period 2* £1.50

Three Band Pricing System	
Left Hand Band:	*The lowest price you will probably be asked to pay for this card.*
Middle Band:	*What you will normally be asked to pay for this card: its average, reasonable price.*
Right Hand Band:	*The highest price you will probably be asked to pay for this card.*
For a full explanation of the system, see page viii.	

CURIOUS/MISCELLANEOUS

In this section are described the odd and the unusual: human freaks, natural phenomena, quaint buildings, record breaking attempts and postcards that do not fit into any of the traditional groupings.

CODES/CYPHERS

Many strange devices were used to disguise the messages on postcards to avoid their being read by postmen, servants, etc. If a postcard has its message written in code, in cyphers, in 'mirror writing', in shorthand, in Greek or Latin, or otherwise disguised, add a premium of 50p to £1 to the card, depending on the complexity of the system used.

CURIOSITIES

Animal Curiosities

Cards of photographic origin, usually by local publishers, may show animals with one leg too many or too few; animals with two heads; animals working treadmills; birds' nests in strange places (e.g. railway trucks); horse that bolted down 66 steps on 6 Feb. 1905; Jonah the Giant Whale; Linus The Wonderful Long Tailed and Double-Maned Horse; or other subjects.

Price range   ..   ..   50p/**75p**/£1.50

Human Curiosities

Many of these appeared on the stage, or in sideshows at circuses (like Barnum & Bailey) or fairs, or in C. B. Cochran's 'Midget City' at Olympia. The cards carry a premium of 25% if they have been hand autographed by the subject.

Dwarfs/Midgets
Anita the living doll (26 in. high). ■119a
Asra, 'der lebenden Puppe'
Baron Ernesto Magri
Baron Paucci (62 cm. high)
Count Primo Magri
Madame Pauline, the Miniature Comedienne
Major and Mrs. Mite
Major Newell
General Tom Thumb
Mrs. Tom Thumb (née Lavinia Warren, Mrs. Magri by her second marriage)
Troupe Lilliputienne Zeynard
Willy Pantzer and his Wonderful Midgets
Others
Price range   ..   ..   £1/**£1.50**/£3

Freaks
Bearded ladies
Siamese twins
Various physical deformities
Price range   ..   ..   50p/**£1**/£2

Giants
Abomah, the Tallest Lady in the World
Hassan Ali, the Egyptian Giant (8 ft. 2 in.)
Machnow, the Russian Giant
The Nottingham Giant Girl
Others
Price range   ..   ..   75p/**£1**/£2

Odd Characters
Bird Charmers of the Tuileries, Paris
Cave dwellers
C. B. Courtenay Thomas (who 'was the means of compelling the Devonport Borough officials to adopt a proper System of Book-keeping, etc.')
Others
Price range   ..   ..£1**£1.50**/£3

Unusual Performers
Conjurers
Contortionists
Escapologists
Hypnotists
Illusionists
Mind Readers
Snake Charmers
Spiritualists
Others
Price range   ..   ..   £1/**£1.50**/£3

■119a

Pub. Rotary. Anita, the smallest adult lady in the world. Hand autographed by Anita. Period 2   £2

Man-made Curiosities

Mannekin Pis, Brussels: many series, comic
and photographic, some in booklet form
.. .. 50p/**£1**/£1.50
Models in icing sugar, made from match-
sticks, other materials .. .. 50p/**£1**/£1.50
Odd-shaped houses, 'smallest' houses and
other curious buildings .. .. 50p/**£1**/£1.50
Ossuaries (e.g. cemetery of Capucin
Monks) .. .. 50p/**£1**/£1.50
Sand sculptures .. .. .. 50p/**£1**/£1.50
Other curiosities .. .. .. 50p/**£1**/£1.50

Natural Curiosities

Crocodile Rock, Millport, USA or other
strange rock formations .. .. –/50p/75p
Double trees (e.g. beech and oak joined)
.. .. –/50p/75p
Giant trees .. .. –/50p/75p
Grottoes/underground caverns .. –/50p/75p
Halley's Comet. 1910. German. Set of 6
Col., signed K. Hesse .. .. .. £2/**£4**/£6
Others .. .. 75p/**£1.50**/£3
Others .. .. –/50p/75p

D.I.Y. POSTCARDS

Sensitised postcards which could be used with
one's own negatives to produce a photographic
picture. Produced by Kodak, Mallandain, Rotary,
Velox and others.
Unused postcards per pack of 10 or 12
.. .. £1/**£2**/£4
Used postcards with photographs **50p**

ESPERANTO (and other International Languages)

Braille
Price range .. .. 50p/**£1**/£2

Deaf and Dumb Sign Language
Price range .. .. 50p/**£1**/£2

Esperanto
For cards written in Esperanto add 50p to £1 to
the value of the card, the earlier the card the
higher the premium.
Cards pertaining to the following (and later)
Esperanto congresses may be found: Boulogne
1905; Geneva 1906; Cambridge 1907; Dresden
1908; Barcelona 1909; Washington 1910; Anvers 1911; Budapest/Cracow 1912; Berne 1913;
Paris 1914 (rare); Tallinn 1920; Budapest/
Prague 1921; Miskolcz 1922; Nuremberg 1923.

Adhesive Congress stamps/Congress rubber
stamps .. .. 75p/**£1**/£1.50
Congress location—viewcards printed in
Esperanto .. .. 75p/**£1**/£1.50
Official commemorative postcards £3/**£5**/£8
Photographic postcards of interiors of
congress halls/organisers/participants
.. .. £1/**£3**/£5
Postmarks—Special Congress .. £1/**£3**/£5
Propaganda cards for Esperanto .. £2/**£3**/£5
Pub. Tuck. Oilette series on Esperanto
.. .. £1/**£2**/£3
Others .. .. 75p/**£1**/£1.50

Esperantists

Bourlet .. .. £2/**£3**/£5
Cunningham .. .. £2/**£3**/£5
Zamenhof, Ludwig (1859–1917) (inventor
of Esperanto) .. .. .. £3/**£5**/£8
Other Esperantists .. .. .. £1/**£2**/£3
Bust of Zamenhof .. .. .. 75p/**£1**/£2
Monument to Esperanto/Zamenhof. ■120a
.. .. £1/**£1.50**/£2
Others .. .. 75p/**£1.50**/£3

■120a

*Pub. Hechl, Jacob, Franzensbad. Monument to
Esperanto and its founder Dr. Zamenhof. Period
4* £1.50

Ido
Revised form of Esperanto, from the initials
International Delegation (1907). For cards writ-
ten in Ido add 50p to £1 to the value of the card,
the earlier the card the higher the premium.
Congresses. Various dates and locations
.. .. 75p/**£1.50**/£5
Propaganda cards for Ido/anti-Esperanto
.. .. £1/**£3**/£5
Others .. .. 75p/**£1**/£1.50

Ido-ists
Marquis de Beaufront, Louis (Inventor)
.. .. £1/**£3**/£5
Other Ido-ists .. ..75p/**£1.50**/£3

Other International Languages
Price range .. .. 50p/**£1**/£3

EXPEDITIONS/FEATS/RECORD-BREAKERS/WAGERS

Allen, W. C.—Walking 2000 miles in 44 days—trained on Bovril (1904). ■121a
Belbin, H. W. G.—Riding his land & water cycle
Buchanan, Capt.—with Ali, Sakari and Feri N'Gashi the camel, during their 3500 miles, 16 month expedition across the Sahara. ■121b
The Crusader walking round the world (£500 reward)
Leach, Bobby—Going over Niagara Falls in a barrel (1911). ■121c
Rolling a barrel from Vienna to Paris (1900)
Schilling, Geo.—Walking round the world in an airship
Walking round the world in an iron mask (£21,000 wager)
Walking from Vienna to Paris, pushing wife and child (*c.* 1900). Pub. Baumann, pram manufacturer, Vienna
Others
Price range .. .. £1/**£2**/£4

GAMES OF CHANCE

Playing Cards
Comic postcards of card games by various artists and publishers (*see also* Comic).
Pub. Stewart & Woolf. Set of 12 chromolithographs of playing cards. Artist J. M. Henman (1903) .. .. .. £1/**£2**/£3
Pub. Welch, J. Col. set of playing cards. Period 2 .. .. £1/**£2**/£3
USA. Series of playing card sets. Period 4
.. .. £1/**£1.50**/£2
Others .. .. 50p/**75p**/£1.50

Roulette and other Gambling Games
For casino buildings *see* Social History.
Croupiers/gamblers. Clear pictures photographic in origin with good detail of people .. .. £1/**£1.50**/£3
French. Rules of Roulette/other gambling games at Monte Carlo and other Casinos.
■121d .. .. £2/**£3**/£4
Others .. .. 75p/**£1**/£3

■121a

Photographer Protheroe, Bristol. C. W. Allen attempting to walk 2000 miles in 45 days, training on Bovril. Period 2 .. .. £2

■121b

Capt. Buchanan, Feri N'Gashi the camel, with Ali and Sakari (both of whom have signed the card on the reverse), after their 16 month 3500 mile expedition across the Sahara. Period 4 .. £1

■121c

Pub. Photo Speciality Co. Bobby Leach and the barrel in which he went over Niagara Falls (1911) £3

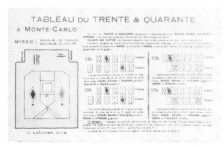
■121d

Pub. F. Laugier, Nice. Tableau du Trente et Quarante à Monte Carlo. *Period 2* £4

GOOD LUCK SYMBOLS

For Pigs, *see* ANIMALS.

Swastikas. Often found on greetings cards
during Periods 2, 3. ■122a .. –/**50p**/75p

MASONIC (and other secret societies)

Artist Drawn

Pub. Millar & Lang. Comic col. series 'Are
You a Mason?' 24 cards. Period 2.
■122b .. .. £1/**£2**/£3
Other comic series .. .. 75p/**£1**/£1.50

Photographic Origin

Masonic regalia .. .. 75p/**£1**/£1.50
People in masonic regalia .. .. £1/**£1.50**/£3

Other Societies

Price range .. .. 50p/**£1**/£2

MISTAKES ON POSTCARDS

For wrongly printed captions, postcards printed
the wrong way round or other mistakes, add 50p
to £1 to the value of the card.

PETOMANIA

The art of breaking wind. Several comic
French series in Patois. Period 2
.. .. 50p/**75p**/£1.50

Q.S.L. CARDS

Radio amateurs' postcards for acknowledg-
ment of radio contact. ■122c. Periods 4
and 5. Posted commemorative designs
.. .. **50p**

'WANTED' CARDS

Pub. USA. with and without stuck on photo
of wanted person .. .. .. **P/A**

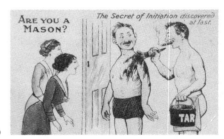

■122a

Pub. 'A.J.C.' Swastika for good luck. PU *1911*
.. .. 50p

■122b

*Pub. Millar & Lang. 'Are you a Mason?' Period
2* £2.50

■122c

Q.S.L. card. German shortwave station DL4LC.
PU *1954* 50p

EARLY CARDS: Period 1/ Early Period 2

The characteristics of an 'Early Card' are perhaps the most difficult of all to define and to value, yet every collector of any experience can recognise an 'Early' card. The good quality board and high standard of printing which are characteristic of many early cards often makes them recognisable by feel as well as by sight. The recent growth in the popularity of postcard collecting has led to an increase in interest in Period 1 and early Period 2 cards (up to 1902). Cards produced between 1869 and 1902 fall into several main themes, e.g. Advertising, *Art Nouveau*, Commemorative, Exhibitions, Official, Royalty, View, etc. These themes have their own sections in this catalogue and valuations should be obtained there. However, there are features, such as the size of the card or its quality of production, which cross the thematic lines between the categories in 'Early' cards. These features, *per se*, make a card collectable. Three of them are considered here: Chromo-litho; Court Size: Gruss Aus. Some preliminary comments about valuations are necessary because cards in this section are extremely sensitive to a number of factors which must be taken into account:

Age: On the Continent card values rise astronomically as the years stretch back from 1900 into the 1890s and the 1880s. Although British collectors are less concerned with the calendar, it is generally accurate to assume that age and value are directly related when dealing with chromo-litho cards, but much less so for monotone or line-drawn examples. Used cards firmly dated by postmark have the edge on unused cards in Period 1.

Condition: Since the collecting reason in this section is not primarily the subject matter of the card, but rather the card itself, condition is of vital importance. A card in pristine condition could be valued at £10, while the same card with a bent corner might rate only £2.

Origin: During Period 1 the finest printing was done in Austria and Germany, and to a lesser extent in Switzerland, Belgium, Italy and France. Cards of equal quality originating from other countries should attract a higher value.

Postal Stationery: In many countries in Europe and also in America the early pictures were printed onto officially issued cards. These picture cards normally carry a pre-printed stamp and attitudes are presently ambivalent towards such examples. On balance they tend to be less valued than an equivalent private card carrying an adhesive stamp.

CHROMO-LITHO CARDS

The majority of these cards were printed on the Continent during Period 1 and early Period 2. They are readily recognised by the excellence of the colour printing (*see also* 'Chromo-litho' in the Glossary), are frequently undivided backs and often have vignettes in the design. Some examples were imported by Continental entrepreneurs like Ernest Nister and may appear to have been published in London. Closer examination usually reveals that they were printed elsewhere. We list below the major printers/publishers of chromo-litho cards. Their postcards are listed and valued under the three headings that follow below:

Printers/Publishers
Bechtold, Rudolph, Wiesbaden
Berardi, E., Milan
Champenois, Paris
Dietrich, Brussels
Franzl, L., Munich
Frey & Sons, Zürich
Hendelsohn, G., Berlin
Huardel, P. G. (P.G.H. & Co.)
Juxberg, F. W., Frankfurt (F.W.J.)
Köhn, Brüder, Vienna (B.K.W.)
Meissner & Buch, Leipzig and London
Menke-Huber, Zürich
Miesler, J., Frankfurt
Moss, Henry (H.M. & Co.)
Munk, M., Vienna (MM)
Nister, Ernest, London and Nuremberg
Pascalis, Moss & Co.
Philipp & Kramer, Vienna
Pinkau, Emil, Leipzig
Ricordi, Milan
Rosenblatt, Frankfurt
Roth, Ludwig, Berlin
Schmidt, Staub & Co., Nuremberg
Stengel, Dresden
Tuck, Raphael & Sons
Winkler & Schorn, Nuremberg
Zieher, Ottmar, Munich

General Designs/Views

Period 1	..	..	..	..	..	£2/**£3**/£5
Others	..	..	..	..	..	£1/**£1.50**/£2

COURT CARDS

The Court Size postcard measures approx. 115 × 89 mm in contrast to the 122 × 75 mm of the normal Periods 1 to 3 cards. Full UPU size in Periods 1 to 3 was 140 × 89 mm. Court cards are indigenous to Britain (though similar size Continental cards exist) and were used from *c.* 1895 until early in Period 2. Court size views of Edinburgh published by George Stewart in 1894 have sometimes been proposed as the first British produced picture postcards, although privately produced court cards were not recognised by the Post Office until the issue of the first official court card (21 January 1895).

Publishers of British Court Cards include:
Beechings (whose views of London and Manchester now command a considerable premium) Blum & Degen; Faulkner; Frith; Photochrom; Pictorial Stationery Co.; Sandle Bros.; Stewart, Geo.; Valentines.

Gruss Aus types

chromo-litho	..	..	..	£8/**£10**/£12
col. (not chromo-litho)		..	..	£6/**£8**/£10
b & w/sepia	..	..	..	£3/**£5**/£8

Official isues—*see* OFFICIAL

Thematic (Advertising, Commemorative, Exhibitions, Royalty, etc.) see the appropriate subject sections in this catalogue. The older the card the higher the value.
Views (general)/vignettes

chromo-litho	..	..	..	£5/**£12**/£20
col. (not chromo-litho)		..	..	£3/**£5**/£8
b & w/sepia	..	..	..	£1.50/**£3**/£5

GRUSS AUS TYPE

(*see also* HISTORY in the Introductory pages)
Literally 'Greetings from . . .'. A type of card popularised in Germany in the 1880s, showing small, one colour line drawings/vignettes — pictures of a beauty spot or a town and its inhabitants—often in an elaborate border of flowers, scrolls, etc. By the mid-1890s these were also being produced in colour, often chromo-litho. Variations on the German words of greeting (according to the language of the country of origin) are: 'Greetings from . . .' (Britain & Colonies incl. India), *Gruss aus* . . . or *Gruss vom* . . . (Germany and Colonies), *Memorias de* . . . (Spain and Spanish-speaking countries), *Ricordi di* . . . and *Saluti di* . . . (Italy), *Souvenir de* . . . (Belgium, France and Colonies, Switzerland). The type was also produced in Russia! Generally speaking the earlier the card and the more obscure the country of origin (e.g. Heligoland) the more valuable it will be. Ultimately, however, the value of a *Gruss Aus* type card will be determined by its sheer appeal and beauty—and beauty is in the eye of the beholder.

Court Size—*see above*

Period 1 pre-1890

chromo-litho	..	..	..	£10/**£15**/£25
col. (not chromo-litho)		..	..	£8/**£12**/£18
b & w/sepia	..	..	..	£5/**£8**/£12

Line drawn, letterpress or intaglio black views on buff official cards. Picture occupies a third or less of the card

..	..	..	..	£13/**£15**/£25

Period 1 post-1890

chromo-litho	..	..	..	£3/**£6**/£18
col. (not chromo-litho)		..	..	£2/**£5**/£10
b & w-sepia	..	..	..	£1.50/**£3**/£5

Early Period 2

chromo-litho	..	..	..	£2/**£3**/£6
col. (not chromo-litho)		..	..	£1.50/**£2**/£4
b & w/sepia	..	..	..	£1/**£1.50**/£2

OTHER EARLY CARDS (Full size, not *Gruss Aus* types)

Period 1 pre-1890

Official issues—*see* OFFICIAL
Thematic (*see* COURT SIZE above)
Vignettes—general views

chromo-litho	..	..	..	£8/**£9**/£12
col. (not chromo-litho)		..	..	£5/**£7**/£10
b & w/sepia	..	..	..	£3/**£5**/£8

Period 1 post-1890/Early Period 2

(incl. 'Intermediate' sizes, which tend to be more highly valued than equivalent normal size cards.)
'Blue' cards *see* SOCIAL HISTORY/TOPOGRAPHICAL .. .. £1/**£2**/£3
Foreign cards will only command two thirds of the valuations for postcards under this heading.
Official issues—*see* OFFICIAL
Thematic (*see* COURT SIZE *above*)
Vignettes—general views

chromo-litho	..	..	..	£2/**£4**/£6
col. (not chromo-litho)		..	..	£1/**£1.50**/£2
b & w/sepia	..	..	..	50p/**75p**/£1

EXHIBITIONS/EXPOSITIONS/ TRADE FESTIVALS/WORLD FAIRS

The first of the great International Exhibitions was that held at the Crystal Palace in 1851, and it was at the 1889 Paris Exhibition, for which the Eiffel Tower had been built, that the picture postcard developed into a commemorative art form. At the 1882 Nuremberg Exhibition an official commemorative card was issued bearing a photo-litho vignette view. It had been produced by the printer Zrenner who afterwards claimed that it was the first true 'picture' postcard (■126a). Whether it was or not, it was in Paris in 1889 that the privately produced picture postcard made the enormous public impact that began the collecting frenzy. After that date every exhibition (or exposition) had its official and privately produced cards. This is a popular collecting theme, particularly for Period 1 and early Period 2 events when the cards produced were often well designed and printed by chromo-lithography. Generally speaking, the higher values relate to especially designed artist drawn cards. We list the significant British and foreign exhibitions together in chronological sequence, and it must be remembered that where cards carry Exhibition postmarks their values will be enhanced.

Nuremberg (1882). ■126a .. .. £25/**£35**/£50
Turin (1884) .. .. £25/**£30**/£40
Paris (1889) .. .. £15/**£20**/£30
London (1890). Penny Postage Jubilee. *See*
  illustration D in Introduction .. £3/**£4**/£5
London (1891). Royal Naval. Eddystone
  Lighthouse. *See* illustration E in Intro-
  duction. .. .. £25/**£50**/£60
Vienna (1892). International Music. Vig-
  nette. Artist Kronstein. PS back
  .. .. £5/**£9**/£11

Chicago (1893). The first commercially produced picture postcards in America were made by Charles W. Goldsmith for the World's Columbian Exposition in Chicago. They are superb chromo-litho prints on an oversize official card. The views are vignetted and there are faint ruled lines for the message. The first set (Series 1) issued was of 10 cards all of which are numbered. In a second printing of Series 1 two of the cards, Nos. 6 and 7, had totally new views. These are shown in brackets below. The premium for a complete set

of the first printing is 50% of the individual card total.
  1. Government Building. ■126b £10/**£12**/£15
  2. Administration Building .. £8/**£10**/£12
  3. Manufacturers & Liberal Arts £8/**£10**/£12
  4. The Agricultural Building .. £8/**£10**/£12
  5. The Electrical Building .. .. £8/**£10**/£12
  6. Horticultural Building .. .. £10/**£12**/£14
     (Fine Art Building) .. .. .. £6/**£8**/£10
  7. Mines Building .. .. .. £10/**£12**/£14
     (Machinery Building) .. .. £6/**£8**/£10
  8. The Fisheries Building .. .. £8/**£10**/£12
  9. The Womans Building .. .. £8/**£10**/£12
 10. Battle Ship Illinois .. .. .. £8/**£10**/£12
London (1893). Gardening & Forestry.
  Eddystone Lighthouse .. .. £30/**£50**/£70
Milan (1894). Philatelic. ■126c .. £4/**£6**/£8
Venice (1894). Postcard Exhibition
  .. .. £15/**£20**/£50
Berlin (1896) .. .. £6/**£8**/£10
Budapest (1896) .. .. .. £6/**£8**/£10
Nuremberg (1896). Chromo-litho .. £7/**£8**/£9
Ditto. Photo-origin .. .. £8/**£9**/£10
Central American (1897) .. .. £5/**£7**/£10
Dresden (1897). Artist drawn. Col. litho
  .. .. £6/**£9**/£12
Hamburg (1897) .. .. .. £6/**£8**/£10
Leipzig (1897) .. .. .. £2/**£3**/£4
Nuremberg (1897) .. .. .. £3/**£4**/£5
Bergen (1898). Artist Carl Dotzler
  .. .. £16/**£19**/£21
Vienna (1898). Jubilee .. .. £3/**£4**/£5
Ghent (1899). ■126d .. .. £5/**£7**/£9
Nice (1899). Exposition de Cartes Postales
  .. .. £7/**£10**/£12
Period 1. General .. .. .. £3/**£6**/£10
Paris (1900). Artist Jack Abeille .. £10/**£15**/£20
Ditto. Postcard entrance pass .. £6/**£8**/£10
Ditto. Others .. .. .. £2/**£3**/£4
Salzburg (1900). Fishing .. .. £2/**£4**/£5
Berlin (1901). Official cards pub. by Klimoff
  and Co. At least 3 series of 6 .. £2/**£3**/£5
Buffalo NY (1901). Pan American. Over 12
  pubs. including Livingston & Strauss
  .. .. £1/**£4**/£6
Dresden (1901) .. .. .. £2/**£3**/£5
Glasgow (1901). The most significant series issued for this first British exhibition of Period 2 is a fine chromo-litho set of 12 un-numbered cards drawn by Cassiers. Although not named, the publisher was Dietrich of Brussels. The premium for a complete set is 25% of the individual card total. All cards have undivided backs with their titles on the picture side. The titles are The Exhibition Glasgow, The Cathedral, Exhibition

Entrance, Royal Exchange, Buchanan Street, Trongate, George Square, The University & Kelvingrove Park, Landing Stage at Broomielaw, On the Clyde, Shipyards on the Clyde.

Value per card	£3/**£4**/£5
Other publishers	£1/**£2**/£2.50
Cork (1902)	£1/**£2**/£3
Wolverhampton (1902)	£1/**£2**/£2.50
Bradford (1904)	75p/**£1.50**/£2

St. Louis (1904). Louisiana Purchase World's Fair. At least 38 pubs. incl. Kropp, Curt Teich & Tuck have been identified. Official pub. Samuel Cupples produced a wide range of chromo-litho vignette cards. Values vary considerably, but are broadly as follows for Cupples:

Artist H. Wunderlich	£1/**£3**/£5
Chromo-litho vignettes ..	75p/**£1**/£1.50
Hold to Light	£1/**£2**/£3.50
Monochrome views	**50p**
Photo-origin views	–/**50p**/75p
Silver finish views	–/**50p**/£1
Others	–/**50p**/£1
Liège (1905). ■127a	£1/**£2**/£5
Milan (1906). Gilded cards ..	£1.50/**£3**/£5
Others ..	50p/**75p**/£1.50
Nuremberg (1906)	£1/**£2**/£3

Dublin (1907). Irish International.

General	–/**50p**/£1
Woven silk. Pub. Grant, W. H.	£12/**£13**/£15

Prague (1908). Radiotelegraphic. R. P.

cards	£1.50/**£3**/£4

White City (1908). Franco-British. The first exhibition to be held at that venue and probably the most fully documented of all on the postcard. Valentines were the official publishers and won several Grands Prix and Diplomas for their designs. Over 10 pubs. have been identified, including Rotary, Davidsons, Beagles & Tuck. Over 500 cards have been attributed to Valentine's.

Comic designs by named artists like	
Crombie, Sarg	50p/**£1**/£1.50
Designs by artist A. K. Macdonald	£5/**£10**/£15
Famous people at the Exhibition ..	50p/**75p**/£2
Flip Flap. ■127b	50p/**75p**/£1
General views	**50p**
Hagenback's Circus	75p/**£1**/£1.25
Mucha advertisement for Job Cigarettes	
with Exhibition overprint ..	£25/**£50**/£75
Ornamental/Patriotic coloured borders	
.. ..	75p/**£1**/£1.50
Oversize views	50p/**75p**/£1
Trade stands	£1/**£1.50**/£2

■126a

Pub. J. B. Obernatter. Artist Zrenner. Period 1. Official card for 1882 Nuremberg Exhibition. Sometimes claimed as the World's first true picture postcard £35

■126b

Pub. Charles W. Goldsmith. Period 1. Official card for 1893 World's Columbian Exhibition Chicago. America's first commercial postcard series. Series 1. Design 1 .. .. £15

■126c

Period 1. Official card for 1894 Milan Philatelic Exhibition. Limited edition of 30,000 .. .. £8

■126d

Period 1. Official card for 1899 Gent Flemish Exhibition £7

Frankfurt (1909). Poster type. Artist
  Correggio .. .. £5/**£7**/£8
Argentine (1910). Republic Centennial.
  Poster type .. .. £3/**£5**/£7
Vienna (1910). Hunting. Poster type.
  Artists Kalmsteiner, Lenhard, Puchinger
  .. .. £2/**£4**/£6
White City (1910). Japan–British. At least
  6 publishers, incl. Rotary, Davidsons &
  Tuck. Valentine's were the official pubs.
  with over 150 attributed cards. General
  categories and valuations as for Franco-
  British above, plus designs by artist Fred
  Spurgin. Pub. Paternoster ..75p/**£1.50**/£2
Crystal Palace (1911). Festival of Empire.
  Rotary Photo Series No. 6799. Over 30
  cards in series .. .. 50p/**75p**/£1
Turin (1911). International. Poster type.
  Artist A. de Karolis .. .. £1.50/**£2**/£3
Chelsea (1912). Royal International Horti-
  cultural (poster type) .. .. .. £4/**£6**/£8
Breslau (1913). Artist drawn .. £4/**£5**/£7
Leipzig (1913). International Architecture.
  Art Deco poster types.. .. £6/**£9**/£11
  Other artist drawn .. .. £1.50/**£2**/£3
Leipzig (1914). Artist drawn .. £2.50/**£3**/£4
San Diego (1915). Panama–Californian. At least
14 different pubs. identified, incl. Curt Teich.
  Pub. Detroit Pub. Co. .. ..75p/**£1**/£1.50
  Pub. Fred Harvey .. .. £1/**£1.25**/£2
  Others .. .. 25p/**50p**/£1
San Francisco (1915). Panama–Pacific Inter-
national. Over 30 different pubs. identified, incl.
Detroit Pub. Co.
  Pub. H. S. Crocker. Pre-Exhibition
  poster .. .. £1/**£1.50**/£2
  Others .. .. 25p/**50p**/£1
Blackpool (1916). Loos Trenches. Re-
  creation of battlefield at Loos. Two
  different pubs. identified .. .. £1/**£1.75**/£2
Wembley (1924/25). British Empire. The official
pubs. were Fleetway Press although other pubs.
produced cards with Fleetways' name as well as
their own, e.g. Tuck, with the Queen's Dolls
House series. At least 16 other commercial pubs.
joined in, incl. Wildt & Kray, Valentine's,
Beagles, Photochrom and Inter-Art (*see* Queen's
Dolls' House).
Exhibitors' cards by Tuck included Anglo-
  Persian Oil Co., Bryant & May, Canadian
  National Railways, Canadian Pacific
  Railway, the Catholic Oratory, Idris,
  Imperial Airways, North British Rubber
  Co., Schweppes, Sharpe's Toffee and
  South African Wine .. .. ..50p/**£1**/£1.50

■127a

*Pub. Lauwers & Co., Brussels. Period 2. Official
card for 1905 Liege Exhibition. First prize winner
in design competition £5*

■127b

*Pub. Valentines. Period 2. Typical 1908 official
Franco-British Exhibition card. The Flip Flap £1*

■127c

*Artist Alfred Martin. Period 4. 1930 Liège
Exhibition £3*

General views/art studies, e.g. Artist Ernest Coffin .. .. −/**50p**/£1

Named artists like Harry Payne .. £1/**£3**/£7

Tuck Oilettes .. .. £1/**£2**/£3

Overprints or sepia views for product advertising, incl. Anglo-Persian Oil Co., Eno's Fruit Salts, Express Dairy, Mersey Docks and Pears Soap .. .. 50p/**75p**/£2

'Super Circus' poster ads, pub. Waterlow .. .. £18/**£20**/£26

Paris (1925). Decorative Arts. Five different pubs. identified, incl. Levy et Neurdein .. .. −/**50p**/75p

Philadelphia (1926). Sesquicentennial. 150th Anniversary of the founding of the USA. Pub. J. D. Cardinell has 100 identified numbered views. At least 6 other pubs., incl. Tichnor **50p**

Strasbourg (1927). International Philatelic. Poster type on official, pre-stamped card .. .. £3/**£5**/£6

Newcastle-on-Tyne (1929). North East Coast. Several pubs., incl. Valentine's. Higher values for photo cards of trade stands .. .. 50p/**£1**/£3

Antwerp (1930). International .. −/**25p**/50p

Liege (1930). International. Higher values for poster types. ■127c .. .. £1/**£1.50**/£3

Milan (1930). Poster type. Fiat. Artist Mizoli .. .. £1/**£2**/£2.50

Vienna (1930). Philatelic. Artist drawn .. .. £1.50/**£3**/£5

Paris (1931). International Colonial .. .. −/**50p**/£1

Chicago (1933). Century of Progress. World's Fair. At least seventeen pubs., incl. Curt Teich & Co. (linen finish cards) and others. ■128a .. .. ..50p/**£1**/£1.25

London (1934). Ideal Home. Photo cards of Heath Robinson exhibits .. .. £1.50/**£2**/£3

Breslau (1935). Col. poster type .. £9/**£10**/£12

Dresden (1936). Olympic Year Stamp Show .. .. £7/**£9**/£10

Paris (1937). International Arts & Crafts .. .. −/**50p**/75p

Glasgow (1938). Empire. Pubs. include Valentine's and at least 3 others .. .. −/**75p**/£1

Wellington (1939). New Zealand Centennial. Five different pubs. identified .. ..50p/**£1**/£1.50

San Francisco (1939). Golden Gate. At least seven pubs. identified, incl. Curt Teich .. .. −/**25p**/50p

New York (1939). World's Fair. Nine pubs. incl. Tichnor Bros. identified as having produced various card types and several more publishers issued linen-faced cards with white borders **50p**

New York (1947). Postal Centennial. 'Souvenir Postal Card', Pub. Lee C. Cray Printed stamp. Illus. both sides £1/**£1.50**/£3

London (1951). Festival of Britain. Pubs. include Salmon, Tuck, Jarrolds & Valentine's. Most cards are photo type .. .. −/**50p**/75p

New York (1964). World's Fair. Most cards pub. by Dexter Color **50p**

New York (1967). 21st Annual Picture Post-Card Exhibition of the Metropolitan Post-Card Collectors' Club. Numbered card, also used as an entrance pass .. .. £1/**£1.50**/£3

Florida (1976). First National Postcard Exhibition. ■128b .. .. .. 50p/**75p**/£1

■128a
Period 4. 1933 Chicago 'Century of Progress' World's Fair £1

■128b
Pub. Postcard Collectors Magazine. Period 7. USA. First National Postcard Exhibition. Feb. 1976. Reproduction of 1906 card by artist G. H. Hilder & Pub. Osborne, NY £1

GLAMOUR/EROTIC/ LANGUAGE OF . . ./NUDES/ ROMANCE/SENTIMENT

The general term GLAMOUR classifies postcards depicting feminine (and/or masculine) charms, from the nude, through the scantily dressed to the fully clothed.

AMERICAN GIRL (THE)

† = *see also* ARTISTS *for more details.*

A species unique to that country, of bright, outgoing, athletic, socialite or collegiate types. Her sophistication is tinged with innocence, in direct contrast to the coy, lingerie-clad creations of the European glamour genre. She is slim and active, in contrast to the static, statuesque Asti or Collins beauties. Her chief exponents were:

Boileau, Phillip†	£1/**£2**/£3
Christy, F. Earl† ■129a	£1/**£2**/£3
Christy, Howard Chandler†	£1/**£2**/£3
Fidler, Pearle (married name Le Munyon)	75p/**£1**/£2
Fidler, Alice Luella	75p/**£1**/£2
Fisher, Harrison†	£1/**£2**/£3
Flagg, James Montgomery	£1/**£2**/£4
Gilbert, Allen	75p/**£1**/£2
Gunn, Archie†	£1/**£1.50**/£2
Hare, J. Knowles Jr.†	75p/**£1**/£2
Kimball, Alonzo†	£1/**£1.50**/£2
King, H.†	75p/**£1**/£2
McFall, J. V.	75p/**£1**/£2
Mayer, Lou	£2/**£3**/£4
Reiter, Brill G.	75p/**£1**/£1.50
Reynolds (Wild West flavour) ..	75p/**£1**/£2
St. John	75p/**£1**/£1.50
Underwood, Clarence†	75p/**£1**/£2
Waskow, Edward G.	75p/**£1**/£1.50

Publishers include: Armour; Langsdorf; M. Munk; National Art; Platinochrome; Reinthal & Newman Rotograph; Tuck; Souvenir P. C. Co.; Stern; Tuck; Ullman.

Series titles include: American Beauty Series; American Girl; American Girl in Foreign Countries; College Campus; College Classes; College Girls (many series); College Girls and Yell; College Mascot; College Queens; National Girls; State Belles; State Girls (several series).

EROTIC/PORNOGRAPHIC

Cards in this section vary from the gently titillating to the blatantly erotic.

Deshabille/Lingerie (Periods 2 to 4)

Artist drawn, signed. Valuations according to artists (listed below)

Artist drawn, unsigned/photographic origin	25p/**50p**/£1.50
RP	50p/**£1**/£2

Erotic

Phallic symbols like asparagus, bananas, flutes, towers, swans, trees, etc. and lesbian interest. The 'suggestive' rather than the explicit.

Artist drawn	75p/**£1.50**/£3
Photographic origin	75p/**£1**/£1.50

Eunuchs and Harems

Artist drawn	£1/**£2**/£5
Photographic origin	£2/**£5**/£8

Fantasy

Girls as neckties. French series ..	£5/**£10**/£15
Heads composed of beauties *en déshabillé*	£4/**£5**/£6
Mechanical incl. Blow-up bosoms and posteriors/Spanking—*see also* NOVELTY	£2/**£4**/£6
Photomontage	£2/**£4**/£6

House of German Art (*see also* WAR)

Period 5. Hitler-approved Aryan beauties.

B & w	75p/**£1.50**/£3
Coloured	£2/**£3**/£5

Nudes

Artist drawn	75p/**£3**/£15
Photographic (Paris Salon, etc.) ..	£1/**£3**/£5
Seldoms and other stage acts. ■130a	£1/**£2**/£4

■129a

Pub. Souvenir P.C. Co. Artist F. Earl Christy. College Series. No. 5. Yale and Yell. Embossed £3

Pornographic

Artist drawn	£3/**£5**/£10
Photographic origin	£3/**£5**/£10

Prostitution

Brothels (interior and exterior) ..	£2/**£4**/£5
Prostitutes	£2/**£4**/£5

EUROPEAN ARTISTS

† = *see also* ARTISTS for more details.

These fall into three types—the slightly risqué, often scantily clad; the robust, bosomy Asti types; and the elegant Gibson-girl types.

Abeille, Jack† (Fr) ■97a	£5/**£15**/£30
Asti, Angelo† (It)	75p/**£1**/£1.50
Aveline, F.† ■37a	75p/**£1**/£1.50
Barribal, W.†	£1/**£2**/£4
Balfour-Kerr (Gibson types) ..	75p/**£1**/£1.50
Bayard-Jones (Gibson types) ..	75p/**£1**/£1.50
Bertiglia, A. (It)	£1/**£2**/£3
Bettinelli (It)	£1/**£2**/£3
Bompard, Luigi (It) (1873–1953)	£1/**£2**/£3
Bonora (It)	75p/**£1**/£2
Bonzagni, Aroldo (It)	£1/**£3**/£5
Brunelleschi, Umberto† (It) ■31b	£20/**£35**/£45
Busi, Adolfo (It) (1891–1978) (*Art Deco*)	
.. ..	£4/**£6**/£8
Calderara, C.† (It)	£1/**£3**/£6
Capiello, Leonetto (It) (1875–1942)	
.. ..	75p/**£1**/£2
Cherubini, M. (It)	£1/**£2**/£3
Collins, G. T. (Asti types)	75p/**£1**/£1.50
Colombo, E. (It)	75p/**£1.50**/£3
Corbella, Tito† (It) ■49a	£1/**£1.50**/£3
English, Archibald† (rather wooden-faced, Period 3) ■54a	50p/**75p**/£1
Fabiano (Fr)	£1.50/**£3**/£5
Fontan, Léo (Fr) ■130b	£2/**£4**/£6
Gibson, Charles Dana† ■56a ..	£1/**£1.50**/£3
Guerzoni (It)	75p/**£1**/£2
Grosze, Manni (*Art Deco* silhouettes)	
.. ..	£1/**£2**/£4
Harbour, Jennie (Crinoline types) ■58a	
.. ..	£2/**£4**/£6
Hérouard (Fr)	£2/**£3**/£5
Horsfall, Mary (colourful, elegant girls) ■60b	£1/**£2**/£3
Icart, Louis (Fr)	£2/**£4**/£6
King, W. R. (Gibson types)	75p/**£1**/£1.50
Kirchner, Raphael† (Aust) ■32a ..	£7/**£12**/£20
Maréchaux, C. (Fr)	£1/**£2.50**/£5

Mauzan, Achille (It) (incl. *Art Deco*)	
.. ..	£2/**£5**/£10
Meunier, Suzanne (Fr)	£3/**£4**/£5
Millière, Maurice (Fr) ■69a ..	£2/**£3**/£5
Monestier, C. (It) (incl. *Art Deco*) ..	£1/**£2**/£4
Montedoro, M. (*Art Deco*)	£3/**£8**/£15
Nanni, Giovanni (It) (1888–1969) (Fashion)	£2/**£4**/£8
Ney (Fr) ■243c	£3/**£4**/£6
Peltier (Fr)	£1/**£2**/£4.50
Penot, A. (Fr)	£2/**£4**/£6
Pepin (Fr)	£1/**£2**/£4
Rappini (It)	£1/**£2**/£4
Sager, Xavier† (Fr) ■83b	£1/**£3**/£10
San Marco (It)	£1/**£2.50**/£5
Simonetti, A. M. (It)	£1/**£2**/£3
Turner (Gibson types)	50p/**75p**/£1
Usaba (Ger)	£1/**£1.50**/£3
Wennerberg, Brynolf† (Ger)	£2/**£4**/£8
Zandrino, Adelina (It) (incl. pierrots)	
.. ..	£2/**£3**/£5
Unsigned	50p/**£3**/£10

■130a

Pub. Rotary. The Seldoms stage act. Period 2 £4

■130b

French. Pub. Libraire de L'Estampe (LE.). Artist Léo Fontan. Les Bas Transparents. Period 3 £5

LANGUAGE OF ...

Type of code or message card to convey an amusing/loving/sexual meaning. Subjects include:

Babies	–/**50p**/75p
Beauty spots (on the face)	–/**50p**/75p
Birds	–/**50p**/75p
Bouquets	–/**50p**/75p
Cards	50p/**75p**/£1
Charms	–/**50p**/75p
Coiffures	50p/**75p**/£1
Colours	–/**50p**/75p
Eyes	–/**50p**/75p
Feet	50p/**75p**/£1
Flowers	50p/**75p**/£1.50
Fruit (sometimes erotic)	50p/**£1**/£2
Gloves	–/**50p**/75p
Jewels	–/**50p**/75p
Kisses	–/**50p**/75p
Knots	–/**50p**/75p
Luck	–/**50p**/75p
Meat	–/**50p**/75p
Plants	–/**50p**/75p
Sausages (erotic)	50p/**£1**/£3
Spiders	50p/**75p**/£1
Stamps	.. 75p/**£1.50**/£2
Tools (erotic)	50p/**£1**/£3
Trousers	–/**50p**/75p
Vegetables (sometimes erotic) ..	50p/**£1**/£3
Window blinds	50p/**75p**/£1
Others	50p/**75p**/£2

Publishers include Alpha Pub. Co., Birn Bros., Inter-Art (incl. Donald McGill), Millar & Lang, Morawetz, Salzburg (Kisses, Luck, etc.), Schwerdtfeger, Stiebel (incl. silvered, embossed), Valentine (incl. scented flowers), Watkins & Kracke (Floral Series), Welch (separate card for each flower), Wildt & Kray (comic series), Woolstone Bros. The highest valuations are for embossed, erotic, scented, silvered, etc.

MALE GLAMOUR

Boxers/wrestlers in 'cheesecake' or fighting poses—named, e.g. A. Aberg (Russian champ.), Launceston Elliott, Gruhn, Hackenschmidt, Tom Jenkins, Eugen Sandow, others. ■131a .. .. £1/**£2**/£4
He-man poses, body-builders, boxers, wrestlers, etc.—un-named .. 75p/**£1.50**/£3
Publishers of the above include Beagles, Rapid Photo Co., Rotary.
Homosexual interest .. .. £1/**£2.50**/£5

ROMANCE/SENTIMENT

Many sentimental wartime postcards exist (notably the embroidered silks) with appropriate verses. (*See also* WAR.) Pre- and post-war series exist in their thousands, of varying merit and artistic quality. Many with *Art Deco* and *Art Nouveau* interest are well above average quality, accounting for the highest valuations. The romantic theme was often given the comic treatment (*see also* COMIC).

Anonymous or Minor Artist Drawn
Beauties, courtship, kisses. Periods 1 to 6.
  Value according to artistic merit and age .. .. 50p/**£2**/£5

Photographic in Origin
Posed subjects as above, many hand-tinted, many of Continental origin by anonymous publishers .. .. 50p/**75p**/£1.50
Cards of British origin .. .. 50p/**75p**/£1.50
  British publishers of the above include Carlton Pub. Co., Corona Pub. Co. (Blackpool), Ettlinger, Hey, E. J. & Co., Schwerdtfeger, Wildt & Kray.

■131a

Whitfort series 103. The wrestler G. Hackenschmidt in cheese-cake pose. Period 2 .. .. £2

> *Remember that the arrangement of this catalogue is alphabetical—both in main section arrangement and in sub-divisions within the main sections.*

GREETINGS/HOLIDAYS

One of the most under-estimated categories of postcard collecting, this section contains examples of some of the printer's finest work.

Some of the best postcard illustrators designed greetings or had their general designs over-printed with seasonal messages.

Because many of the Greetings cards refer to public holidays, the genre is often known as HOLIDAYS in the USA, and merges or overlaps with COMMEMORATIVE and PATRIOTIC in many cases. As transatlantic trading increases, more of these colourful, often amusing, postcards are now becoming available and collected in Britain.

See also NOVELTY where several types of greetings cards are described.

AMERICAN GREETINGS/HOLIDAYS/PATRIOTICS

Several festivals and holidays are celebrated more in America than in Europe, with resultant appropriate greetings postcards.

Decoration Day/Memorial Day (April)

Anniversary of the end of the US Civil War; a day when the fallen heroes' graves are decorated with flowers. Many Period 2 cards in this category show strong Northern (Union) or Southern (Confederate) sympathies.

Ground Hog Day (2 February)

The day when the hibernating ground hog would emerge if the weather promised to be mild.

Hallowe'en (31 October) ■132a

A European celebration, now more enthusiastically observed in the New World. Themes are black cats, candles, broomsticks and witches, pumpkin lanterns, etc.

Independence Day (4 July)

When America ceased to be a British Colony! Themes include scenes from the War of Independence, the US flag and other patriotic symbols, and characters like Betsy Ross, Miss Liberty, Paul Revere, Uncle Sam, etc.

Jewish New Year (September) (*Rosh Hashana*)

Themes include family devotional and feasting scenes. Synagogue and Rabbi scenes. A sought after category

Labor Day (September)

A Public Holiday, adopted in 1894. Themes include parades and various workers and working scenes, workers on holiday.

Lincoln's Birthday (12 February)

Portraits of the great President, with flags and other patriotic symbols, scenes from his life and 'martyrdom'. Highest values are for the centenary of his birth in 1909, particularly the 'Open Book' series published by Anglo-American.

Rally Day ■132b

Sent by chapels, churches, Sunday Schools to encourage children to attend. Themes include various places of worship, often incorporating a religious text.

St. Patrick's Day (17 March)

Themes include Irish symbols like harps, shamrocks, and phrases like *Erin-go-bragh* (Ireland for Ever) and *Cead Mile Failte* (A hundred thousand welcomes), Irish types, etc. Green is the predominant colour!

Thanksgiving Day (November)

Favourite themes are family feasts, Pilgrim Fathers, Turkeys, etc.

■132a

Pub. Tuck. Hallowe'en Postcard Series. No. 150. PU *1908* £1.50

■132b

Rally Day. Message on back: from a Washington DC Sunday School. PU *1931* 75p

Washington's Birthday (22 February)
Portraits of the great President, with flags and other patriotic symbols, scenes from his life, cherry trees, etc.

Artists of the above include: Banks, E. C.; Beck, Charles; Brundage, Frances; Chapman, Cyrus; Clapsaddle, Ellen; Griggs, H. B.; Schmucker, Samuel; Wall, Bernhardt; Wiederseim, Grace.
Higher values are for the better artists and the highly embossed, decorated examples.
Price range .. .. 75p/**£3**/£6

Publishers of the above include: Anglo-American Co.; Bien, Julius; Birn Bros., London; Brown & Bigelow; Gabriel, Samuel; Illus. P. C. Co.; International Art Co.; Lounsbury; Nash, E.; Taggart; Tuck; Ullman; Winsch.
Price range .. .. 75p/**£3**/£6

APRIL FOOL/POISSON D'AVRIL
A day celebrated more on the postcard in France than any other country, with their 'April Fish' jokes.
April Fool. Various British publishers
.. .. –/**50p**/75p
Poisson d'Avril. Various French publishers
.. .. 50p/**75p**/£1

BIRTHDAY
Add a premium to the following prices for the work of well-known artists, according to their general valuation.

Period 1/Early Period 2 UB
Chromolithographed artist signed, some-
    times embossed .. .. £1/**£3**/£5
Chromolithographed unsigned, sometimes
    embossed. ■133a .. .. .. 75p/**£2**/£4

Periods 2, 3
Artist drawn .. .. 50p/**75p**/£1.50
Appliquéd, embossed, gilded, silvered, tin-
    selled, etc. .. .. 50p/**75p**/£1.50
Others .. .. –/**50p**/75p

Periods 4, 5
For specified ages/friends/members of
    family .. .. –/**50p**/75p
Photographic, often with deckle edges or
    embossed edges, sometimes hand-tinted
.. .. **50p**
Others .. .. –/**50p**/75p

Publishers of the above include Birn Bros., Carlton Pub. Co., Davidson Bros., Ettlinger, Hildesheimer, Millar & Lang, Philco, Rotary, Schwerdtfeger, Stewart & Woolf, Stiebel, Tuck, Valentine, Wildt & Kray, and many un-named Continental publishers.

CHRISTMAS ■133b
Values and publishers as for 'Birthday' above. Themes include angels, animals, bells, children, food and drink, robins, Santa Claus (*qv*), religious subjects, snow scenes, etc.

■133a

Pub. Tuck. 'Art' postcard. Birthday Greetings. Photochromed in Prussia, beautifully embossed and gilded. PU *1908* £3

■133b

Pub. Wildt & Kray. Artist Ellen Clapsaddle. Christmas greeting. PU *1924* £2

EASTER

Values and publishers as for 'Birthday' above. Themes include angels, chickens, flowers, rabbits, religious subjects.

FAITH, HOPE & CHARITY

Often known as 'FHC' or 'The Virtues'. Some beautiful series on this theme of Victorian/Edwardian virtues exist, often extending to Innocence, Patience, Prudence, Purity and others.

Artist drawn, signed. ■66c .. .. 50p/**75p**/£2
Artist drawn, unsigned .. .. .. –/**50p**/75p

GENERAL GOOD WISHES

Values and publishers as for 'Birthday' above. Themes include Forget-me-not, friendship, hearty greetings, kind thoughts, 'sorry', 'write to me', etc.

GREETINGS FROM/GRUSS AUS/ SOUVENIR DE *see* EARLY CARDS

HANDS ACROSS THE SEA

Type of card which came into prominence with the wave of emigrations to the Commonwealth and other countries in early Period 2. They are amongst the most colourful and exuberant postcards printed. They show clasped hands, means of transport and national symbols.

Publishers include Birn Bros., Ettlinger, Gross, E. D. (New York), Heal, Wm. (New York), Millar & Lang (many colourful series) ■134a, Rotary, Schwerdtfeger, Taylor, A. & C., Thridgould, John (at least 36 designs), Valentine, Vertigen, Wildt & Kray, Woolstone Bros.

Price range .. .. 75p/**£1.50**/£2

LARGE LETTER

Alphabet Series

Actresses with *Art Nouveau*/Fantasy letters
 .. .. 50p/**75p**/£1.50
Multi-Baby Alphabets .. .. .. 50p/**75p**/£1
Musterschutz (Ger. Pub.) *Art Nouveau*/Children/Fantasy/Females. Period 2. Per set of 26 .. .. £35/**£50**/£70
Photo Printing & Pub. Co. ABC postcards.
 ■134b .. .. 75p/**£1**/£2
Rotary Photo Co. .. .. 50p/**75p**/£1
Others .. .. 50p/**75p**/£1

Calendar Cards

Various designs, incl. New Year
 .. .. 50p/**75p**/£1.50

Dates

The year, often with New Year greetings.
 Various designs .. .. 75p/**£1**/£1.50
25 December (Premium if posted on that date)
1 January (Premium if posted on that date)
The Year (e.g. 1909)
 Various designs .. .. .. .50p/**75p**/£1.50

Days of Week

Birn Bros. series .. .. 75p/**£1**/£1.50
Others .. .. 50p/**75p**/£1

Leap Year

Various comic series .. .. 50p/**75p**/£1.50

Mizpah

'God be with you till we meet again'. Various designs .. .. –/**50p**/75p

■134a

Pub. Millar & Lang. 'Hands Across the Sea'. Period 2 .. .. £2

■134b

Pub. Photo Printing & Pub. Co. Alphabet Card 'T for Tailor'. PU *1909* £2

Names
Made up of flowers, photomontages of actresses, etc. Various designs
.. .. 50p/**75p**/£1.50

Numbers (1–10, etc.)
Musterschutz (Ger. Pub.) *Art Nouveau/ Children/Fantasy/Females.* Period 2. Per set of 10 .. .. £17.50/**£25**/£30
Others. Per Card .. .. 50p/**£1**/£2

Towns
Made up of photomontages of views, etc. Various designs. ■135a .. ..50p/**£1**/£1.50

MONTHS OF THE YEAR
Many well known artists, from Sydney Carter to Mucha, produced sets of 12 of the months, making this a highly desirable type, especially if the set is complete. Value according to the artist. Per set .. .. £6/**£24**/P/A

MOURNING/SYMPATHY CARDS
To announce a death, or offer sympathy—rare subjects .. ..75p/**£1.50**/£5

NEW YEAR ■135b
Values and publishers as for 'Birthday' above. Themes include angels with trumpets, calendars and dates.

SANTA CLAUS (Father Christmas)
A type much collected in the USA and now being sought after in Britain. The best designs were printed in Germany. Santas come in green and other colours, as well as the traditional red, and US Santas wear a suit rather than the European long robe. Many Santas are given the NOVELTY treatment—with appliqué, embossing, H.T.L. Others are by well known artists. All these factors will add a premium to the prices below.

Tuck were amongst the finest and most prolific of Santa postcard publishers. Other publishers include Langsdorf, Nash, Schwerdtfeger and Winsch.
Period 1/Early Period 2. Highly decorative
.. .. £2/**£5**/£8
Later designs .. ..75p/**£1.50**/£3

SEASONS, THE
Many artists have treated this attractive subject of the 4 Seasons—Spring, Summer, Autumn, Winter. There also exist fine, unsigned sets in distinct *Art Deco* or *Art Nouveau* style.
Artist signed—value according to artist. Per set .. .. £8/**£30**/PA

Well-designed, unsigned sets. Per set
.. .. £4/**£12**/£20
Others. Per card .. .. 50p/**£2**/£3

VALENTINES
Comic Designs
Artist drawn, value according to artist
.. ..75p/**£1.50**/£3
Photographic origin .. .. .. –/**50p**/75p

Sentimental
Early chromolithographic, embossed, etc.
.. .. £1/**£2**/£4
Later designs .. .. 50p/**75p**/£1

WEDDING GREETINGS AND CONGRATULATIONS
Rarely seen on postcards, and then usually in Period 4.
Early, good quality productions .. £1/**£1.50**/£3
Later designs .. .. –/**50p**/75p

■135a

Pub. Hodges, Birmingham. Greetings from Birmingham. PU *1905* 75p

■135b

Pub. Giesen Bros. Embossed, coloured New Year card. Period 2 .. .. £1.50

HISTORICAL/MILITARY/ TRADITIONAL

This section deals with cards whose subject matter is, in the main, historical rather than contemporary. Thus, for example, the military cards here are those featuring uniforms, traditions and past battles—like Agincourt. Cards that reflect events or conflicts contemporary to themselves may be found under COMMEMORATIVE and WAR respectively. Thus, photo-origin cards are of minor interest except, perhaps, where there are strong topographical connections such as with local publishers cards of pageants. Valuations may then be more appropriate under the SOCIAL HISTORY/ TOPOGRAPHICAL heading. The major specialist British publisher of military cards was Gale & Polden, although Tucks produced hundreds of titles. Artists who stand out in this field are Richard Caton-Woodville, Harry Payne and Reginald Phillimore (*see* ARTISTS). Particularly splendid chromo-litho cards were produced in Italy from around 1890 carrying the flags and battle honours of military regiments and these are currently attracting attention.

ARTISTS

Caton-Woodville, Richard† .. .. £1/**£1.50**/£2
Ibbetson, Ernest† (*see also* Gale & Polden
   under 'Publishers' below) .. .. £1.50/**£2**/£4
McNeil, J. (*see also* Gale & Polden under
   'Publishers' below) .. .. .. £1.50/**£2**/£4
Payne, Harry† ■136a .. .. .. £2/**£3**/£4
Phillimore, Reginald P. (who both drew and
   published his own cards, and some 700
   different designs have been identified.
   Many of these are named as the 'Historical Series' and concentrate upon
   churches, castles and cathedrals, etc. To
   the central design Phillimore usually
   added a small historical cameo. Local
   publishers issued the designs as the
   'Phillimore' series) (*see also* ARTISTS for
   checklist) .. .. £1/**£2**/£3

FOREIGN

French

Military figures published by L'H (probably
   L'Hirondelle) of Paris. Cards are numbered and initialled, 'P.K.' At least 40
   cards. .. .. £1.50/**£2**/£5.50
Others .. .. 50p/**75p**/£1

Italian

Period 1. Chromo-litho. UB.		£4/**£6**/£8
Period 2. Chromo-litho. UB		£2/**£3**/£4
Others		50p/**75p**/£1

PAGEANTS

A pageant consists of dramatic scenes enacted by local (usually amateur) performers. They are connected with local history and probably most major towns have staged one at some time. This listing does not claim to be exhaustive, but it does reflect a sampling of what might be found readily. Feasts, processions and tattoos are included in this general category. Most pageants of postcard interest were held during Period 2 and values tend to be modest unless the cards are photographic with a strong topographical content, in which case they should be valued as Social History.

Bath (1909). Pub. Lewis Bros. & R. Wilkinson	–/**50p**/75p
Bradford	–/**50p**/75p
Bury St. Edmunds (1908)	50p/**75p**/£1
Carlisle (1928). Pub. Tassell	**50p**
Chelsea (1908)	–/**50p**/75p
Chester (1908)	**50p**
Chester (1910)	**50p**
Chester (1926). Official pub. Phillipson & Golder	**50p**
Colchester. Real Photos. Pub. Rogers, Colchester	50p/**75p**/£1
Ditto. Others	**50p**
Coventry (1907)	**50p**
Dover (1908). Official pub. W. H. Smith. Series with official device on picture side	–/**50p**/75p
Ditto. Others	**50p**
English Church (1908). Official pub. Rotary	**50p**

■136a
Artist Harry Payne. Pub. Tuck—Oilette series 9884. The Gordon Highlanders £3

Festival of Empire, Crystal Palace (1911).
Official pub. Bemrose & Sons. Artist
series .. .. 50p/**75p**/£1
Ditto. Photo series .. .. 75p/**£1**/£1.50
Gloucester (1908). Official pub.
Debenhams .. .. –/**50p**/75p
Liverpool. Official pub. G. G. Walmsley,
Liverpool. Series with official device on
picture side. 12 cards. ■137a .. 75p/**£1**/£1.50
Ditto. Others .. .. –/**50p**/75p
Madame Tusaud's (1922). Pub. Tussaud's
.. .. –/**50p**/£1
Newcastle on Tyne (1931). Official pub. R.
Johnstone & Sons Ltd **50p**
Oxford (1907) Official pub. Tuck, e.g. Oilette
series (each of 6 cards) Nos. 9516, 9517, 9518.
Artists include Bowley, Finnemore, Ludovici.
Series with official heraldic device on picture
side .. .. 50p/**75p**/£1
Pub. George Davis. Oxford Pageant Series
.. .. **50p**
Pageant of Empire (1924). Pub. Campbell
& Gray **50p**
Pageant of Wales (1909). Official pub. F. G.
Pawsey & Co. .. .. 50p/**75p**/£1
Porchester (1907). .. .. 50p/**75p**/£1
Reigate (1913). .. .. –/**50p**/75p
Romsey (1907). .. .. 50p/**75p**/£1
Runnymeade (1934). Official pub. Fleetway
.. .. 50p/**75p**/£1
St. Albans (1907). Official pub. Tuck.
Artist R. E. Groves.
Series with official device on picture
side .. .. 75p/**£1**/£1.50
Others .. .. 50p/**75p**/£1
Scarborough (1912). Official pub. Sarony
.. .. –/**75p**/£1
Sheffield (1906). Empire Day. Pub.
Chadwick & Allan .. .. 75p/**£1**/£1.25
Sherborne (1905) Pub. R. Wilkinson &
Co. **50p**
Warwick (1906). Pub. Water Colour Post
Card Co. .. .. 75p/**£1**/£1.50
Others .. .. –/**50p**/75p
Winchester (1908). Pub. Gandey –/**50p**/75p
York (1908). Official pub. C. & G.
Walmsley .. .. –/**50p**/£1

PERSONALITIES

Covers Kings and Queens (*see* 'Publishers' Tuck
below) and famous figures, as well as unnamed
individuals (listed as 'Poses') whose purpose may
have been only to display a uniform. Photo-origin
cards are of interest in the latter case but value
usually depends upon artistic and printing quality
rather than subject. *See also* ART REPRODUC-
TIONS.
Abraham Lincoln .. .. .. 50p/**75p**/£1
Drake .. .. –/**50p**/70p
Joan of Arc **50p**
Napoleon .. .. –/**50p**/70p
Nelson (*see also* Gale & Polden under
'Publishers' below) .. .. –/**50p**/75p
Poses—photo type. ■138a .. 50p/**70p**/£1.25
Wellington **50p**
Others **50p**

PUBLISHERS

The major specialist publisher in this field is Gale
& Polden.

Gale & Polden

Badge series. Gold border. About 120
cards .. .. 50p/**£1**/£2
British Army (History & Traditions) series. UB.
120 cards in Period 2. Welsh Guards added in
Period 3. First issues unnumbered. Artists
J.McNeil & Ernest Ibbotson.
No. 1–31 Cavalry .. .. .. £2/**£3**/£4
Nos. 32–104 Infantry. ■138b .. £2/**£2.50**/£3
Nos. 105–117 Corps .. .. £1.50/**£2**/£3
Lord Kitchener .. .. .. £1/**£2**/£2.50
Sir John French .. .. .. £1/**£1.50**/£2
King George V .. .. .. £1/**£1.50**/£2
Military Mail .. .. £3/**£4**/£5
Nelson series .. .. 50p/**£1**/£1.50

Recruiting cards. Regimental recruiting
offices used G & P cards picturing their
Regiment but changed the text to give
details of rates of pay. Many such cards
were not postcards. We refer only to
postcards printed for HMSO. ■138c
.. .. £8/**£10**/£12

■137a

*Pub. G. G. Walmsley, Liverpool. Period 2.
Liverpool Pageant—King John handing down the
Charter* £1.50

Wellington series. Inset photo-origin cameo views with surrounding artistic military design. UB .. .. £2/**£3**/£4
Others .. .. 50p/**75p**/£1

Jarrold & Son Ltd.
Pageant series and others .. 50p/**75p**/£1

Knight Bros.
Chromo-litho Regimental series .. 75p/**£1**/£1.25

Salmon, J.
Various historical and military artist-drawn designs (incl. A. R. Quinton) .. 50p/**75p**/£1

Tuck
Empire series 664. B & w. UB. ■138d
.. .. 75p/**£1**/£1.50
History & Tradition series .. .. –/**50p**/75p

Kings & Queens of England (*see also* COLLECTIONS).
Series 614—12 cards .. .. .. £4/**£6**/£8
Series 615—12 cards .. .. .. £4/**£6**/£8
Series 616—12 cards .. .. .. £4/**£6**/£8
Series 617—1 card (6 variations) £4/**£6**/£8

Our Army/Our Navy. Oilettes .. **50p**
Our Generals. Series 68. UB .. .. £1/**£2**/£3

Valentine
The Kings Army. Artotype series.■138e
.. .. –/**50p**/75p

OTHER HISTORICAL INTEREST
Price **50p**

■138a
Pub. Rotary. Period 2. Series 3518. 'Soldiers of the King'. Corporal of the Life Guards .. £1.25

■138b
Artist Ernest Ibbetson. Pub. Gale & Polden. Period 2. British Army 'History & Traditions' series. Royal Irish Rifles. No. 97 .. .. £2.50

■138c
Pub. Gale & Polden for HMSO. Period 2. Recruiting card for the Middlesex Regiment giving Rates of Pay £10

■138d
Pub. Tuck. Period 2. Empire series 664. Photo-origin b & w. Our Indian Army. UB .. £1.50

■138e
Pub. Valentines. Period 2. Artotype series. The King's Army 1415 Agincourt 50p

LITERARY/MUSICAL

ARTISTIC REPRESENTATIONS
† = *see also* ARTISTS *for more details.*

Alice in Wonderland/Through the Looking Glass
Pub. Black, A. & C. Artist Charles Folkard†. Series of Songs from *Alice in Wonderland* and *Through the Looking Glass*. Period 4 .. .. .. £1.50/**£2**/£2.50

Pub. Faulkner, C. W. Artist Kathleen Nixon†. Series 1819 set of 6 *Alice* cards. Period 4 .. .. £1/**£2**/£3

Pub. Fuller & Richard. Artist Tenniel. Reproductions of his original illustrations for *Alice*. Set of 8 cards (1910) £1/**£2**/£3

Pub. King, Gerald M. Twenty-one cards reproduced from his book, *Alice through the Pillar Box*, all hand stamped and designed. Period 7. The set .. **£20**

Pub. Guinness. Set of advertising cards with re-written episodes from *Alice*. Period 4 .. ..75p/**£1**/£1.50

Pub. Lester, Leslie. Artist Mendoza. Set of 6 *Alice* cards by permission of Walt Disney. Period 6 .. .. £1/**£1.50**/£2

Pub. Merrimack. Reprints of Tenniel's illustrations for *Alice*. Period 7 **50p**

Pub. R.P.S. Series. Artist Studdy†. *Alice in Wonderland* dog .. .. .. £1/**£2**/£3

Pub. Salmon, J. Artist Flora White†. Series No. 1472 .. .. 50p/**75p**/£1.50

Pub. Savory Ltd. Cheshire Cat with *Alice* quotation. Period 2 .. .. ..75p/**£1**/£1.25

Pub. Post Office 1979 Year of the Child 13p stamp—scene from *Alice* (PHQ 37d) **25p**

Andersen, Hans
Pub. Henderson. Illustrated Fairy Tales. Artist Sydney Carter†. Period 2 .. ..50p/**£1**/£1.50

Burns, Robert
Pub. Art Pub. Co. Burns Souvenir cards. Period 2 .. ..75p/**£1**/£1.25

Pub. Johnston W. & A. K. Several series of Burns sets from 1902 .. .. —/**50p**/75p

Pub. Stoddart & Co. Burns Pictorial series Period 2 .. .. **50p**

Pub. Tuck. Oilette series 7703, 7694 (1918) .. .. 50p/**75p**/£1

Byron, Lord
Pub. Tuck. Oilette series 2750 (1918) .. .. 50p/**75p**/£1

Dickens, Charles
Pub. Beagles. Centenary of Dickens' birth (1912) .. .. £2/**£3**/£4

Pub. Cassell & Co. Character Sketches from Dickens. Artist Frederick Barnard. Three sets of 6 (1904) .. .. .. 50p/**75p**/£1

Pub. Chapman & Hall. Set of 13 cards reproducing monthly parts of Dickens' novels (1905) .. .. .. 50p/**75p**/£1

Pub. Hildesheimer. B & w Dickens characters. Artist E. F. Manning UB .. —/**50p**/75p

Pub. Jones, A. V. N. Dickens Characters. Artist Frank Reynolds .. .. £1/**£2**/£3

Pub. London Stereoscopic Co. Set of 12 cards illustrating the production of The Only Way (adaptation of *Tale of Two Cities*) (*see also* John Hassall poster advertisement for David Allen in THEATRE) .. .. —/**50p**/75p

Pub. Stewart & Woolf. Dickens' Characters. 3 sets by Artist Alfred Crowquill (1902) .. ..75p/**£1**/£1.25

Pub. Tuck. At least 15 series of 'In Dickens Land' Oilettes (from 1903) .. 50p/**75p**/£1

Ditto. 'With Famous Authors and Painters' (1918). Eight Dickens sets .. 50p/**75p**/£1

■139a

Pub. Tuck. Artist Joseph Clayton Clark ('Kyd').
Characters from Charles Dickins, 'Mr. Stiggins'.
UB *chromolithograph. Early Period 2* **£3**

Pub. Valentine. Several series of Dickens designs. Period 2 .. .. .. –/**50p**/75p

For the many fine series of Dickens characters by Artist Joseph Clayton Clark ('Kyd'), *see* ARTISTS. ■139a

Fairy Tales

Pub. Anon. (Dutch). Artist Kirchbach. Col. Princess and the Pea .. .. 50p/**75p**/£1

Pub. Tuck. 'Art' Nos. 3471/3/5. Puss in Boots, Hansel & Gretel, Little Red Riding Hood, Little Snowhite, etc. Period 2
.. ..75p/**£1**/£1.50

Others .. .. –/**50p**/75p

Hardy, Thomas

Pub. Tuck. Oilette series 7700, 7755, 7763 (1918) .. .. 50p/**75p**/£1

Jerome, Jerome K.

Pub. Blum & Degen. 'Three Men in a Boat' series with Jerome seal of approval on reverse (1907). .. ..75p/**£1.50**/£2

Lorna Doone

Pub. Photochrom 'Celesque'. Scenes from Lorna Doone. Period 2 .. .. 50p/**75p**/£1

Pub. Valentine. Characters from Lorna Doone. Period 2 .. .. .. –/**50p**/75p

Various scenes from 'Lorna Doone Country', etc. **50p**

Milton

Pub. Tuck. Oilette Series 7039, 7420/1 (1918) .. .. 50p/**75p**/£1

One Thousand and One Nights

Kunstlerkarten Series 1102 (Ger). *Marchen aus 1001 Nacht*. Artist Mackott. Beautiful col. series. UB. PU 1900. Titles include Aladin, Sinbad the Sailor, Scheherzerade (*sic*) .. .. .. £1/**£2**/£4

Pilgrim's Progress

Pub. Religious Tract Soc. Four sets of 6 by Artist Harold Copping† (1911) 75p/**£1**/£2

Scott, Sir Walter

Pub. Hildesheimer. Sketches from Scott. Artist Sydney Carter†. Period 2
.. ..50p/**£1**/£1.50

Pub. Ritchie & Sons. Home & Haunts of Sir Walter Scott. Artist J. Douglas (1906)
.. .. 50p/**75p**/£1

Pub. Ritchie & Sons. Comic characters from Sir Walter Scott (1907) .. .. 50p/**75p**/£1

Pub. Valentine. Scenes from Scott –/**50p**/75p

Shakespeare, William (*see also* THEATRE)

Pub. Collins, Wm. Shakespeare characters in sepia by Artist Dudley Hardy†. Period 2 .. .. £1/**£1.50**/£2

Pub. Faulkner, C. W. 'Shakespeare Series'. Superb UB chromolithographed £1/**£2**/£4

Pub. Hildesheimer. Sketches from Shakespeare. Artist Sydney Carter. Period 2 .. ..50p/**£1**/£1.50

Pub. Lyon, Wm. Set of ping-pong cards with titles from Shakespeare. Period 2
.. .. 50p/**75p**/£1.50

Pub. Nister. ■140a. Scenes from Shakespeare. Superb col. UB chromolithographs .. .. £1/**£2**/£4

Pub. Nister. Later series divided backs
.. ..75p/**£1.50**/£3

Pub. Stewart & Woolf. Comic series with Shakespeare quotes UB chromolithographs. ■98b .. .. £1/**£1.50**/£2

Pub. Tuck. Set of 12 cards from *Hamlet* by Artist Harold Copping† (1901) £1/**£2**/£4

Pub. Valentine. Characters from Shakespeare. Several designs. Period 2
.. .. –/**50p**/£1

Thackeray, William Makepeace

Pub. Hildesheimer. Sketches from Thackeray. Artist Sydney Carter. Period 2 .. ..50p/**£1**/£1.50

Pub. Tuck. *Vanity Fair* Oilette series
.. .. 50p/**75p**/£1

■140a

Pub. Nister. 'Jolly Jack Falstaff'. Artist 'H.M.P.' UB. Chromolithograph. Early Period 2 .. .. £4

LITERARY FIGURES

Ger. Series. 1989. Col. Subjects include Burns, Byron, Dickens, Goethe, Longfellow, Schiller, Scott, Tennyson. Two versions exist: one with portrait of author only, the other incorporating a scene as well .. .. £2/**£4**/£6

Grosse Jahrhundert series—*see* COLLECTIONS.

Pub. Abraham, Keswick. Wordsworth and members of his family. Period 2 —/**50p**/75p

Pub. Alcock, K. Knutsford. Mrs. Gaskell, etc. Period 2 .. .. **50p**

Pub. Blum & Degen. Eminent Writers (1899) (Burns, Byron, Dickens, Longfellow, Scott, Shakespeare, Tennyson) .. .. £1/**£2**/£3

Pub. Hildesheimer. Homes of Literary Men. Artist Sydney Carter† .. ..50p/**£1**/£1.50

Pub. Rapid Photo Co. Photographs of authors, war correspondents, etc. Period 2. ■141a .. .. .. 50p/**75p**/£1

Pub. Rotary. Charles Dickens, etc. **50p**

Pub. Smith, H.J. Charles Dickens, etc. (1903) .. .. —/**50p**/75p

Pub. Tuck. Sets of famous poets/writers by Artists Joseph Finnemore, Geo. G. Kilburne, Robert Sauber (1900) .. £1/**£1.50**/£2

Pub. Valentine. Shakespeare, etc. Period 2 .. .. **50p**

Pub. Wrench. Hall Caine, etc. early Period 2 .. .. 50p/**75p**/£1

Others .. .. —/**50p**/£1.50

NEWSPAPER SERIES

Photomontage

These interesting b & w postcards take the form of the front page of a newspaper through which a pretty girl is pushing out. Most major postcard producing countries had their own versions—of local and national newspapers. They are usually found postally used around 1904.

France. *L'Echo de Paris, La Fronde, La Liberté,* etc. Pub. 'S.I.P.' (1903). ■141b .. ..75p/**£1**/£1.50

Germany. *Berliner Illustrirte Zeitung* (1902–1904) .. ..75p/**£1**/£1.50

Deutschezeitung (with Bismarck silhouette) .. .. £1/**£2**/£4

Rigaer Tageblatt. Period 4 .. .. £1.50/**£3**/£5

Great Britain. *Military Mail,* Pub. Gale & Polden (1903). .. .. .. £3/**£4**/£5

Italy. *Il Corriere della Sera, Il Giornale d'Italia, La Lotta, Il Messaggero, La Plebe, Il Trovatore* .. .. .. 75p/**£1**/£2

Peru. *Vanguardia.* Pub. H. Vaz, Frankfurt .. .. 75p/**£1**/£2

Russia. Newspaper in Cyrillic script (1904) .. .. £1.50/**£3**/£4

Other photomontage postcards .. 50p/**75p**/£1

Other Newspaper postcards

Period 1 (1893). London series.

Period 2 (1903). Fr. *Le Carte Journal,* Paris

Period 2 (1905). *Illustrated Daily Postcard*

Price range .. .. 50p/**75p**/£1.50

■141a

Pub. Rapid Photo Co. Mr. A. G. Hales (war correspondent and author). Period 2 .. .. 75p

■141b

Pub. 'S.I.P.'. Newspaper montage, La Liberté (1903) £1

MUSICAL

Bands
Clear pictures of photographic origin with good detail of people, etc.
Brass bands, ■142a
Dance bands
Military bands
Pipe bands
Religious groups' bands
School bands
Others
Price range .. .. 50p/**£1.50**/£3

Bandstands—*see* SOCIAL HISTORY

Comic Musical Cards
Pub. DeLittle, Fenwick & Co. Songs and Singers. Period 2 .. .. .. 50p/**75p**/£1
Pub. Moss, Henry & Co. Musical Terms up to Date. Artist P. V. Bradshaw†
.. .. £2/**£4**/£6
Pub. Ponajowski, E. Humorous Musical Series in Write-Away style. Period 2
.. .. 75p/**£1**/£1.50
Various publishers. Various artists, signed and unsigned. Value according to artist, period, etc. .. .. 50p/**75p**/£3

Composers
Pub. Ackerman, Munich. Tonkünstler Silhouetten Series (Composers' Silhouettes) Artist W. Bithorn. Period 2 .. £1/**£2**/£3
Pub. Blum & Degen. Musical Composers (1899) .. .. £1/**£2**/£3
Pub. Brüder Köhn. Col. series by Artist Ulreich (1908) .. .. .. £1/**£2**/£3
Pub. Gerstmayer, J. Col series by Artist O. Elsner of Schubert Lieder. Period 2.
.. .. £1/**£2**/£3
Pub. J. B. B. Fantasy Heads of Composers. Period 2 ■142b .. .. .. £10/**£20**/£30
Pub. *La Revue Musicale.* Paris. Portraits of Rimsky Korsakov, etc. by Lebedoff. Period 4 .. .. 75p/**£1**/£2
Pub. Philipp & Kramer. Tondichter (Composer) Series XXVII. Artist Percy N. F. Hedley .. .. £2/**£4**/£5
Pub. Rotary. Composers and Music
.. .. –/**50p**/75p
Others .. .. –/**50p**/£1.50

Concerts
Clear pictures of photographic origin with good detail of people.
Indoor views .. .. –/**50p**/75p
Exterior views .. .. .. 50p/**75p**/£1.50

Conductors
Big Band .. .. 50p/**75p**/£1
Classical orchestras **50p**
Famous names .. .. .. 50p/**75p**/£1

Instruments
Bells/Bell ringing .. .. .. 75p/**£1.50**/£2
Orchestral instruments .. .. –/**50p**/75p
Organs—church .. .. –/**50p**/75p
Organs—cinema .. .. £1/**£2**/£3
Others **50p**

Instrumentalists
Big band bandleaders and musicians (e.g. Count Basie, Bennie Goodman, Glen Miller, Tommy Dorsey, etc.) Periods 4 to 6 .. .. 75p/**£1.50**/£3

■142a
The English members of the famous Waterloo Band, Canada. Period 2 .. ..75p

■142b
Pub. 'J.B.B.'. Fantasy Head of Mozart. Period 2 .. ..£25

Opera

Gilbert & Sullivan. Savoy Co.	£1/**£1.50**/£3
Ditto others	50p/**75p**/£1.50

Madame Butterfly. Rare Early Period 2. Set
of 6. Col. Per set .. .. .. £20/**£35**/£50

Opera Heroines. Early Period 2. Artist
drawn col. vignettes (Ger) .. £2/**£4**/£5

Pub. Breitkoff & Hartel. Series of 60 cards
of Wagner operas, incl. portraits of
conductors, singers, etc. Period 2
.. .. £1/**£1.50**/£5

Pub. Faulkner, C. W. Series of 12 Wagner
operas. Col. Period 2 .. 75p/**£1.50**/£2

Pub. SA Nazionalie del Grammofono,
Milano. Period 4. HMV ads. by Artist
Nanni, incl. Toti dal Monte as 'Lucia di
Lammermoor' .. .. .. £6/**£12**/£18

Pub. Tuck. Period 2. Col. chromo-litho
Wagner series. Nos. 691, 693, 694
.. .. £1/**£2**/£4

Others .. .. –/**50p**/75p

Singers

Cabaret/Concert/Singers (*see also* THEATRE)
(e.g. Dame Clara Butt, Ben Davies, John
McCormack, Edith Piaf, Kennerley Rum-
ford, Charles Trenet, etc.) .. 50p/**£1**/£2

Jazz singers (e.g. Louis Armstrong)
.. .. £1/**£1.50**/£2

Opera singers (e.g. Enrico Caruso*, Feodor
Chaliapin*, Geraldine Farrar, Benjamino
Gigli, Dame Nelly Melba ■143a, Toti dal
Monte, Dame Adelina Patti, Luisa
Tetrazzini, etc.) .. .. .. 75p/**£2.50**/£5

Other singers .. .. –/**50p**/75p

(* = commands the highest price)

Song Cards

Pub. Augener. Little Songs of Long Ago.
Artist Henriette Willebeek Le Mair†
.. .. 50p/**75p**/£1.35

Pub. Bamforth. Several thousand designs. Periods
2 to 4:

Per pair	50p/**75p**/£1.25
Per set of 3	75p/**£1.25**/£2
Per set of 4	£1/**£2**/£3
Single cards	–/**50p**/75p

Pub. Davidson Bros. *See also* COMIC. Many
series by well known artists .. 75p/**£1.50**/£4

Pub. Shamrock. Nearly 400 titles (1908)
.. .. –/**50p**/75p

Pub. Tuck. Many Oilette series .. –/**50p**/75p

Pub. Valentine. Several series of songs
.. .. **50p**

Other pubs.	–/**50p**/£1

National Anthems. Period 3. Patriotics
.. .. –/**50p**/75p

Other National Anthems **50p**

Songs with Musical Notations/Words

Pub. Musical Post Card Syndicate. Musical
Invitations (1903) .. .. 75p/**£1**/£1.50

Pub. Musical Post Card Syndicate. Popular
Songs series .. .. .. –/**50p**/75p

Pub. Reid Bros. Six sets of 6 (1906)
.. .. –/**50p**/75p

Others **50p**

Other Musical Series

Price range .. .. –/**50p**/75p

■143a

*Pub. Rotary. Photographer Reutlinger, Paris.
Madame Melba.* UB. *Early Period 2* £1

Three Band Pricing System

Left Hand Band: *The lowest price you will
probably be asked to pay
for this card.*

Middle Band: *What you will normally
be asked to pay for this
card: its average,
reasonable price.*

Right Hand Band: *The highest price you
will probably be asked to
pay for this card.*

For a full explanation of the system, see
page viii.

LOCAL PUBLISHERS

Following the publication of the first edition of this catalogue, the compilers sought the assistance of Postcard Clubs throughout the country with a view to including a 'Local Publishers' section in this second edition. The response has been so generous and full that it has been impossible to collate all the information in time to print it in this edition in a form that would do justice to its importance. Information is still coming in (and even more would be welcome) and, therefore, it has been decided to make a major new section for Local Publishers in a future edition of the catalogue. At that time full acknowledgement will be made to the many individuals who have kindly supplied listings. Here we wish to record our thanks to those Clubs that have gone to particular trouble to join with us in this research: Canterbury and East Kent; Maidstone; Norfolk; North of England; Northern Ireland; North Wales; Rushden; Pickering & District and Tayside.

It is anticipated that future Local Publisher entries will consist of two parts, as follows:

1. Area Analysis. Listings of (a) Local Publishers and (b) National publishers (and smaller localised publishers not based in the area under consideration) who published cards of the area.

2. Local Publisher Checklists. Details of the cards issued by individual publishers.

Here we give an example under each heading as a guide to what could doubtless be repeated for every town/publisher in the country, and we will be pleased to receive similar details for other areas—however small the list.

The following information was supplied by Paul Harthoorn, Robert Appleton, Roger Amos, Alan Pickup and Terry Hougham.

Area Analysis: Canterbury

Local Publishers
Ackland & Youngman
Austen's Library
Bailey, Frank
Charlton, J. G.
Crow, E. & Son
Field, J.
Fisk-Moore, B. & W.
Fullagar, F.

Goulden, H. J.
Kentish Wholesale Supply Co.
Muir, H. G
Noakes & Co.
Palmer, Fred C.
Parry, J. H.
Parsons, F. J.
Pettit, S. B. & Son
Pierce, Edith
Sinclair & Sons
Snow of Walmer
Teal, S.
Wheeler, Fisk-Moore Ltd.
Wilder, A.

Non-Local Publishers
Arcadia Bazaar Series
'BAC'
Beagles
Bell's (Leigh on Sea)
Black, A. & C.
Boots Cash Chemist
British Mirror Series
Burrow (Cheltenham)
Cornish Riviera Press
Cynicus
Daily News Wallet Guide Series
Davidson Bros.
DeLittle, Fenwick & Co.
Dennis, E. T. W.
'Excel' Series
Faulkner, C. W.
Foto Artistry
Frith & Co.
Gaines of Leeds
G. D. & D.
Gale & Polden
Hartmann
Hildesheimer
Hills of London
Jackson of Grimsby
'JaJa' (Stoddart)
Jarrold
Judges
'LL' (86 identified designs)
London View Co.
Lovering & Co.
Mack, E.
Millar & Lang
Palatine Pictorial
Pencil Sketch Co.
Photochrom
Pictorial Stationery Co.

Rapid Photo Co.
Rotary
SPCK
Salmon, J.
Sargent Bros.
Schwerdtfeger
Scott, Walter
Shoesmith & Etheridge, Hastings
Smith, W. H.
Stengel
Stewart & Woolf
Taylor, A. & G.
Tuck
Valentine's
Vivian Mansell
Walker, J. & Co.
Warren, A. P.
Watercolour P. C. Co.
Weekly Tale Teller
Welch (J. W. S.)
West & Son, Whitstable
Wildt & Kray
Williams, C. G.
Woolstone Bros.
Wrench
Wyndham Series

Local Publisher Checklist: Sydney Smith (1884–1958)

A photographer/publisher who lived and worked in Pickering, Yorkshire. His earliest cards are thought to be a series of three produced in 1909 to record the laying of the foundation stone of the Liberal Club. Over the next 30 or so years he published photo cards recording Pickering events and is a perfect example of a 'Local Publisher' of the type whose works are now sought by collectors and historical societies around the country. The listing below is indicative of the sort of output that most local publishers produced and doubtless could be repeated for towns and villages of any size throughout the land. Sydney Smith's major series and the probable number of cards, where known, are:

1909. Laying the foundation stone of the Liberal Club (3)
1910. Funeral of John Franks (3)
1911. The Coronation (32)
1914. Captain Vane's hounds (3 or more)
1914. Floods (10)
1919. Victory Celebrations (16)
1921/22. Rosedale Hill motor cycle trials (unknown)

1922. Raising of spur flag on the Memorial Hall (2)
1924. Opening of the Memorial Hall (12)
1925. Floods (5 or more)
1927. Floods (33)
1930. Floods (32)
1931. Floods (24)
1931. Visit of Lloyd-George (7 or more)
1932. Floods (9 or more)
1933. Lord Howard opening Goslipgate council houses and sewage works (5 or more)
1933. Pickering from the air (9 or more)
1933. The great blizzard (unknown)
1935. Hailstorm (10)
1935. Jubilee celebrations (32)
1936. Memorial Service for George V (8 or more)
1936. Proclamation of Edward VIII (3 or more)
1936. Queen Mary's Visit (4 or more)
1937. Coronation of George VI (14 or more)
1940. Lord Howard inspects the ARP (13 or more)

In addition to these there are individual cards covering Wesley Day and Remembrance Day Services, the landslide at Riseborough, the visit of Gipsy Smith, the fire at Welburn Hall and 4 cards on the Eastgate accident. Ascribing valuations to cards such as those produced by Sydney Smith is difficult. Local enthusiasts, seeking the elusive missing link to complete a series, would pay high sums. To people with no local interest the cards mean, and would fetch, significantly less. However, the price range here gives within its three bands the lowest price likely to be asked, the average price and what might reasonably be expected to be the highest price.

Price range .. .. 50p/**£1.50**/£10

Readers are cordially invited to send in details to Mr. and Mrs. Holt of cards, series, publishers, artists . . . indeed any relevant information which they may have upon any postcard topic which adds to what appears in this edition. All correspondence addressed to them at the publishers will be answered and all contributions will be formally acknowledged in the next edition.

MODERN CARDS

The Postcards Produced During Period 7

Although it remains true that more collectors appreciate modern cards in France than do in Britain, the compilers have had many requests to expand this section. Certainly interest is growing, and 1980 saw a spate of modern productions. Collectors are now extending their thematic collections throughout all the seven periods, and interesting postcards on current events and political themes are now being produced in the USA and the UK. The large size of many of the new cards prevents them fitting into the standard modern albums, which has deterred many from collecting them. However, albums are now being produced (*see* ACCESSORIES) which hold all but the largest, and some publishers, with collectors' tastes in mind, are now producing normal size postcards.

There has also been a visible trend in the past two years to re-establish the original dynamism of the postcard: to use cards again for advertising, to make social and political points, to commemorate events as varied as Royal milestones like the Queen Mother's 80th Birthday to current events like the Egypt–Israel Peace Treaty. It is not commercially viable to produce postcards today to the high quality printing standards of the Golden Age. Some publishers have experimented with limited editions designed specifically for the serious collector, commissioning talented contemporary artists and using high quality production methods and materials. As yet this trend has achieved a limited success.

Because of the low price of most modern postcards—which makes them particularly attractive and interesting to new and young collectors, and to those on a small budget—they attract a low profit margin, and many dealers do not stock them. However, some can be found in specialist retail shops and are advertised in the postcard and philatelic press.

A selection of some of the most interesting and collectable issues of Period 7 (some of which started in Period 6) are listed below.

Where one price only is quoted, that is the current standard retail price.

Athena B.
Pub. Pip Barker. Limited Edition. Grounding of the ship on Brighton Beach (1980). **25p**

BIPEX 79
Card issued as a season ticket. Cost price £1.50. All cards numbered. .. **50p**

Carousel Limited Editions
Standard size, number printed in brackets.
Nos. 1–4. Bath subjects (1250) **50p**
No. 5. SS *Great Britain* (1250) .. **£1**
No. 6. 1977. 50th Anniversary of *King George V* railway engine (approx 1250) **75p**
No. 7. 1977. Fleet Review (4500) **£1**
No. 8. 1977. HM Victory Silver Jubilee (2500) **40p**
No. 9. 1977. World Hot Air Balloon Championships. Released 1980 (under 1000) **35p**
No. 10. 150th Anniversary of *The Rocket*/ Liverpool & Manchester Rly. (under 1000) **35p**
Nos. 11/20. Giants of Steam. Set of 10 (1000) per set **£1.75**
No. 21. 1980. 16–19 November. Lombard RAC Rally (1000) **35p**
All the cards are designed and published by Michael Dummer.

Collector Cards/Pamlin prints ■147a
Produced in Croydon by Kenneth Carr, a collector of historic photography, to make interesting items from his collection available to students and enthusiasts of social history through good quality reproductions. The first card—No M1—'The Centenary of Croydon's Trams' was issued in 1966. Since then 2900 cards have been published, 1250 issues being currently in print, with many popular issues being reprinted and new titles constantly being added. Print runs vary from 250 to 1000. The major series (with the number of titles in each in brackets) are as follows:
Aircraft (100)
Bikes and Motorbikes (30)
Canals and Rivers (30)
Commercial Vehicles (30)
Docks and Harbours (30)
Ferries & Chain Ferries (25)
Fire Engines (30)
Historic Advertisements (30)
Historic Buses/Trolleybuses (200)
Literature (20)

Motor Cars (30)
Piers (30)
Pop Artists/Film Stars (30)
Railway
 Steam subjects (200)
 General (200)
Ships (100)
Sport (20)
Theatre History (25)
Topographical
 Old England (1000)
 Old Wales (100)
 Old Scotland (20)
 Old Paris (20)
 Contemporary (300)
Trams (200)
War (30)
Current retail price per card **12p**

Coral-Lee Postcards ■147b
Published in the USA by retired schoolmistress
Coralie Sparre and printed by Mike Roberts,
these are interesting, imaginative and well pro-
duced postcards. Themes are in the current event,
entertainment and political fields, many in sets of
12.
Mount St. Helen Eruption. Set of 12 **£2**
Personalities. Groucho Marx, Bob Hope etc.
 Set of 12 .. .. **£2**
Pope John Paul's Visit to USA. Set of
 12 .. .. **£2**
Popular Entertainers
Olivia Newton John, Cat Stevens, Led
 Zeppelin, etc. Sets of 12 .. .. **£2**
Elvis Presley. Set of 5 .. .. .. **£1.25**
President Carter
Inauguration/First 100 Days/End of First
 Year/End of Second Year/End of Third
 Year. All sets of 12 .. .. .. **£2**
The Carter Family/Friends: Amy, Billy, Bert
 Lance, Miss Lilian, Rosalynn, etc. **15p**
Presidents Ford, Nixon, Reagan .. **15p**
US Bicentennial. Two sets of 12—one
 normal size, one oversize **75p**
(*Prices are per set.*)

Dalkeith 1000 Series ■147c

Big Four Railway Museum, Bournemouth
Attractively designed sets of 6, each limited to
1000 and presented in an ornate, numbered
envelope.

No. 1. (1–6) Liverpool & Manchester Rly.
 Col. Line drawings of train, plus design
 on reverse. Per set **£1.20**
 (6a) Extra card of Royal Mail Coach
 .. .. **20p**
No. 2 (7–12) Somerset & Dorset Joint
 Rly. Sepia pictures of trains with
 ornate pale blue heading and company
 crest. Per set **£1.20**

■147a
*Pub. Pamlin Prints. 'The Beatles'. Collector-Pop
C8501. Period 7* 12p

■145b
*Pub. Coral-Lee. Photo David Burnett. The
Reagans visit the Carters at the White House
shortly after the US Presidental Election 1980*
.. ..12p

■147c
*Pub. Dalkeith. 1000 Series. Liverpool &
Manchester Rly. Period 7* 20p

147

No. 3 (13–18) Stratford-upon-Avon & Midland Junction Rly. Blue tinted photo. views on pink background with map. Per set **£1.20**

More sets are planned in this series.

Dutch Royalty 1980

Abdication of Queen Juliana .. **15p**
Accession of Queen Beatrix **15p**

London Transport

Reproductions of London Transport Posters
■148a

Two hundred and fifty designs have been produced, of which only about 10 are un-numbered. This is a most interesting and attractive series, which, if it were not for their over-large size (ranging from 15 × 9.5 cm to 17 × 10.5 cm) would be more popular with collectors.

Following in the great poster tradition of Cheret, Lautrec and Mucha, London Transport's policy has been to produce, first and foremost, works of art. The contrasting styles represented in the long series range from the conservatively traditional to the *avant-garde*. The postcard reproductions form a fascinating panorama of the London scene and the best of contemporary art from John Hassall (1908), through M. Lawrence (1912), Mabel Lucie Attwell (1913), G. McKnight Kauffer (1922 to 1928), Alfred Leete (1928), Abraham Games (1937) to a talented collection of modern artists. These include Hans Unger (whom London Transport were amongst the first to commission after WW2), Carol Barker, Tom Eckersley, John Farleigh, Harry Stevens, Betty Swanwick, etc.

The subjects, too, are interesting and varied—from London's art galleries, buildings, monuments, museums, parks, special exhibitions, 'Types' to suburban scenes. The range is so wide it imposed no limits on the artists' imagination.

Price range **5p–15p**
Recent printing of 12 of the titles by Camden Graphics, stocked by London Transport Museum **15p**

National Railway Museum Series
Twelve cards of famous engines from 1928–1936 printed by Camden Graphics
.. .. **15p**

Transport Postcards
A series of 56 (intermittently numbered 1–67) photographic and artist drawn postcards depicting buses, trams and trollies.

■148a

Pub. London Transport. Reprint of 1969 poster by Hans Unger. Tower of London. No. 195. Period 7 .. .. 10p

■148b

Pub. Harenberg Kommunikation. Reprint of Period 2 postcard 'Snapshots from this Town'. Period 7 .. .. 20p

Thirty-six are currently stocked by the Museum **10p**
Uncut sheet of these 36 cards .. **£2.99**

Eric Maylin
Attractive and well printed reproductions from the illustrations for a German series of books on Ephemera published by Harenberg Kommunikation of Dortmund. The following series were taken from original postcards and are reproduced in 'Continental' (o/s) size:

008 *Jugendstilpostkarten* 1. (col.)
From Viennese *Art Nouveau/Art Deco* designs
009 A further selection as above
023 *Reklame Postkarten* (col.)
Advertising postcards from *c.* 1900

025 *Der Kuss* (col.)
'The Kiss' as depicted by postcard artists
032 *Herzlichen Glueckwunsch* 1 (col.)
German greetings postcards of Period 2
033 A further selection as above
037 *Bitte recht Freundlich* (col.) ∎148b
'Smile Please', postcards with a camera theme
039 *Angeberpostkarten* (col.)
Tall stories/boasts
046 *Riesen, Zwerge, Schauobjekte* (col.)
Freaks, etc. from Period 2
052 Playgirls von Damals
'Postcards our Grandfathers thought daring'
055 *Potztausend, die Liebe* (col.)
Postcards of love and the erotic. Period 1
156 *Die Liebe Lust* (col.)
From erotic French lithographs
Price range (per card) **20p–25p**

'FAGA' (Frederick G. Foley)

Faga was born within the sound of Bow Bells, and after a varied career, studied calligraphy. Linked with his love of history, his penmanship has created a unique genre of design. Historical tit-bits jostle with maps, line drawings and photographic portraits. The whole is an energetic, original and 'busy' picture. There is a growing band of Faga collectors and the early, small print-run designs have greatly appreciated in value. The size of some of the postcards (the first 129 were reductions of detailed wall maps) is, however, regarded as too large to display by some collectors. A list of Faga's first 20 postcards follows, together with his 1980 issues.

No.	Date	Title	Variations	No. printed	
1.	1961 (*Issued 1962*)	Gunwalloe		1000	
2.	1961	Hendon	blk. on white	1000	
			blk. on blue	1000	
			navy on white	2000	£2
2a.	1964–75	Hendon redesigned		5000	50p
3.	1962	Hampstead	pale blue	2000	
			dk.blue	1000	£2
			sepia/red	2000	
			dk. blue/red	2000	
			grn./blue	7000	£1
			red overprint/ free issue on above	1000	
3a.	1965–76	Hampstead redesigned	multicol.	1000	
4.	1962	Highgate	navy on white gloss	1000	
			pale blue on white matt	1000	
	1963		mauve on white matt	2000	£1
	1964		navy on white matt	1000	
4a.	1965	Highgate redesigned	multicol.	9000	

No.	Date	Title	Variations	No. printed	
5.	1962 (Mar.)	Riverside Taverns of London	blk./blue	1000	
	1962 (Jul.)		blk./blue	1000	
	1962 (Oct.)	Amended design	blk./blue	2000	
	1963	Amended design	red/blue	1000	
	1964	Amended design	red/blue	3000	
5a.	1965	Redesigned	multicol.	80,000	
6.	1962	Mill Hill	grn. on white	2000	60p
6a.	1964–75		multicol.	7000	£1
7.	1962	Bristol	sepia/red	1000	£1
7a.	1967–70	Bristol	multicol.	1000	50p
8.	1963–67	Westminster	multicol.	8000	50p
8a.	1964–67	Westminster redesigned, Small card	multicol.	7000	
8b.	1965–72	Westminster redesigned		33,000	
9.	1963–65	Westminster	grn./blue	3000	
	1963–65	(*cf.* No. 8) ($7\frac{3}{4}'' \times 5\frac{3}{4}''$)	mauve/grn.	1000	
10.	1963–67	City of London (Buildings/ Map) ($7\frac{3}{4}'' \times 5\frac{3}{4}''$)	sepia/gold/blue	1000	
			sepia/blue/red	6000	£1.50
10a.	1966–77	City of London (Costume/ pageantry) ($4\frac{1}{2}'' \times 7\frac{3}{4}''$)	multicol.	37,000	
11.	1963–66	Hampstead & Environs	blk./apple grn.	1000	
			blue/bt. grn.	1000	80p
			blue/lime	1000	
			red/lt. grn.	3000	
12.	1963	Chelsea Trial printing	multicol.	1000	£4
		do.—inscr. 'Chelsea Pottery . . . 1952'	multicol.	37,000	£3
13.	1963–66	Edinburgh ($5\frac{1}{2}'' \times 7''$)	navy/red/yel.	1000	
			lt. blue/red/yel.	1000	£1.50
13a.	1964	Edinburgh ($6'' \times 4\frac{1}{2}''$)	Pale blue/ mauve/yellow	5000	£3
13b.	1964	As 13a ($7'' \times 5\frac{1}{2}''$)		2000	
14.	1963–69	Little Venice in London	red/blue	1000	
			or./grn./blue	1000	
			dk. blue/cerise/ grn.	6000	
14a.	1969–76	*do*—'Water Bus Issue' sold aboard	multicol.	7000	65p
14a.	1970	*do*—Amended for private use for local residents		1000	
15.	1963–70	Straford-upon-Avon. Shakespeare's 400th Anniversary (Large)		15,000	
16.	1963–70	Edgware & Environs	multicol.	3000	£2.50
17.	1964	London Shakespeare ($5\frac{1}{2}'' \times 4\frac{1}{2}''$)	yel./lime/blue	6000	£2
18.	1964–69	Southwark	lt. blue/lime/red	5000	
			navy/yellow/ red	3000	
19.	1964–69	Stratford-upon-Avon (small card)	multicol.	10,000	
20.	1964–76	Wimbledon	multicol.	25,000	

Further details of Faga postcards will be printed in future editions of the catalogue.
Over 200 designs have been printed, including variations.
Note: 13a 4310 of the 5000 printed were later destroyed.

1980 Issues
R100 Airship. 50th Anniv. of 1930 flight	**35p–£3.50**
R101 Airship. 50 Anniv. of fatal 1930 crash	**35p–£2**
Mrs. Thatcher. Anniv. of 21 years as an MP (6″ × 4¾″)	**£1–£4.50**

Fotofolio 1979 ■150a
USA. Horst P. Horst/Rapoport Printing Co.
Series of reproductions of superb photographs of historic themes and personalities by named famous photographers. Subjects include: New York street scenes (Italian Ghetto, Rag Pickers, Tenement Fire, Immigrants at Ellis Island), Red Indians, etc. Personalities include: Louis Armstrong, Isadora Duncan, Albert Einstein, Greta Garbo, Martha Graham, Mae West, etc. **25p**

■150a
Pub. Horst P. Horst. 'Fotofolio'. Reproduction of 1934 photo of Mae West by George Hoyningen-Huene 25p

People's Republic of China ■150b
Attractively presented in pictorial folders, often with explanatory notes in English, these colourful, well-printed postcards (with English captions) show a fascinating glimpse into aspects of life in Red China. Produced in the 1970s, they are no longer being printed and are becoming scarce to find. About 50 sets have been identified, of which the following are typical examples:
Foreign Languages Press
    Modern Revolutionary Peking Operas. Bright photographic scenes
        Taking Tiger Mountain by Strategy. Set of 12. Per set **£1.25**
        The White haired Girl. Set of 17. Per set **£1.75**
        The Great Wall. Ten Photographic cards. Per set **£1**
Kwangsi People's Publishing House
    Woodcuts. A beautiful set of 10 by artists Teng Fu-chueh and Chang Wen-hsiang. Per set **£1**
People's Sports Publishing House
    Sports in China, At least 2 sets of 10 photographic cards. Per set .. **£1**
Shanghai People's Publishing House
    Ivory carvings. Beautiful set of 10 photographic cards, incl. scenes from modern revolutionary ballet. Per set .. **£1**
Unknown Pub.
    Changchun. Set of 10 modern photographic views, incl. Auto plant, Ice sculpture, Stalin Boulevard. Per set **£1**
    Summer Palace. At least 2 sets of 10 photographic views. Per set .. **£1**
    Tomb Bricks from Chiayukuan. Set of 10 primitive brick drawings. Per set **£1**

■150b
Pub. Foreign Languages Press, Peking. 'Taking Tiger Mountain by Strategy.' Scene 10. Period 7 .. .. 10p

Plaistow Pictorial
Sixteen Historic Cars in colour from photographs at the National Motor Museum, Beaulieu, Hants. Titles include Alfa Romeo, Austin, Bentley, Daimler, Rolls Royce Silver Ghost, etc. Per set **£1**

Postcard Collectors Gazette
Card issued as a promotional item within USA and UK announcing the opening of an American office in 1979. Each card numbered. Limited edition of 2000. .. .. **50p**

Reflections—Sports Series
Limited Editions of 1000. Artist Russell Fisher. b & w. No. 1 Muhammad Ali, Billy Beaumont (rugby player), Brian Clough (football manager), Robin Cousins (ice-skater), Illie Nastase (tennis player), Derek Randall (cricketer). Per set **75p**

Republic of Naura Postcards

Limited edition postcards designed by the popular graphic designer and artist, David Gentleman.

1.	Girl with Coral (rare)	**75p**
2.	Girl Catching Fish	**25p**
3.	Wading Bird	**25p**
4.	Reprint of 1.	**25p**

"I'M SORRY MR MELLORS — I'VE GOT A WHOLE DRAWER FULL OF MANUSCRIPTS BY RETIRED GAMEKEEPERS"

■151a

Pub. Shire Publications. Shire Cartoons. Limited Print Series. Artist Hector Breeze. Period 7 35p

Shire Publications ■151a

This company has now ceased publication of postcards, so those in existence may gradually increase in value. Reproductions of line drawings on art board, $5\frac{1}{2}'' \times 4''$.

No. printed

Series 1	Rural Industry (10 cards)	32,000
2	Victorian Farming (10 cards)	50,000
3	Old Fashioned Christmas (6 cards)	9000
4	Gilbert & Sullivan (12 cards)	2000
5	Old Carts & Wagons (6 cards)	18,000
6	Bewick's Dogs (6 cards)	2000
7	Agriculture (6 cards)	8000
8	Corn dollies (6 cards)	5000
Games	2 'Board Games' postcards	2000

Per set .. .. –/50p/75p

Privately printed, promotional set of Shire cartoons by Hector Breeze, 'Larry', Martin Honeysett, Ken Taylor, Bill Tidy and Mike Williams. 1000 sets printed. Per set **£2**

Social History

It is pleasing that the postcard is again being used as a propaganda medium by various organisations to promote often controversial themes. A varied selection of these postcards would form an historical collection, an idea for future generations of the issues that concerned the 1970s and 1980s. The following is a list of typical subjects.

Pub. The American Opinion Bookstore. 'Remember the Hostages'. Flag designed by Bianco & Oglesby. 1980 .. **50p**
Pub. Atlantis Studios, NY. Col. photos of New York graffiti **25p**

Pub. Boycott of Olympic Games Organisation (Fr) Set of 8 b & w drawings by Filipandre & Christine Lesieur. Per set **£4**
Pub. Bruce Peters. 'Stop Using the Bloody Phone' (anti-Busby design) .. **15p**
Pubs. Carto-Breiz and Siphula (Fr) 'Marées Noires'—protest against pollution from oil tankers.
 Carto-Breiz. Limited Edition set of 10 by artist André Coupe. Per set .. **£4**
 Siphula. Shipwreck of tanker *Tanio*/ Breton fishermen march on Paris, 1980 .. .. **25p**
Pub. 'It's a Knockout' (*Jeux Sans Frontières*) 1980 Winner. Bar le Duc, France. Limited Edition (1000) b & w photo. **50p**
Pub. Ligue Nationale Française contre le péril vénérien. 'Attention les Jeunes' **50p**
Pub. NTS (Scandinavian anti-smoking organisation). 'More and More of us are Set Free' 1979 .. .. **25p**
Pub. 'Rock Against Racism'. Series of pictures of fans at 'gigs' (concerts) 1977/ 78 .. .. **25p**
Other subjects inlcude Anti-apartheid, Anti-nuclear weapons, Free Speech in Ireland, 'Overdose' (effect of too much TV on children), Prisoners' Rights, Pro-abortion, etc.
Price range (according to current availability) .. .. 15p/**25p**/£1

TVH Current Event Postcards

Limited edition of 500 only. Two col. print, designed by cartoonist Bryan Reading.

1. Teheren, 1979. Red/black. The Ayatollah, Pres. Carter and the hostages
   .. .. **£1.25**
2. Dallas, 1980. Blue/black. 'Who Shot J.R.?' **£1.15**

Tor Line Fresh Air

Set of 3 cards posted as an advertising idea during November 1979. One card per week posted to 4500 travel agents announcing the coming of a 'Breath of fresh air.' The latter turned out to be the Tor Line Holiday Brochure. 5000 sets printed. .. .. **–/50p/75p**

21st Century Postcards Pub. Monahan, Salop.

Sets of 6 cards, produced from February 1976, in coloured presentation folders.

Series 1. The National Exhibition Centre, Birmingham, from photographs taken by *The Birmingham Post* of the official opening. Per series **£3**

Series 2. Political Cartoons by Cummings of Labour Party personalities: Benn, Callaghan, Foot, Healey, Jenkins, Wilson. Per series **£4.50**

Series 3. Silhouettes by Mark Haddon, theatrical designer. Per series .. **£4**

Series 4. *Not issued.*

Series 5. *Eclat Vingt et Un.* Colourful 'pin-ups' by Kasia Charko (designer for 'Biba'). Per series **£5**

The above are the current published retail prices, but as stocks of these attractive limited editions dwindle, the sets are now rapidly appreciating in value.

Veldale Covers ■152a

Limited edition postcards designed to complement Post Office commemorative issues. All are offset-litho on dark cream board, normal postcard size (with the exception of CBS 4/1, which is 8″ × 3½″)

		No. printed	
CBS 1/1	Mrs. Gaskell (9 Jul. 80)	700	**15p**
CBS 2/1	British Conductors (10 Sep. 80)	500	**15p**
SE 1/1	Queen Mother's 80th Birthday (4 Aug. 80)	1000	**25p**
CBS 3/1	Sporting Centenaries. (10 Oct. 80)	500	**15p**
V 5/1–4	Shakespeare Players. Artist 'Jarvis' (Nov. 80) Set of 4	1000	per set **60p**
CBS 4/1	Christmas 1980. Artist 'Jarvis' (19 Nov. 80)	700	**15p**
CBS 5/1	Folklore/Valentine (6 Feb. 81)	1000	**15p**
SE 3/1	Engagement of the Prince of Wales (Feb. 81)	3000	**25p**

Zandra Rhodes ■152b

Advertising for this controversial, sometimes outrageous, sometimes brilliant, fashion and life-style designer. Eighteen card set produced in 1975/76. Subjects include photographs of shop interior and window, models (incl. Zandra herself) wearing her creations, stylised heads drawn by Zandra, 'pleated satin' sculptures, also by Zandra. Per set .. **£5**

■152a

Pub. Veldale Covers. Engagement of the Prince of Wales to Lady Diana Spencer, February 1981
.. .. 25p

■152b

Pub. Zandra Rhodes. Artist Zandra Rhodes. Series 1. No. 3. Period 7 .. .. 25p

NOVELTY

A novelty postcard is one that deviates from the normal rectangular item made of standard board. It may have something stuck on it, may be made of unusual material or be of an unusual size or shape. It may also *do* something—squeak, smell or move—in which case it is a 'mechanical' postcard. Many novelty cards contravened existing Post Office regulations for postcards because of their irregular size, shape or material. They were then subject to letter or book rate (1*d*. instead of ½*d*. as for normal postcards in Periods 1 to 3). Some, like jewelled or tinselled items, had to be sent through the post in protective envelopes.

APPLIQUED MATERIALS

Buttons
Dried flowers
Envelope (to enclose a tiny letter)
Glass (eyes for animals)
Hair (on heads and other parts of the body)
Jewelling/glitter (usually mica)
Lace
Mirror (i.e. metal that reflects an image)
Photographs (inset personal portrait)
Pocket (to enclose a card or tiny hankie)
Pussy willow (to make the bodies of kittens)
'Real Japanese' ■154a (Tuck series with linen finish)
Sand paper (to strike matches)
Seeds (shamrock and others)
Velvet and other materials (in the shapes of bloomers, flowers, hats, etc.)
Other materials
Price range .. .. £1/**£3**/£6

BANKNOTES/COINS

In Period 2 cards were printed to represent the banknotes and coins of various countries. Some of the gilded/silvered, embossed versions are most realistic.
Pub. Armstrong, M. H. Series with national flags and coins.
Pub. Osnabrucker Paper Mfg. Co. Banknotes and coins series.
Others. ■154b
Price range .. .. £2/**£4**/£6

BAS RELIEF

A deep form of embossing with a three-dimensional effect, often with 'jewelling'. Subjects are normally important personages. *See also* ROYALTY.
Publishers include Stengel & Co., and Sutton, Sharpe & Co.
Price range .. .. 75p/**£1**/£1.50

BEER MATS

Period 7 cards produced by brewers in Britain and on the Continent (e.g. Munchner Hofbrau) often o/s.
Price range .. .. –/**25p**/50p

COMPOSITE

A composite set is a number of postcards (from 2 upwards) which fit together to make a complete picture.

American

Santa. Pub. Hild 1906. Set of 4. Per set .. .. £8/**£10**/£15
Uncle Sam, etc. Period 2. Sets. Price according to no. of cards in set. Per set .. .. £10/**£45**/£100
Period 7. Per set .. .. £3/**£5**/£10

Austrian

Pub. Brüder Köhn. Artist Carl Josef, (e.g. Series 410: 'Korso', set of 6). Period 2.
Per set .. .. £20/**£45**/£100
Others. Per set .. .. £10/**£15**/£30

Belgian

King Albert I. Pub. Legia with Namur views. Set of 8. Per set .. .. .. £20/**£30**/£35
Ditto. With Antwerp views. Set of 8. Per set .. .. £20/**£30**/£35

British

Edward VII G.P. Tea, etc. Period 2. Per set .. .. £20/**£50**/£120
Pub. Hildesheimer. Series 5190.
Negro with Spear. Set of 4. Per set
.. .. £50/**£60**/£75
Pub. Wrench. No. 4822. Giraffe
Instalment cards. Set of 5. Period 2. Per set .. .. £30/**£50**/£60
Other Period 2. Per set .. .. £15/**£35**/£50

French

Chasseurs a Pied. Mesange series 222. Set
   of 10. Per set .. .. .. £25/**£35**/£50

Jeanne d'Arc. Fauvette series No. 1685. Set
   of 10. Per set .. .. .. £15/**£25**/£35

La Gaite a la Caserne. Artist A. P. Jarry.
   Period 3. Set of 10. Per set .. £25/**£50**/£75

Life of Jesus. Mesange series 528. Set of 10.
   Per set .. .. £15/**£25**/£35

Life of Jesus. Set of 12. Old Masters
   surround. Per set .. .. £15/**£30**/£40

Life of Napoleon. Artist Mastroianni. Period
   2. Set of 10. Per set .. .. £25/**£50**/£75

Life of Napoleon. Mesange series 528. Set of
   12. Per set .. .. .. £15/**£35**/£60

Kaiser's Head Atrocity sets (*see* War)

Others. Per set .. .. .. £10/**£50**/£75

German

Crocodile. Set of 5. Early Period 2. Per
   set .. .. £10/**£15**/£25

Kaiser Wilhelm II. Period 2. Set of 8. Per
   set .. .. £50/**£75**/£100

Others. Per set .. .. .. £10/**£15**/£50

Italian

Life of Christ. Rubens paintings surround.
   Set of 12. Per set .. .. £10/**£20**/£40

Others. Per set .. .. .. £10/**£15**/£35

Japanese

Samurai, warriors, etc. Period 2. Per set
  .. .. £20/**£50**/£120

Others

Period 2. Per set .. .. .. £20/**£50**/£120

Period 7. Per set .. .. .. £3/**£5**/£10

EMBOSSING

Many beautiful early Continental embossed
designs exist. *See also* Greetings. British publishers include DeLittle, Fenwick & Co., Hildesheimer, Ettlinger, Tuck ('Art' and 'Connoisseur' series).

Price range .. .. 75p/**£1.50**/£3

FANTASY

This is an imaginative, frequently surrealist, type
of design, often with a *trompe l'oeil* element,
sometimes using photomontage.

Girls in neckties .. .. .. £10/**£20**/£30

Heads composed of figures, e.g. Composers
   Kaiser, Mephisto, Napoleon, Skulls
   ■155a, etc. .. .. .. £5/**£10**/£15

Mountains with faces and figures. Artist
   'Hansen' (Emile Nolde). Pub. Killinger,
   etc. ■71b .. .. .. £5/**£8**/£12

Multi Babies. A phenomenon which appeared on postcards throughout the Continent. Various designs incl. Alphabet.
   Period 2 .. .. £1/**£1.50**/£2

HAND PAINTED/TINTED

Amateur artists .. .. .. 50p/**75p**/£1.50

Commercially produced hand coloured artist
   drawn .. .. 50p/**£1**/£2

Continental commercially produced water
   colours of flowers, etc. .. 75p/**£1.50**/£2.50

Japanese oil paintings, miniature works of
   art which are much underrated. ■156a
   .. .. £1/**£2**/£3

Japanese water colours .. .. 75p/**£1**/£1.50

Photographic origin. Hand tinted
   .. .. 50p/**75p**/£1.50

Others .. .. –/**50p**/£1.50

■154a

Pub. Tuck. 'Real Japanese' Connoisseur series.
Period 2 .. .. £6

■154b

The Flag and Coinage of Great Britain and
Ireland. Period 2 .. .. £5

HOLD TO LIGHT (HTL)/ TRANSPARENCIES

These are cards which, as their title implies, reveal a surprise when held to the light. They came in two forms—cards that appear quite standard until held to the light (transparencies) and those that have cut out sections representing a source of light—candles, moons, suns, windows, etc.—(cut outs).

Christmas and other greetings. .. £4/**£8**/£10
Cupples, Samuel (incl. World's Fair 1904)
.. .. £1/**£2**/£3
Hartmann transparency series .. £2/**£3**/£4
Meteor transparencies (incl. Paris Exhibition 1900) .. .. .. £6/**£8**/£10
W.H., Berlin (HTL and transparencies)
.. .. £1/**£1.50**/£3
Others .. .. £1/**£2**/£4

MECHANICAL

Postcards demanding some kind of action.

Action Cards
Moved by levers, wheels, etc.

Barometers
Changing colour in the damp.

Blow Up
With rubber inflatable sections.

Cigarette Cards
Pub. Ettlinger. Artist Browne, Tom. 2 cigarettes attached.

Cut Outs
Notably Tuck 'Birds and Butterflies on the Wing', Dolls for Dressing, etc. (*see also* CHILDREN).

Deeks Puzzle Cards
USA. Changing pictures

Girls' Own Paper Postcards
1900. Two sets of 4 postcards printed on one page to cut out. Views from the Editor's window, readers' portraits, signatures, etc.

Gramophone Records
Modern. Melody cards. Series of 8″ × 6″ cards with 45 rpm discs. Titles include: 'Whole Lotta Woman', 'For You', 'April Love', 'Somebody Loves Me', etc.
Pub. Ettlinger, at least 12 designs
Pub. Tuck, at least 40 designs.

Heat-activated Cards
To show hidden pictures.

Jigsaw Cards
Notably Tuck Picture Puzzle Postcards, miniature 'zag-zaw' puzzles in boxes of 6, each of 30 pieces. Thirty sets (1918).

Kaleidoscopes
Pub. Alpha, at least 20 designs.

Reversible Cards
Showing a different picture when turned upside down.

Scented Cards
With impregnated pads to rub to release perfume.

Squeakers
Various publishers.

Windows
Or boxes that open to show another picture.

Wire Coils
Used for 'flying' butterflies, wagging tails, etc.

Others
Price range for all above .. .. £2/**£8**/£15

PULLOUTS

The commonest kind of novelty card where a flap is raised to reveal a concertina of small pictures,

■155a

French. Fantasy head 'Un Faune'. PU *1912* £10

usually views. Pullouts exist for most categories of postcards including ADVERTISING, ANIMALS, COMIC, ROYALTY, SOCIAL HISTORY, etc.

Artist drawn, signed .. .. .. 75p/**£1**/£3
Artist drawn, unsigned .. .. 50p/**75p**/£1.50
Photographic origin .. .. .. –/**50p**/75p

SHAPES

Cards were produced in a variety of unusual
  shapes, e.g. animals, circular, leaf, others
  .. .. 75p/**£1**/£3

SILK

This is the best documented type of novelty postcard (in the booklets of C. Radley). Three main types exist: embroidered, printed and woven. *See also* WAR.

Embroidered Silks

Period 2. Mostly Floral in Design
Austrian from 1903
British. Pub. Birn Bros. Town Series
French from 1907
German from 1906. Pub. Duroldt, A.
Swiss from 1907 (for Embroidery Exhib.)
Others
Price range .. .. £4/**£6**/£12

Period 4
Continuation of Continental sentimental Period 3 type designs.
British. Pub. Tuck. 'Broderie d'Art' series.
Price range .. .. £2/**£3**/£5

Printed on Satin/Silk

The least collectable type of silk card, though some fine Continental *Art Nouveau* designs exist and the British 'Fab' Patchwork series is interesting.

1900–1903. Ger. Pub. Krieger. Four
  Seasons series. Per set .. £20/**£40**/£60
1900–1903. Various Continental designs
  .. .. £3/**£5**/£10
Period 2. 'Fab' Patchwork. Clan Crests/
  Flowers/Views .. .. .. £4/**£6**/£8
'Fab' designs for the USA market of State
  Capitals (Series 5) .. .. £5/**£6**/£8
Others .. ..75p/**£1.50**/£3
  N.B. Cards with plain backs (e.g. Cinema stars, Edith Cavell, etc.) are *not* postcards and are not listed.

Woven

These are the most artistic, skilfully produced and the most sought after of all the 'Silks'.

Alpha. Flags, greetings, etc. .. .. £9/**£14**/£28
American. St. Louis Exhibition (1904)
  .. .. £14/**£28**/£40
Austrian. Periods 2, 4 .. .. .. £10/**£20**/£28
French. 1900. Pub. Benoiston, Paris
  Exhibition .. .. £20/**£28**/£35
French. Period 2. Pub. Neyret Frères. *Art Nouveau*, Classical, Portraits, Views (the highest value is for col. *Art Nouveau*)
  .. .. £20/**£35**/£135
German. Periods 1/Early Period 2. Pubs.
  include Knuffmann and Knieger
  .. .. £14/**£28**/£40
Grant, W. H. & Co. Exhibitions, Greetings, Hands Across the Sea, Portraits, Ships, Subjects, Views (the highest value is for col. subjects) .. .. .. £14/**£35**/£50
Japanese. 1908–1910. Admiral Togo, View
  of Amanohashitate .. .. .. £6/**£14**/£20
Stevens, Thomas. ■156b Exhibitions, Greetings, Hands Across the Sea, Portraits, Religious subjects, Ships, Subjects, Views (the highest valuation is for col. views and rare personalities) .. .. £14/**£35**/£100
Others .. .. £3.50/**£5**/£7.50

■156a
Japanese. Hand painted in oils £3

■156b

Pub. Thomas Stevens. 'Ye Peeping Tom of Coventre' in woven silk. Period 2 .. .. ..£40

SIZES

Book Mark ■157a

Approx. 137 × 45 mm. Subjects include animals, personalities like actors and actresses, military leaders, royalty and views.

Pub. Rotary Photo Co.	50p/**75p**/£3
Pub. Rumsey & Co., Toronto ..	50p/**75p**/£3
Pub. Tuck	50p/**75p**/£3
Others	50p/**75p**/£3

Giant

Oversize postcards, subject to Book Post/Letter Rate in Period 2. Subjects include exhibition and view cards.

Pub. Graphotone Co. 310 × 210 mm	..75p/**£1**/£1.50
'Panoramic'—double size postcards	..75p/**£1**/£1.50
Pub. Photochrom. 'Reform' View Card 245 × 200 mm	..75p/**£1**/£1.50
Pub. Trent Pub. Co. 315 × 135 mm	..75p/**£1**/£1.50
Pub. Valentine, incl. Franco British and other exhibitions	..75p/**£1**/£1.50

'Midget'

Rectangular or diamond-shaped. 88 × 71 mm. Subjects include animals, children, actresses.

Pub. Ettlinger	50p/**75p**/£1
Pub. Rotary	50p/**75p**/£1
Others	50p/**75p**/£1

STAMP CARDS

Cards reproducing the postage stamps of various nations.

Embossed

Pub. Guggenheim	£3/**£5**/£6
Pub. Menke-Huber	£3/**£5**/£6
Pub. Zieher, Otmar	£4/**£6**/£7
Others	£3/**£5**/£6

Non-embossed

Heller, Henry. Bern	£3/**£6**/£7
Others	..50p/**£1**/£1.50

Collages of Cut Up Stamps

Pub. Alpha	£2/**£4**/£5
Chinese, hand made	£2/**£4**/£5
Others	£2/**£4**/£5

UNUSUAL MATERIALS

Postcards were manufactured from the most curious substances, which include aluminium, bark, celluloid ■157b, cork, ivory, leather, panel cards (on stout board), peat, wood, others.

Price range .. .. £1/**£3**/£10

The highest value is for postally used cards of unusual substances.

One of the most original materials ever used was pulped paper currency in the USA—known as 'Macerated Money Cards'. Rare.

■157a

Pub. Tuck. 'Bookmarker'. Artist Phil May .. £3

■157b

French. Handpainted celluloid card with appliquéd velvet iris (1919) £2.50

OFFICIALS

The postcard started its life as an 'official', i.e. government owned, publication. As new countries followed Austria's lead of 1869 and adopted the postcard, so more official cards were issued. Such cards, together with letter cards, newspaper wrappers, etc. were catalogued and collected during Period 1 and early Period 2. The generic title given to them all was—'Postal Stationery'. Now that postcards are once more 'collectable', interest is growing in the early officials of different countries. Of course official postcards are much more than first issues. There are the cards used by government departments, those produced in war-time, etc. (*see also* WAR). However, as a first step in bringing early official cards back into the mainstream of postcard collecting we list here the dates on which the major postcard nations adopted the idea, together with a brief description of the first card issued.

Austria
1869. Two kreuzer printed stamp. Yellow on white. Bordered. Inscriptions on back and front in black. *See* illustration A in Introduction .. .. £1/**£2**/£3

Belgium
1871. Five centimes printed stamp. Brown on buff. Instructions at ends. Picture design in centre heading .. .. £1/**£2**/£3

Canada
1871. One cent printed stamp. Light blue on pale buff. 'Montreal and Ottawa' inscription .. .. £1/**£2**/£3

France
1873. No stamp. Black inscriptions on white. Space for two 5 centimes stamps .. .. £1/**£3**/£5

German Empire
1870. No stamp. Black inscriptions on buff. Headed 'Correspondenz-Karte' £1/**£1.50**/£2

Great Britain
The first British postcards were put on sale on 1 October 1870, precisely one year after the world's first postcard had appeared in Austro-Hungary. The British version measured 121 × 88 mm, exactly the same size as its illustrious predecessor, and was very similar in design (■A & B). Within a few days it was realised that the shape of the card was such that it stuck out of the bundles of mail carried by the postman and was damaged by the string which was tied around the packages. Very quickly a slimmer 'oblong' card was introduced, 121 × 74 mm, and it began to replace the earlier issue from about the middle of November 1870. These first cards were solely for inland use, were sold only at Post Offices and carried a pre-printed halfpenny stamp.

The first chink in the armour of the PO monopoly appeared on 17 June 1872 when privately produced printed cards were allowed to be used. However, they could not carry adhesive stamps but had to be delivered to the Post Office authorities who then impressed a pink/orange stamp upon them. That eminent politician, William Ewart Gladstone, favoured the postcard as a carrier of brief messages, but complained about the flimsy board from which the cards were made. Accordingly, on 1 February 1875, the PO issued an oblong card made of thicker board. It became known as 'Mr. Gladstone's stout card'. On 1 July 1875 the first British postcard designed to be sent abroad was introduced. It was named, appropriately, 'Foreign Post Card' (■160a) and reverted to the old size of 121 × 88 mm.

Over the following years commercial pressures gradually forced the PO, and De La Rue their printers, to relinquish their total monopoly of the postcard business. Minor design changes were made in the cards, both Inland and Foreign, with few significant postcard events except perhaps the following (*see* A BRIEF HISTORY):

1 January 1878—the border removed from the card design. 122 × 75 mm.

1 July 1879—adhesive stamps could be added to the printed stamps on Foreign postcards to 'make-up' an overseas rate.

1 October 1882—the 'Reply Paid' card was introduced. 122 × 75 mm.

September 1889—the 'British Empire' card introduced for use to the Australian Colonies (■160b). 140 × 88 mm.

21 January 1895—official court size cards put on sale. Stout card 115 × 89 mm. (Private court size cards were in use earlier.)

1 November 1899—privately produced post-

cards were allowed to be produced up to full size of 140 × 89 mm and to be used with adhesive stamps.

The valuations given do not take account of philatelic properties such as first day cancellations. The value attached to such items is currently PA. Dimensions may vary by 1 mm from card to card.

First issue. 1870. Half-penny printed stamp.
Violet on buff. Bordered. 121 × 88 mm
(see ■B in INTRODUCTION) .. £1/**£3**/£5
Second issue. The oblong card. 121 × 74
mm .. .. 50p/**£1**/£2
Privately printed. Impressed stamp.
.. .. 75p/**£1**/£2
Mr. Gladstone's stout card .. .. −/**50p**/75p
The foreign postcard. ■160a .. £1.50/**£2**/£3
Reply paid. Complete .. .. −/**50p**/75p
British Empire. ■160b .. .. 50p/**£1**/£1.50
Official court card. Printed ½d. stamp
.. .. −/**50p**/75p

Italy

1874. Ten centesimi printed stamp. Brown
on buff. Bordered .. .. 50p/**£1**/£1.50

Japan

1873. One half sen printed stamp. Brown.
Frame in red .. .. .. 50p/**£1**/£1.50

Russia

1872. No stamp. Black on greyish card.
Bordered .. .. 50p/**£1**/£1.50

Switzerland

1870. Five centimes printed stamp. Vermilion on cream. Bordered .. 50p/**75p**/£1

USA

The first American postcards were put on sale on 13 May 1873, although current American terminology refers to 'postal cards' beginning in 1861. In December 1861 J. P. Charlton and H. L. Lipman of Philadelphia, copyrighted the 'Lipman Postal Card'. It had one side blank for the message, and on the other side were ruled lines for the address plus a stamp box. However, these cards were not true postcards because they were treated as letters by the postal authorities; there was not a postal rate that recognised postcards in 1861. Indeed the postcard rate, and hence the 'postcard' (as opposed to the letter) did not appear until 1 October 1869 and that was in Austro-Hungary (see A BRIEF HISTORY). The cards issued by the American Post Office from 1873 are known as 'government postals' and from the first day they were bought in quantity by business houses who then printed their own messages or advertisements upon them. On the address side was a printed 1c. brown stamp and the words 'United States Postal Card'.

On 1 July 1898 privately produced postcards were allowed (a full 16 months ahead of Britain) thus permitting the free development of the picture postcard. These cards had to carry the legend 'Private Mailing Card—Authorized by Act of Congress, May 19, 1898', but could be used with an adhesive stamp. However, picture cards carrying advertisements for products, services and exhibitions were printed on government postals from 13 May 1873 and such cards produced before private cards became legal (i.e. before 1 July 1898) are known as 'pioneers'. However, although private 'cards' were also issued, only official government postals are true pioneer postcards because privately produced 'cards' were treated as letters until 1898.

Picture cards produced using government postals, in the period before private cards were allowed, fall into two main categories—advertising and exhibition (exposition). They are known as 'pioneer advertising cards' and 'pioneer exposition cards' respectively. Thus while the pictures on these cards were privately produced the cards themselves are official issues and the category is included in this section.

We would welcome ideas and information from American collectors and dealers with a view to expanding this category.

First issue (1873). 1c. printed stamp, brown
on buff. Bordered. Watermarked
'USPOD' .. .. £1/**£3**/£4
Pioneer advertising .. .. .. £8/**£10**/£12
Pioneer exposition
World's Columbian (1893) .. £6/**£10**/£15
California Midwinter International
(1894) .. .. £3/**£6**/£8
Cotton States & International (1895)
.. .. £3/**£5**/£6
Trans-Mississippi & International
(1898) .. .. £3/**£4**/£5

■160a
*1875. The first British postcard for foreign use.
Brown on buff. 122 × 87 mm* £1

■160b
*1889 'British Empire' card for use to Australia.
Carmine on buff. 140 × 88 mm* £1.50

■160c
*1978. National Postal Museum, London. Penny
Black card. NJ corner letters* 25p

■160d
*N.E.P.R. 1980. One of series of 6 depicting
Yorkshire Dales* 25p

■160e
*Scottish P.B. 1979. Postbus at the Harbour,
Kirkcudbright* 25p

Post Office PHQ Cards

*Since 1973 the Post Office have issued
picture cards showing commemorative
stamps. Initially cards were only issued for
certain issues but since June 1976 cards
have been issued for all new special stamps.*

*A listing of these cards up to and including
the Liverpool & Manchester Railway stamps
of March 1980 appeared in the first edition
of this catalogue. A priced listing is included in Stanley Gibbons Collect British
Stamps checklist published twice a year—in
May and November.*

*The Summer 1981 edition (published May
1981) includes all cards up to and including the International Year of Disabled
People stamps issued on 25 March 1981
(PHQ50).*

PHQ1 issued in July 1973 is shown above.

PHQ = Postal Headquarters.

PHILATELIC

In recent years many philatelists have become more interested in postcards and in particular in those cards which have a postal theme—i.e. illustrations of post offices, posting boxes, mail trains, etc. These are dealt with in the SOCIAL HISTORY and other sections in this catalogue. To cater for this interest many post offices, philatelic societies and some stamp dealers have produced cards having a direct appeal to the stamp collector. The British Post Office began in 1973 a series of cards reproducing in large size the designs of various commemorative stamps. These have been issued for most sets of stamps since 1975. They are known as 'PHQ cards' as they are issued by Postal Headquarters and bear a 'PHQ . . .' reference number on the back. A list of these issues was given in the first edition of this catalogue and they are listed and priced in each edition of our *Collect British Stamps* (published each May and November). In addition other cards have been issued by the National Postal Museum (since 1969) and by the regional headquarters of the various postal regions (since 1971). A simplified listing of these is featured here. We also list those cards issued in behalf of the Philatelic Section of the British Library and in future editions intend listing some of the other cards—those issued by the British Museum, local philatelic societies and stamp dealers. In 1980 the Guernsey Post Office produced its first set of PHQ-type cards and the Jersey Post Office is expected to follow suit this year. Many of the regional cards proved very popular, were quickly sold out and reprinted. Usually the reprints can be distinguished from the original printing. In the listings which follow the number of printings known are given in brackets. Where there has been more than one printing two prices are quoted—the lower price for the most common printing and the top price for the rarest printing. In most instances the original print is the most sought-after and commands the highest price.

National Postal Museum

Museum Series (sets of 6)
1. Personalities (2). Nov. 69 .. .. 75p/£2
2. Development of 1*d*. Black and 2*d*. Blue
   (2). Nov. 69 .. .. 75p/£25
3. Mulready (2). Nov. 69 .. .. 75p/£2
4. De La Rue (2). Nov. 69 .. .. .. 75p/£2
5. Q. V. Jubilee issue (2). Nov. 69 .. 75p/£15
6. Edward VII Essays. May 80 .. .. **75p**
7. George V Essays. May 80 .. .. **75p**
8. George V Commens. May 80 .. .. **75p**

Other Cards
Penny Black. Corner Letters 'P.M.'. 1971/
  2 .. .. **£10**
Penny Black. ■160c. Corner Letters 'N.J'
  (2). May 78 .. .. 25p/£1
Rowland Hill. Set of 5. Aug. 79 .. .. **75p**
VC Exhibition. Jan. 81 .. .. **25p**
Valentine Exhibition. Feb. 81 .. .. **25p**

Eastern Postal Board
Oxford Philatelic Counter. Jun. 71 .. **25p**
Norwich Philatelic Counter. Oct. 79 .. **25p**
Diss Postbus. Mar. 80 .. .. **25p**
Colchester Postbus. Jun. 80 .. .. .. **25p**
Cambridge Philatelic Counter. Aug. 80 **25p**

Midland Postal Region
1. Chetwynd House, Stafford. Oct. 74
     (5) .. .. 25p/£1.50
2. Richard Brinsley, Sheridan. Oct. 74
     (5) .. .. 25p/£1.50
3. Rowland Hill statue, Kidderminster.
     Dec. 74 (8) .. .. 25p/£18
4. Rowland Hill (col. o/s). Aug. 79 .. **50p**
5. }
6. } Historic and unusual posting boxes.
7. }   To be issued during 1981
8. }
9. Victoria Sq. PO, B'ham. (4 cards).
     Mar. 81 .. .. **75p**
10. 'Hen & Chickens' cycle 1881. Mar.
     81 .. .. **25p**

North-Eastern Postal Region ■160d
1–5. Yorkshire Dales (reproductions of
  paintings) (Set of 5). Apr. 74 .. .. **£2**
6–10. Yorkshire Dales (reproduction of
  paintings) (Set of 5). Aug. 80 .. .. **75p**

North-Western Postal Region
1. L'pool & Manchester Rly. Passenger
     Train. Nov. 76 (8) .. .. 25p/£8
As above but with 150th Anniv. logo and set
  of railway stamps affixed. Mar. 80 .. **£1**
2. L'pool & Manchester Rly. Goods Trains.
     Mar. 80 (2) 25p/50p
As above but with 150th Anniv. logo and set
  of railway stamps affixed. Mar. 80 .. **£1**

Postbus Cards
Duddon Valley (single view). Mar. 74
  (3) .. ..   25p/£3
Duddon Valley (multi-view). Jun. 79 (3)
  .. .. 25p/£1.50
Penrith/Martindale (single view). Apr. 74
  (3) .. .. 25p/£50
Penrith/Martindale (multi-view). Jun. 79
  (3) .. .. 25p/£1.50
Grizdale Forest (multi-view). Jun. 79 (2)
  .. .. 25p/50p

Scottish Postal Board ■160e

Postbuses
1. Kelso–Stichill. Nov. 79 .. .. ..   **50p**
2. Killin–Callander. Nov. 79 .. ..   **50p**
3. Kirkcudbright–Borgue. Nov. 79 ..   **50p**
4. Inveraray–Dalmally. Nov. 79 ..   **50p**
5. Brodick–Shannochie. Nov. 79 ..   **50p**
6. Bettyhill–Kimbrace. Jul. 80 .. ..   **25p**
7. Grotaig–Drummadrochit.Jul. 80 ..   **25p**
8. Arnisdale–Kyle. Jul. 80 .. ..   **25p**
9. Colonsay. Jul. 80 .. .. ..   **25p**
10. Ballater–Lynn of Dee. Jul. 80 ..   **25p**

South-Eastern Postal Region

Postbus Cards
Canterbury–Crundale
  Captions on front. Nov. 74 .. ..   **£3**
  Captions on reverse. Jun. 78 .. ..   **25p**
  City wall Canterbury (SEPR 1). Jul.
  80 .. ..   **25p**
Dorking–Ockley
  Single-view. Aug. 73 (2) .. .. 50p/£30
  Coldharbour (SEPR 2). Oct. 80 ..   **25p**
Hailsham–Bodle Street Green
  Bodle Street Green (SEPR 11). Jul.
  80 .. ..   **25p**
Heathfield–Waldron
  Star Inn (SEPR 7). Jul. 80 .. ..   **25p**
Henley–Frieth
  Multi-view. Oct. 78 (2) 25p/50p
  Single view (SEPR 17). Oct. 80 ..   **25p**
Hungerford–E. Garston
  Multi-view. Oct. 78 (2) 25p/50p
  E. Garston (SEPR 8). Oct. 80 .. ..   **25p**
Hungerford–Gt. Shefford
  Denford Mill (SEPR 9) Oct. 80 ..   **25p**
Hungerford–Kintbury
  Denford Mill House. Jul. 74 .. ..   **£3**
  Kintbury crossing. (SEPR 10) Oct. 80   **25p**
Newbury–Chaddleworth
  North Heath (SEPR 16). Oct. 80 ..   **25p**

Newbury–W. Ilsley
  Donnington Castle (SEPR 15). Oct.
  80 .. ..   **25p**
Newbury–W. Ilsley/Chaddleworth
  Multi-view. Apr. 76 (2) .. .. 50p/£4
  Multi-view. Apr. 79 .. .. ..   **25p**
Newport–Brightstone
  Chillerton (SEPR 13). Jul. 80 ..   **25p**
Newport–Newtown
  Carisbrooke Castle (SEPR 12). Jul.
  80 .. ..   **25p**
Oxted–Lingfield
  Postbus at Crowhurst. Sep 73 (2) ..   **50p/£2**
  Crowhurst Place (SEPR 3). Oct. 80   **25p**
Petersfield–Froxfield
  Froxfield Grn. (SEPR 14). Jul. 80 ..   **25p**
Petworth–Bignor
  Sutton Village (SEPR 4). Jul. 80   **25p**
Redhill–Outwood. ■162a
  Old Mill Outwood (SEPR 18). Oct. 79
  (2) 25p/50p
Sittingbourne–Wormshill
  Bus at shell centre. Mar. 74 .. ..   **£6**
  Bus at Wormshill. Mar. 74 (2) .. £1/£35
  Milstead Village (SEPR 5). Jul. 80   **25p**
Tunbridge Wells–Wadhurst
  Bus at Wadhurst. Mar. 74 (2) .. £1/£15
  Bus at Mayfield. Mar. 74 (2) .. .. £1/£8
  Bus in country lane. Dec. 78 .. ..   **25p**
  Mayfield High Street (SEPR 6). Jul.
  80 .. ..   **25p**

Other Cards
Loading mail at Gatwick Airport. Oct. 73
  (2) .. .. 30p/£1.50
Farnham Post Office–1. Nov. 73 .. ..   **£1.50**
Farnham Post Office–2. Aug. 78 .. ..   **30p**
Brighton Centre. No logo. Sep. 78 ..   **£1.50**
Brighton Centre. Giro logo. Feb. 79 ..   **25p**
Brighton Landmarks. May 80 .. ..   **25p**

■162a

S.E.P.R. 1979. Redhill—Outwood Postbus   25p

South-Western Postal Region

Dorchester Mural (2). Oct. 71 .. 25p/£1.25
Weymouth Mural (2). Jul. 72 .. .. 25p/£1
Ralph Allen; Studio of Thomas Hudson (5).
   Apr. 73 .. .. 25p/£6
  1. Bath Mail Coach (2). ■163a. Apr.
     73 .. .. 25p/£30
    Bath Mail Coach (Jumbo Size) (3). Jul.
     73 .. .. 25p/£1
  2. West Country Mails (3). Jul. 74 .. 25p/£5
  3. Lioness Attacking horse (3). Jul. 74
     .. .. 25p/£5
  4. Russell's Wagon 1833 (4). Jul. 74 25p/£30
  5. Oldest Pillar Box (2). May 78 .. 25p/50p
  6. Honiton Postbus (2). Sep. 78 .. 25p/50p
  7. Postal Services in Cornwall (2). Apr.
     79 .. .. 25p/50p
  8. Swindon Mailtrains. Nov. 79 .. **25p**
    Swindon Mailtrains (Jumbo Size) (2).
     Mar. 80 .. .. 25p/50p
  9. Cotswold Post Offices. Mar. 80 . **25p**
10. Bournemouth Royal Mail Air Services.
     May 80 .. .. **25p**
11. Salisbury; Badge of PO Rifles. Jul.
     80 .. .. **25p**
    Salisbury; Badge of PO Rifles (Jumbo
     Size). Jul. 80 .. .. .. **25p**
12. South Devon Royal Mail Services. Apr.
     81 .. .. **25p**

Wales and The Marches Postal Region

  1. Civic Centre Cardiff. Aug. 74 .. **£1**
  2. St. David's Cathedral. Aug. 74 .. **£1**
  3. Llanidloes Postbus. Aug. 74 .. **£4**
  4. Brecon Beacons. Aug. 74 .. .. **£1**
  5. Llangorse Lake. Aug. 74 .. .. **£1**
  6. Caswell Bay. Aug. 74 .. .. **£1**
  7. Eastgate Chester. Aug. 74 .. .. **£1**
  8. Lledr bridge. Aug. 74 .. .. **£1**
  9. Llandrindod Wells Postbus (2). Jan.
     79 .. .. 25p/50p
10. Llandovery Postbus (2). Jan. 79 .. 25p/50p
11. Llanidloes Postbus. Jan. 79 .. 25p/50p
12. Rhyl Postbus. ■163b. Jan. 79 .. 25p/50p
13. Usk Postbus Usk. Jan. 79 .. 25p/50p
14. Usk Postbus Ragian. Jan. 79 .. 25p/50p

British Library ■163c

Famous Stamps
  1. Penny Black (1979) **50p**
  2. 1855. 4*d*. Carmine (1979) **50p**
  3. 1847. 1/- Green (1980) **50p**
  4. 1971. Christmas 3p (1979) **50p**
  5. LNWR. Letter stamp (1980) **25p**

■163a

S.W.P.R. 1974. Palmer Mail Coach 25p

■163b

W.M.P.B. 1979. Rhyl–Meriadog Postbus .. 25p

■163c

British Library. 1980. L.N.W.R. 1892 2d railway letter stamp. o/s 50p

Details of new Post Office regional cards are given in Gibbons Stamp Monthly.

Available from all newsagents and many stamp dealers.

POLITICAL/PROPAGANDA/ PUNISHMENT & JUSTICE

The postcard was a medium greatly utilised by civil, military and political commentators. Sometimes this was spontaneous comment by the artist, sometimes it was inspired or commissioned by governments and other bodies for their campaigns. This vehicle flourished in wartime, so consult also WAR. This is another section where artists reign supreme, although, sadly, much fine work is unsigned and as yet unidentified. To make the pointed barbs palatable to the collecting public, many political/propaganda drawings appear as cartoons. Therefore a high proportion of designers of political cards will also be found under COMIC. Several themes in this section also overlap with SOCIAL HISTORY/TOPOGRAPHICAL.

Listed below are the CAUSES AND THEMES of importance in this category which are commented upon on the postcard, or which use the postcard as their mouthpiece or shop window. Cards illustrating these themes are covered by the artists, publishers and series described in this section. Whatever the treatment (photographic, artist drawn—even anonymous) cards featuring these causes or themes will attract the valuations shown, apart from those specified later.

Alsace-Lorraine (Periods 2, 3) ..	£3/**£4**/£5
Anti-British (*see also* WAR for Boer War, WW1, WW2)	£5/**£15**/£25
Anti-Royalty. Q. Victoria, Boer War, Edward VII debauchery, George V, WW1)	£3/**£10**/£25
Anti-Semitic (*see also* WAR for National Socialism)	£5/**£15**/£25
Berlin Blockade (1948)	£15/**£25**/£30
Bolshevism/anti-Bolshevism ..	£5/**£10**/£20
Communism (incl. Period 7) ..	£3/**£8**/£10
Edith Cavell (*see also* WAR)	£1/**£3**/£4
Fascism	£3/**£5**/£10
Freemasonry	£1/**£3**/£5
Irish Home Rule/Sinn Fein	£1/**£3**/£5
Lusitania (*see also* WAR)	£1/**£3**/£5
Maternity benefit (1914). ■164a	£1/**£2**/£3
National Insurance Acts	75p/**£1.50**/£3
National Socialism (*see also* WAR)	£3/**£7.50**/£15
Sidney Street Siege	£1/**£3**/£5
Socialism (throughout Europe) ..	£2/**£4**/£10
Spartakist uprising (1919)	£3/**£5**/£8

State Visits (e.g. Czar to France 1896)	£7/**£15**/£25
Strikes (*see also* SOCIAL HISTORY)	£2/**£4**/£8
Suffragettes	£2/**£4**/£8
Tariff Reform	75p/**£1.50**/£3

NOTABLE SERIES

American
Pub. Austen, J. I. America's Famous Men. Series of 50. Period 2 .. .. £1/**£3**/£5
Pub. Coral-Lee. Political series, *see* MODERN
Pub. Donaldson, R. M. Famous Americans (1908) .. .. £1/**£3**/£5
Pub. Sheehan, M. A. (Topanga, California).

■164a

Pub. C. & H. Gurney. Maternity Benefit. Lloyd George caricature 'Thank you Kindly Noble Sir'. 1914 .. .. £1.50

■164b

USA. Pub. Sheehan. President George Washington from set of 32. No. 247 of limited edition of 2000. Period 5 .. .. £2.50

The Presidents of the United States from Washington to Truman. Black silhouettes on yellow background, gilded, marked 'Hand-made original Serigraph'. Limited edition of 2000. ■164b. Period 5. Per card .. .. £1/**£2**/£3
Per set (32 cards) .. .. .. £45/**£75**/£110

British
Pub. Birn Bros. Suffrage series E19, E23. 'This is the House that Man Built'. Per set .. .. £20/**£30**/£45
Pub. Davidson Bros. Fiscal Games, Mr. Chamberlain at . . ., Political Dances, etc. Artist Ludovici (*see* ARTISTS) and others. Per card .. .. £2/**£3**/£4
Pub. Faulkner, C. W. Chamberlain, Fiscal, John Bull, Suffragette series. Artist Arthur Moreland (*see* ARTISTS) and others. Per card .. .. .. £2/**£3**/£4

Hartmann
Eminent Men in their Youth. Period 2 .. .. 75p/**£1**/£2

Inter-Art
'Licker' (National Insurance stamps) series. Period 2. ■166a .. .. .. £1/**£2**/£3

Jarrold
Punch War Cartoons. Period 3 .. £1.50/**£3**/£4

Millar & Lang
Freemason series. Period 2 (*see also* CURIOUS). ■122b .. .. .. £1/**£2**/£3

Tuck
Aesop's Fables by Sancha (*see also* WAR). Period 3 .. .. £4/**£5**/£7
Empire series. UB chromolithographed Statesmen .. .. £3/**£4**/£5
Fiscal series/Game Birds .. .. £2/**£3**/£4
'Political Leaders' .. .. .. £2/**£3**/£4
Others .. .. £1/**£3**/£5

Valentine
Various Political series .. .. £1/**£2**/£3

Wrench
Punch Cartoons (1901) .. .. £2/**£3**/£4

Anonymous
Many anonymous (as to artist and/or publisher) series exist, with powerful political themes .. .. .. £1/**£3**/£5

French
Many are reproductions from satiric publications like *Le Rire*. † = *see also* ARTISTS for more details.
Musée des Sires. Artist Roubille .. £5/**£10**/£15
Musée des Souverains. Artists E. Cadel, Léal de Camara†, P. Kauffmann, Charles Léandre .. .. £5/**£10**/£15
Le Burin Satirique and other limited edition series by Orens† .. .. £7/**£15**/£20
Les Organisateurs de la Guerre and other limited edition series by Léal de Camara† ■165b .. .. .. £7/**£15**/£20
Les Monstres des Cathédrales. Period 3 caricatures .. .. £2/**£3**/£4
Anonymous anti-Establishment series .. .. £3/**£10**/£15

■165a
Pub. Lustigen Blätter *newspaper. The epicurean Edward VII. Period 2* £5

■165b
The Organisers of the War. No. 14 General Orloff. Edition limited to 100 by Léal de Camara. Period 3 .. ..£15

Italian

Many fine series of propaganda cards exist for Periods 2 to 5 notably 'Edith Cavell' by Corbella (*see also* WAR) .. £2/**£15**/£20

Portuguese

Series of 14 col. postcards published by the Information Dept. of the Armed Forces Movement showing the political revolution from 28 Sept. 1974–25 Nov. 1975. Artists: Alves, Amaral, Joao, Manta, Rosa, Ruivo, Velez, Vespeira.
Per set **£3.50**

POLITICAL ARTISTS

† = *see also* ARTISTS for more details.
Camara, Léal de, Noel. ■165b. French. Powerful political satire. Period 1. Usually small limited editions .. .. £5/**£15**/£25
Carter, Reg.† Political cartoons. Pub. E. Mack .. .. £1/**£1.50**/£2
Corbella, Tito† Edith Cavell .. £2/**£4**/£6
Crane, Walter. *Punch* contributor, famous for illustrations of children's books .. .. £2/**£3**/£5
Davey, Geo. Sometimes signed 'Geo. D'. Valentine's Suffragette series .. £1/**£2**/£4
'Dudley'. Joseph Chamberlain caricature (as Bubbles). Pub. W. McKenzie .. 75p/**£1**/£2
Furniss, Harry. Political cartoons with a humorous slant. Pub. John Walker & Co. .. .. £1/**£2**/£4
Ludovici.† Pub. Davidson Bros. Several series incl. Rosebery at Sheffield, Joseph Chamberlain at Glasgow ■112c £2/**£3**/£4
Maurice, Reg. Signed 'Reg. M.'. Pub. Regent Pub. Co. (1906) .. .. 75p/**£1**/£1.50
Mirko. Italian artist. Fascist propaganda in a distinct *Art Deco* style. Period 4 .. .. £2/**£4**/£8
Moreland, Arthur. John Bull series. Pub. C. W. Faulkner ■69b .. .. £2/**£3**/£4
Orens.† Also signed 'Denizard', 'Godillot'. French. Powerful caricatures of political/war leaders. Often small limited editions .. ..£3/**£7.50**/£22
Partridge, Bernard. Humour with a political flavour, incl. cartoons from *Punch*. Pub. Wrench (1901) .. .. £2/**£3**/£4
Raemaekers, Louis.† See also WAR. Period 3 cartoons .. ..£1/**£2**/£2.50
Raven-Hill, Leonard. Pub. Wrench. Pictures from *Punch* (1901) .. .. £1.50/**£2**/£3

Raven-Hill, Leonard. Pub. Jarrold. *Punch* war cartoons. Period 3 .. ..50p/**£1**/£1.50
Retrosi, Virgilio. 1892–. Italian artist. Fascist propaganda. Period 4 .. £2/**£4**/£6
Rostro (Fr). Several editions limited to 250 and other political caricatures. Period 2 .. .. £5/**£10**/£15
Roubille (Fr). Anti Militarist. 'Musee des Sires' etc. Period 2 .. .. .. £5/**£10**/£15
Roverini, Mario. Italian artist. Fascist propaganda. Period 4 .. .. £1/**£3**/£5
Spurgin, Fred.† (Also under his initials, 'FS'.) Suffragette/National Insurance themes for several publishers, notably Inter-Art. ■166a .. .. .. £2/**£4**/£6
Thiele, A.† Period 3. German propaganda/military .. .. £2/**£4**/£6
Sancha. Pub. Tuck. Aesop's fables WW1 style (*see also* WAR) (also in Dutch, French) .. .. £4/**£5**/£7

■166a

Pub. Inter-Art. 'Licker' series. National Insurance stamps. Artist Fred Spurgin (unsigned) .. £4

POLITICAL LEADERS/PERSONALITIES

Heads of State, Members of Parliament, Presidents, Prime Ministers, Royalty. Favourite subjects are—*Britain*: Balfour, Campbell-Bannerman, Joseph Chamberlain, Churchill, Edward VII, Sir Edward Grey, Lloyd George and Queen Victoria; *France*: Clemenceau, Felix Faure, de Gaulle, Loubet and Poincaré; *Germany*: Bismarck, Hitler and the Kaiser; *USA*: Eisenhower, Kennedy, Lincoln, Nixon, Washington (*see also* GREETINGS/HOLIDAYS).
Period 7 subjects include: Ayatollah Khomeini, Giscard d'Estaing, Elizabeth II, Pope John Paul II, Jeremy Thorpe (*see also* MODERN).

Cartoons/Caricatures
Value according to quality of the artist
.. .. £2/**£5**/£20

Political Campaigns/Candidates/Election Results/Groups of Cabinets/Governments
Artist drawn ■167a .. .. .. 75p/**£1.50**/£3
Photographic in origin. ■167b .. £1/**£3**/£5

Straight Portraits
Artist drawn. Value according to quality of
artist .. .. £1/**£2**/£3
Photographic. Publishers include Beagles,
Rotary, Tuck, F. W. Woolworth 75p/**£1.50**/£2

PUNISHMENT & JUSTICE

Famous Trials
Dreyfus Affair. Periods 1, 2. Several series,
of 6 to 12 cards, from 1900 to 1914
(add premium for complete set) £5/**£10**/£15
Haarmann the Mass Murderer (1924)
.. .. £2/**£4**/£6
Landru. Period 2. Artist Poulbot.† £6/**£8**/£10
Ditto. Others .. .. £2/**£3**/£5
Other trials. British and French. Periods 2,
7 .. .. £2/**£5**/£10

Punishments
Chain gangs/convicts/prisoners and prisons/
slave ships. Clear photographs .. £1/**£2**/£4
Decapitation/flogging/hanging/various exe-
cutions and punishments. Clear photographs .. .. £1.50/**£3**/£5
Tottenham Assassins. Privately produced,
real photo cards of the siege and the
suicides .. .. 75p/**£1**/£3

Unusual Punishments
Fr. Series of comic artist drawn penalties of
gossip—hideously enlarged tongues.
Period 2. ■167c .. .. .. 75p/**£1**/£1.25
Ger. Pub. Nister. col. artist drawn series
which includes ducking, muzzling, neck
collars, pillories, stocks, etc. Period 2
.. .. 75p/**£1**/£1.50

■167a

Pub. U.S.S.P.C. Co. No. 456. Artist Gossett. The Politician. 1905 .. .. £1.50

■167b

Pub. Newcastle Socialist Society. Portrait of R. B. Cunninghame-Graham. Period 2 .. .. .. £3

■167c

French. Pub. 'G.P.', Paris. Penalty for speaking ill of others. Period 2 .. .. £1

PUBLISHERS

This is a new section, and our object here is to establish a pattern for the development of a major PUBLISHERS section in future editions. Included here is a detailed listing of 'LL' cards of central London and Inter-Art cards of pre-1918. Such detailed listings are only possible by the discovery of a wholesaler's stock book/publisher's trade lists or through the exhaustive study of a vast number of postcards. The following lists have been compiled by using both methods, and we invite contributions from Clubs, individual collectors and dealers for future entries.

DAVIDSON BROS.

This company is associated with good quality humorous cards drawn by the best British artists of Period 2. Production probably began in 1902 at about the time that the divided back card was introduced, because few UB Davidson cards are to be found. Series 2502, their second series, exists both in divided and undivided versions. Their most prolific artist was Tom Browne, who often signed himself 'Tom B', and Davidson's claimed to have a monopoly on Browne's drawings. Nevertheless Tom Browne did do some work for Alexander Baird, Hartmann, Tuck, Wrench and Valentine's, as well as a number of advertisement cards. However, the sum total of Browne's other postcard work is less than his Davidson's output. His Davidson series, each of 6 cards, run consecutively from No. 2500 to No. 2648, i.e. about 900 designs. An artist by artist analysis of the 1905/06 McMullen stock book shows the following numerical make-up amongst the 828 different cards on offer.

Artist	No. of different cards
Browne, Tom.	318
Bull, René	6
Duncan, Hamish	36
Fuller, Edmund	6
Hardy, Dudley	72
Hassall, John	54
Ludovici, Anthony	48
May, Phil	24
Owen, Will	18
Pyp	12
Stanlaws, Penrhyn	6

The remaining cards are unsigned comics, photographic pictures of stage personalities, panel cards and midget series.

INTER-ART (International Art Company)

This company is associated with humour by most collectors and in particular with the work of Donald McGill. Of the over 8000 different designs accredited to Inter-Art the majority are indeed comic, but there are other themes as we indicate below. The first cards were issued in 1909 and the firm's output seems to have been unaffected by the First World War. Mysteriously, production stopped in 1935 and began again 16 years later in 1951—but only for that year. Various addresses appear on the cards and may be approximately attributed as follows: Southampton House, London WC (pre 1914); Kinofilm House, Red Lion Square, London, WC (1914 onward); Florence House, Barnes, London, SW (post WW1). Some cards published at an earlier address were republished at a subsequent one and occasionally renamed as a 'Comique' series.

The listing here has been divided into three parts:

Artists. Artists whose signed work was published by Inter-Art.

Themes. An alphabetical listing of collectable themes that may be followed through Inter-Art cards.

Check List. The listing is in chronological order, for cards issued 1909–1918

Artists

	No. of cards
G.A. (or could be G.B.)	32
Barribal, W.	91
Butcher, Arthur	343
Buxton, Dudley	146
A.C.	6
Calport	10
Cowham, Hilda	24
Earnshaw, Harold	1
Ellam, W. H.	1
Felix	60
Gay, Helen B	12
Hassall, John	7
Hayes, F. W.	24
Hudson, Isabel	36
Kit-Cat	12
O'Brien, Kitty	1
Lewin, F. G.	61
Martin, P.	24

McCrum, R.	1
McG., H.	6
McGill, Donald	3459
Meadon, Charles	1
Morgan, Val	6
Morgan, F. E.	16
Mike	27
C.M.	4
Nash, A. A.	156
Overnell	6
Peddie, Tom	27
Quiggel, C. W.	6
Richardson, Agnes	66
Rutherford	5
Sherie	36
Spurgin, Fred	551
Studdy	12
Ⓢ	24
Valter, Eugene	36
Valter, Florence	12
Vere, Audry de	6
Wain, Louis	1
Widdowson	18
William	12
Wilson, Oscar	54
Wood, Lawson	49
Woollett	6
Young, G. H.	7 or 18

Themes

Art (Scenic); Bathing Beauties; Bonzo; Cats; Charabanc humour; Chicks; Children; Crossword humour; Dancing (Tango); Dogs; Fashions (Harem Hobble); Felix the Cat; Glamour; Greetings (Birthday, Christmas, Easter, New Year, Valentine); Horses; Humour (Bobbed hair, Children, Chinese, Drink, Egyptian, Golf, Hiking, Leap Year, Military, Negro, Police, Political, Seaside, Scottish, WW1); Insurance Act (humour); Language of (stamps, vegetables); Mickey Mouse; Nursery Rhymes; Nutime (Summertime); Patriotic (Child, humour, serious); Political; Red Cross; Roller Skating; Scouting; Sentimental; Silks; Song; Suffragette; Summertime; Telephone; Wireless.

Check List

Numbers	Series	Artist	Year
501–524	Photogravure	Rutherford (*et al.*)	1909
601–643	Kute Kiddies		1909
701–771	Artcolor		1909
801–807	Cock-a-Doodle Doo	Kit Cat	1910

Numbers	Series	Artist	Year
807–812	Kute Pets		1910
814–819	Sherie	Sherie	1911
820–825	Dainty Girls		1911
826–837	Coronation		1911
838–849	Hobble	Spurgin	1911
850–861	Harem	Spurgin	1911
862–885	Katchy		1911
886–891	Happy Kiddies		1911
892–987	Simple		1911
898–905	Winning		1911
907–911	Cupids	Sherie	1911
915–924	Spurgin	Spurgin	1911
925–930	Haremette	Spurgin	1911
931–936	Bloomer Kids	Spurgin	1912
937–942	American Kiddies		1912
943–948	Novel		1912
949–960	Leap Year	Spurgin	1912
961–966	Johnny		1912
967–972	Turks	Spurgin	1912
973–978	Amour	Sherie	1912
979–984	Nipper	Spurgin	1912
985–996	Do Write		1912
51–60	Kute Kristmas Kiddies	Kit Kat	1912
62–84	Topical Christmas	Spurgin	1912
102–112	Springtime		1912
115–137	Seaside	Spurgin	1912
138–145		Sherie	1912
150–161	Pastel		1912
162–167	Katchy Kids	Spurgin	1912
168–173	Pannier	Spurgin	1912
174–179	Hudson		1912
180–191	Xmas	Spurgin	1912
192–197	Licker		1912
198–203	Mephisto	Spurgin	1912
204–209	Beauty	Spurgin	1912
210–215	Mal-de-Mer		1912
215–227		Spurgin	1912
228–233		Sherie	1912
234–237	Quaint Kids		1912
239–240	Tartan	Spurgin	1912
244–249	Bobby	Spurgin	1912
250–255	Cinema		1912
264–265	Target	Spurgin	1912
267–273	Quaint Kiddies	Spurgin	1913
274–279	Birthday	Spurgin	1913
282		Spurgin	1913
286	Fireflies		1913
287–292	Cat Bow		1913
293–298		I. Hudson	1913
299–304	Monk		1913
305–310	Yankee Kids		1913
311–316	English Kids	Spurgin	1913
317–322	Dutch Kids	Spurgin	1913
323–328	Jack Tar	Spurgin	1913
329–334	Katz		1913
335–340	Art Kids	Overnell	1913
341–346	Cafe	Spurgin	1913
347–352	Birthday	Hudson	1913
353–358	Kitty Kats	Spurgin	1913

Numbers	Series	Artist	Year	Numbers	Series	Artist	Year
361		Barribal	1913	754–756	Artistic	Spurgin	1914
364–370		Tom Peddie	1913	772–777	Camp		1914
371–376	Tiny Tots	Spurgin	1913	778			1914
377–388	Kiddoo	Spurgin	1913	784–789			1914
389–394	Hennery	Spurgin	1913	791–795	Patriotic II	Spurgin	1914
402		Peddie?	1913	796–807	Patriotic III	Spurgin & Ellam	1914
402–406	Brine	Spurgin	1913	808–819	Patriotic IV	McGill	1914
424	Knuts		1913	820–825	Our Heroes	Quiggel	1914
432–437	Wedding Bells	Barribal *et al.*	1913	828–833	Allies	Nash	1914
328–443	Fairies	Cowham	1913	834–845	Remembrance		1914
444–449	Scout	Spurgin	1913	846–850	Patriotic VII	Spurgin	1914
450–455	C.O.H.		1913	852–857	Boy Scouts	Spurgin	1914
456–461	Panel	Spurgin	1913	858–869	Patriotic V or VII		1914
462–467	Odd Kids	Spurgin	1913	870–881	Patriotic Xmas		1914
468–473	Patriotic 1	Spurgin	1913	884–889	British		1914
474–479	Wee Mites	Spurgin	1913	890–895	British	Nash	1914
480–485	Bow-Wow	Spurgin	1913	896–901		McGill	1915
486–491	Youngster	Spurgin	1913	902–907	Navee	McGill	1915
492–497	Xmas	Spurgin	1913	908–913	Armee	McGill	1915
498–503	Xmas	Cowham	1913	914–919	Huns		1915
504–509	Xmas	Nash	1913	920–925	Recruits	McGill	1915
510	Pelican		1914	926–931	Bulldog	Spurgin	1915
511–519	Mirth	Spurgin	1914	932–937	Bulldog	McGill *et al.*	1915
523–534	Girlie	Spurgin	1914	938–943	Steadfast	Spurgin	1915
535–536		Hudson & Hassall	1914	944–949	Patriotic Kids	Nash	1915
540–549	Waifs	Spurgin	1914	950–955	S.P.C.	McGill	1915
550	Tango	Spurgin	1914	956–961	R.C.	McGill	1915
551–552		Rutherford	1914	962–973	Comrade II	Spurgin	1915
554–559	Chic	Spurgin	1914	974–979	Birthday Remembrance		1915
560–565	Chic Kids	Spurgin	1914	980–991	Greetings		1915
566–571	Wee Rogues	Spurgin	1914	101–112	Birthday I		1915
572–577	Freak		1914	111–124	Silk		1915
578–583	Luvnot	Spurgin	1914	119–124	Good Luck	Spurgin	1915
584–589	Topics	Spurgin	1914	125–130	Pelican		1915
590–595	Nash	Nash	1914	131–136	N.V.R.	McGill	1915
596–601	Cowham	Cowham	1914	137–148	Birthday II		1915
602–607	Babes		1914	149–154	One-Four-Nine	Spurgin	1915
608–613	Catchem	H. McG.	1914	155–160	Birthday Tommy	McGill	1915
614–619	Fairy	Spurgin	1914	161–172	One-Six-One	McGill	1915
620		Hudson	1914	173–178	K.A.	McGill	1915
624–631	Coon	Some Spurgin	1914	179–	Cheer Up		1915
632–636	Tango	Spurgin	1914	197–202	One-Nine-Seven	Spurgin	1915
638			1914	203–208	Two-o-Three	McGill	1915
640–645	Komic Kids	Spurgin	1914	209–220	Two-o-Nine	Nash	1915
652–657		A. De Vere	1914	221–226	Cherie	Spurgin	1915
664–669		Spurgin	1914	227–232	Cherie	Butcher	1915
670–675			1914	233–244	Beach	Spurgin	1915
676–681	Witty	Spurgin	1914	245–250	Good Luck	McGill	1915
684	Kitty	L. Wain	1914	251–256	New Love	Spurgin	1915
688–692	Robert	Spurgin	1914	257–262	Terrier	Spurgin	1915
693–698	Holiday		1914	263–268	Two-Six-Three	McGill	1915
699–707	Holiday	Spurgin	1914	269–274	Forget-Me-Not	Spurgin	1915
712–717	Racy	Spurgin	1914	275–280	Alliance	Spurgin	1915
718–728	Doggie	Nash	1914	281–292	Two-Eight-One	McGill	1915
724–729	Ocean		1914	293–304	Two-Nine-Three	Nash *et al.*	1915
730–735	Kiltie		1914	305–316	Relation Birthday		1915
736–741	Golf		1914	1001–1006	N.A.	Spurgin	1915
742–747	Tommy	Spurgin	1914	1007–1012	N.A.	Spurgin	1915
748–753	Spooney		1914	1013–1018	Our Fair Allies	Widdowson	1915

Numbers	Series	Artist	Year	Numbers	Series	Artist	Year
1019–1024	Our Own Girls	Butcher	1915	1559–1560	Nutime	McGill	1916
1025–1036	Local	McGill	1915	1569–1574	Artistique		1916
1037–1042	Protection	McGill	1915	1587	Artistique	Barribal	1916
1043–1048	I2U	McGill	1915	1591–1596	Artistique	Lawson Wood	1916
1049–1060	Khaki	Spurgin	1915	1597–1602	Artistique	Richardson	1916
1061–1066	Ten-Six-One	Spurgin	1915	1603–1608	Comique		1916
1072–1084	I2U	McGill	1915	1609–1620	Comique	McGill	1916
1091–1096	A.N.	Nash	1915	1621–1638	Xmas	McGill	1916
1098–1103	Ten-Nine-Eight	Butcher	1915	1639–1644	Xmas	Butcher	1916
1104–1109	Eleven-o-Four	Nash	1915	1645–1650	Comique	McGill	1916
1110–1115	Home Sweet Home	Spurgin	1915	1651–1656	Comique	McGill	1916
1116–1121	Valient		1915	1657–1668	Comique	McGill	1916
1122–1127	Eleven-Twenty-Two	McGill	1915	1669–1674	Artistique	Nash	1916
1128–1133	Eleven-Twenty-Two	Spurgin	1915	1675–1680	Artistique	O. W.	1916
1134–1139	Xmas I-2-U	McGill	1915	1681–1686	Artistique	Butcher	1916
1140–1152	Xmas Gift	McGill	1915	1687–1692	Artistique		1916
1153–1176	Xmas Greeting		1915	1693–1698	Artistique	Nash & Butcher	1916
1177–1182	United Six	Butcher	1915	1699–1728	Comique	McGill & Morgan	1917
1183–1188	A.B.	Butcher	1915	1729–1734	Artistique	Barribal	1917
1189–1194	Sentinel	Nash	1916	1735–1740	Artistique	E. M. Valter	1917
1195–1200	Waiting	Widdowson	1916	1741–1746	Artistique	Nash	1917
1201–1206	Thistle	McGill	1916	1747–1752	Artistique	Barribal	1917
1207–1209	Thistle		1916	1753–1758	Artistique	Wood	1917
1214–1225	The Front	McGill	1916	1759–1764	Artistique	E. M. Valter	1917
1232–1237	Song	Butcher	1916	1765–1770	Artistique	Richardson	1917
1238–1249	Twelve Thirty Eight	McGill	1916	1771–1776	Comique	Buxton	1917
1250–1255	Twelve Fifty	Nash	1916	1777–1788	Comique	McGill	1917
1256–1261	Twelve Fifty Six	Nash	1916	1789–1812	Comique	McGill	1917
1262–1267	Twelve Sixty Two		1916	1813–1818	Comique	McGill	1917
1268–1273	Twelve Sixty Eight	McGill	1916	1852–1875	Local Comique	McGill	1917
1274–1285	Twelve Seven Four	McGill	1916	1876–1890	Comique	McGill	1917
1286–1291	Twelve Eighty Six	McGill	1916	1891–1892	Comique	Buxton	1917
1292–1303	Twelve Eighty Six	Buxton	1916	1898	Comique	McGill	1917
1298–1303	Artistique	Nash	1916	1901–1906	Artistique	Nash & Wood	1917
1304–1309	Artistique	Widdowson	1916	1911	Artistique	Wilson	1917
1310–1315	Artistique		1916	1917–1922	Artistique	Wilson	1917
1324	Artistique	Butcher	1916	1939–1943	Artistique	Nash	1917
1325–1334	Comique	McGill	1916	1951–1956	Artistique	Wood	1917
1335–1339	Comique		1916	1957–1963	Artistique	Richardson	1917
1343–1345	Comique		1916	1969–2005	Comique	McGill & Buxton	1917
1347–1357	First Line	McGill	1916	2010–2058	Comique	McGill (mostly) & few	1917
1361–1364	Comique		1916			Morgan & Buxton	
1365–1376	Comique	Buxton	1916	2059–2064	Artistique	Richardson	1917
1377–1408	Comique	McGill, Buxton	1916	2065–2070	Artistique	Nash	1917
1410–1418	Artistique	Butcher & Anon	1916	2071–2076	Artistique	A. C.	1917
1421–1426	Comique	Nash	1916	2077–2082	Artistique	Wooller	1917
1427–1434	Artistique	McGill	1916	2083–2088	Artistique		1917
1438	Artistique	O.W.	1916	2089–2100	Artistique Songs	McGill & *Anon*	1917
1441–1444	Artistique	Butcher	1916	2106	Artistique	Nash	1917
1447–1452	Comique	McGill	1916	2007–2112	Artistique	Barribal	1917
1453–1457	Comique	Buxton	1916	2113–2118	Comique	McGill	1917
1458–1492	Comique	McGill	1916	2119–2154	Comique	McGill (one Morgan)	1917
1469–1474	Comique	McGill	1916	2155–2160	Comique	Buxton	1917
1481–1489	Comique	McGill	1916	2162–2195	Comique	McGill	1917
1493–1498	Artistique	McGill	1916	2199	Artistique	Richardson	1917
1517–1522	Floral		1916	2213–2218	Artistique Xmas		1917
1529–1534	Comique	A. Butcher	1916	2229–2231	Artistique		1917
1535–1558	Comique	McGill	1916	2233–2238	Artistique	Barribal	1917
1551–1557	Comique	D. Mc.	1916	2239–2244	Artistique	Wood	1917

Numbers	Series	Artist	Year
2245–2250	Artistique	Nash	1918
2251–2256	Artistique	E. M. Valter	1918
2257–2262	Artistique	F. E. Lewin	1918
2263–2268	Artistique	Richardson	1918
2275–2280	Comique	McGill	1918
2281–2298	Comique	McGill	1918
2299–2304	Comique	Buxton	1918
2305–2310	Comique		1918
2311–2316	Comique	McGill	1918
2317–2334	Comique	McGill	1918
2335–2346	Artistique	G B	1918
2359	Artistique	F. E. Valter	1918
2363–2368	Artistique	Barribal	1918
2371–2382	Comique	McGill *et al.*	1918
2383–2388	Comique	McGill	1918
2389–2448	Comique	McGill *et al.*	1918
2411–2424	Comique	McGill	1918
2455–2466	Comique	McGill	1918
2467–2472	Comique		1918
2473–2478	Artistique	Richardson	1918
2485–2490	Artistique	Nash	1918
2491–2496	Artistique	Barribal	1918
2497–2502	Artistique		1918
2509–2514	Artistique		1918
2515–2520	Artistique	F. C. Lewin	1918
2521–2526	Artistique		1918
2527–2544	Comique	McGill	1918
2545–2550	Comique	McGill	1918

LL   Louis Levy

Every postcard collector knows the initials 'LL'. In recent years there has been considerable debate concerning the interpretation to be placed upon the double 'L' sign. Most collectors accept that the initials derive from the name 'Louis Levy', but many do not believe that every card carrying the letters was produced by Levy, or originated from a photograph taken by him. Levy cards cover France, the French Colonial Territories of Period 2, Spain, North Africa and the battlefields of WW1 as well as much of England south of the Wash. It does seem a mammoth task for one man to accomplish. One theory suggests that Louis Levy was not only a photographer and publisher but also an inventor. There were two brothers— Louis F. Levy and Max Levy—of Philadelphia, who perfected the half tone screen in 1888 and an advanced acid etching system in 1899, both of which led to a greatly improved printed picture. The techniques were combined in a piece of equipment which became known as the 'Levy Machine'. It is proposed that they franchised their technique and sold their machines in Europe and America. When used by other printers the letters 'LL' had to be displayed on the final product. This theory has not been disproved.

LL cards do not often carry details of the publisher but the following variations (in a range of styles) are known:

> 'Levy Sons & Co. Paris'
> 'Levy et Neurdein Reunis Paris'.

This does suggest that the whole Levy family was involved in the business and that the Paris end may have been run by Louis Levy Junior. Neurdein was a publisher with a product very similar to the *LL*, but active mostly in France, and his 'by-line' implies an amalgamation with *LL*. In Britain *LL* operated through a London agent and cards can be found with a retailer's imprint on the reverse. The *LL* view card is a near masterpiece. Most are superbly printed and provide clear details, but they are not quite close-up enough. It is the very clarity of the picture that makes the absence of close-up views irritating. Nevertheless the cards are most collectable, particularly in the provinces.

Almost without exception the cards are captioned and numbered on the front. The numbers begin from 1 in each area or theme and it is sometimes difficult to distinguish one sequence from another. Coloured cards are in the minority but their relative scarceness does not necessarily add to their value because the colouring sometimes reduces the clarity hence making them less desirable.

The listing here first indicates those areas in England for which a significant number of *LL* cards is known to exist and then considers a London category in detail under the heading *A London Listing*.

LL Areas

Alfriston (Sussex); Amesbury (Wilts.); Arundel (Sussex); Banbury (Oxon); Bath (Som.); Bexhill (Sussex); Birchington-on-Sea (Kent); Bognor (Sussex); Boscombe (Hants); Bournemouth (Hants); Bourne End (Bucks.); Brighton (Sussex); Broadstairs (Kent); Bromley (Kent); Cambridge; Canterbury (Kent); Channel Islands; Cheddar (Som.); Cheltenham (Glos.); Chichester (Sussex); Chislehurst (Kent); Christchurch (Hants); Cliftonville (Kent); Corfe (Dorset); Combe Martin (Som.); Cosham (Hants); Crediton (Devon); Cromer (Norfolk); Deal (Kent); Dover (Kent); Ealing (London); Eastbourne (Sussex); Eton (Berks.); Exeter (Devon); Felixstowe (Suffolk); Folkestone (Kent); Frinton-on-Sea (Essex); Gloucester; Gorleston-on-Sea (Norfolk); Great Yarmouth (Norfolk); Hastings (Sussex); Hayes (Kent); Herne Bay (Kent); Hythe (Kent); Ilfracombe (Devon); Isle of Wight;

Kenilworth (Warwickshire); Kingsgate; Leamington (Warwickshire); Lee-on-Sea; Littlehampton (Sussex); Lowestoft (Suffolk); Lynmouth (Devon); Margate (Kent); Norwich (Norfolk); Oxford; Portsmouth (Hants); Rye (Sussex); Ramsgate (Kent); Salisbury (Wilts.); Southampton (Hants); Southsea (Hants); St. Leonards (Sussex); Seaford (Sussex); Swanage (Dorset); Stratford-on-Avon (Warwickshire); Torquay (Devon); Tunbridge Wells (Kent); Westgate (Kent); Weston-Super-Mare (Som.); Weymouth (Dorset); Winchester (Hants).

LONDON LISTING

We have set out information describing the cards which, beginning from the number one, are the 'London' series by *LL*. They cover the Central London area. Most of the cards are black and white. A few are repeated in colour with the same number, e.g. No. 80, and it may be that some only exist in colour, e.g. No. 48, although that seems unlikely. There are a few cards in brown, e.g. No. 77 and a smaller number in brown with gold lettering, e.g. No. 14. Brown card views are also found repeated in colour, each type carrying the same number, e.g. No. 89. The complexity of the possible permutations may be illustrated by examining cards where a number is repeated, e.g. No. 105. There are 3 versions. The brown one is a view from exactly the same place as the black and white and coloured versions, but it was photographed at a different time and has a postal district (EC) in the title. The picture in the other two, however, is identical in each one.

Most titles are on the front of the cards together with the identifying number, but examples exist with the title repeated on the address side, or not on the picture side at all. Cards with the same title are generally different views, e.g. No. 84 and No. 86, but since several photographs were usually taken at each spot, cards with the same view but marginally separated in time can turn up with different numbers, e.g. No. 55 and No. 65. In some cases where a clock (e.g. Big Ben) is captured by the camera the exact time between photographs can be estimated, e.g. the separation between No. 8 and No. 11 is 8 minutes (7 to 15 minutes past 4).

LL cards may be found postmarked from 1902 to the 1920s and immediately following WW1 a large number were reprinted from the original plates. These later printings are very black and often clearer than the earlier ones. On the address

side the stamp box is without a border, and the dividing line is often slightly off centre.

We wish to expand this list and to extend it beyond London. Contributions are invited. All information received will be acknowledged.

LL. London & District

1. St. Paul's Cath. & City—Birds Eye View
2. Birds Eye View of St. Paul's Cath. & City from St. Bride's Church
3. St. Paul's Cath. from River
4. Houses of Parliament
5. SW—Houses of Parliament
6. Houses of Parliament
7. SW—Houses of Parliament
8. House of Parliament—Clock Tower (V)
11. Houses of Parliament—(V)
12. SW—House of Lords—Victoria Tower (V)
13. House of Lords from Victoria Gardens
14. SW—House of Commons—Terrace
15. St. Stephen's Hall Westminster
16. Houses of Parliament—Clock Tower (V)
17. House of Lords—Royal Entrance (V)
18. House of Lords—King's Robing Room
19. House of Lords—King's Robing Room
21. House of Lords
22. House of Lords—Throne
24. House of Lords—Prince's Chamber
25. House of Lords—Marble Group, Prince's Chamber (V) (*1909*)
26. Clapham—Common (South) (*1920s*)
27. House of Lords—Library (*1908*)
28. House of Lords—Lobby—Brass Gate (V) (*1908*)
29. Houses of Parliament—Central Hall
30. House of Commons—Crypt Chapel
31. House of Commons
32. House of Commons
33. House of Commons—Lobby (*1918*)
34. House of Commons—Cloisters (V)
35. House of Commons—Bust of Oliver Cromwell (V)
36. Stephen's Hall, Westminster—Statue of Pitt (V)
37. House of Commons—Statue of Gladstone (V)
38. Westminster Abbey
39. House of Commons—Crypt Chapel (*1919*)
39. SW—Westminster Abbey & St. Margaret's Church
40. Westminster from Dean's Yard (+C)
41. Westminster Abbey—NW (V) (*1908*)
42. Westminster Abbey—NW (V) (*1910*)
43. Westminster Abbey—NW
44. Westminster Abbey—N entrance (V)

46. Westminster Abbey—Coronation Stone Chair (V)
48. British Museum (C)
50. Waterloo Bridge
51. National Gallery & St. Martin's Church (C)
52. National Gallery
53. Tower Bridge—Looking NW
54. Tower Bridge & Tower of London (+C)
55. EC—Tower Bridge—Looking N (V)
55. Tower Bridge—Looking N (V) (+C)
56. Tower Bridge—Looking N (V)
57. View down Thames from London Bridge
60. Tower of London & Tower Bridge (*1911*)
61. St. Paul's Cath.—Monument of Lord Nelson (V)
62. Tower of London from River
63. Tower of London from top of Tower Bridge
65. Tower Bridge—Looking N (V)
65. Lambeth Palace from Lambeth Bridge
66. High Holborn (V)
67. WC—Hotel Cecil & Victoria Embankment (*1906*)
67. Victoria Embankment & Hotel Cecil
68. WC—Victoria Embankment Gdns. showing Hotel Cecil & Cleopatra's Needle (*1908*)
69. Victoria Embankment (+C)
69. Victoria Embankment
70. Cleopatra's Needle (V)
71. WC—Westminster Pier (*1923*)
72. Carlton Hotel (V)
74. London Bridge
74. EC—London Bridge
75. London Bridge
76. SE—Blackfriar's Bridge (*1907*)
77. Royal Exchange & Bank of England
77. Royal Exchange & Bank of England
78. Royal Exchange & Bank of England. ■176a
80. Cheapside—Looking W (*1923*) (+C)
81. The Strand
82. Charing Cross Station
84. Charing Cross & Trafalgar Sq. (V) (*1909*)
86. Charing Cross & Trafalgar Sq.
88. Trafalgar Sq. (*1909*) (+C)
89. Trafalgar Sq. (+C)
93. Trafalgar Sq. & St. Martin's Church (V)
94. Nelson's Monument—Trafalgar Sq. (V)
94. Nelson's Monument—Trafalgar Sq. (V)
95. View from National Gallery
96. The Strand
96. The Strand & Aldwych (+C)
97. The Strand
98. WC—Strand from Charing Cross
99. Strand & St. Clements Danes Church
100. Fleet Street (*1914*). ■175a
101. Griffin on site of old Temple Bar (V)

102. EC—Cheapside—Looking E (V) (*1908*)
104. Law Courts & Strand (V)
105. EC—Ludgate Circus (V)
105. Ludgate Circus (V) (+C)
108. Cheapside—Looking E (V) (*1916*)
108. Cheapside—Looking E (V)
109. St Paul's Churchyard from Cheapside (V)
110. Piccadilly Circus
110. Piccadilly
112. Piccadilly (+C)
113. Piccadilly
115. Regent Street
116. Regent Street
118. Regent Street
118. Regent Street
119. Holborn Viaduct
120. EC—Holborn Viaduct & City Temple E
123. EC—Holborn Viaduct. ■176b
125. Shaftesbury Avenue
127. Leicester Sq. & Alhambra
128. Royal Entrance to Houses of Lords (V)
128. Waterloo Place & Crimean Memorial
129. Crimea Memorial, Waterloo Place (V)
132. Regent Street
133. Oxford Street
135. Oxford Street (V)
136. Oxford Street W from Tottenham Court Rd.
138. W—Oxford Circus
139. Oxford Circus
143. EC—General Post Office & St. Martins-le-Grand (*1907*)
145. General View from the Monument (+C)
146. EC—Whitehall & Nelson's Monument (*1907*)
147. Whitehall
148. Big Ben (V)
149. Foreign Office Whitehall (*1907*)
150. War & Foreign Offices from St. James' Park
150. War & Foreign Offices (+C)
152. Horse Guards & War Office from St. James' Park (+C)
153. Natural History Museum
154. Imperial Institute
156. EC—St. Paul's Cath.—Interior Looking E.
157. St. Paul's Cath.—Interior (V)
158. St. Paul's Cath.—Choir looking E (V) (*1909*)
159. The Coliseum (V)
160. St. Paul's Cath.—Crypt Chapel
161. St. Paul's Cath.—Monument of Nelson (V)
162. The Guildhall (V)
163. EC—Liverpool Street Station
166. EC—Ludgate Hill Stn. & New Bridge St. (*1906*)
167. SW—Pall Mall (*1907*)

■175a

Pub. 'LL' London Series 'Fleet Street' No. 100 £8

283. Old Curiosity Shop
284. Tottenham Court Road (V)
288. Queen's Hotel—Leicester Sq. (V)
290. Haymarket Theatre (*1914*)
292. Alhambra & Leicester Sq. (*1911*)
299. Hyde Park—Feeding the Pigeons
301. London Types—Beefeater at the Tower of London (V)
302. London Types—Pavement Artist (V). ■176c
303. London Types—The Fireman (V)
304. Guards' Band at St. James' Palace
306. Tower of London—Middle Tower (*1914*)
307. Tower of London—Byward Tower
308. Tower of London—Traitor's Gate & St. Thomas Tower
310. Tower of London—Armoury Hall in Council Chamber
311. Tower of London—Armoury Hall in Council Chamber
313. Savoy & Cecil Hotels
316. Natural History Museum—Central Hall
317. Natural History Museum—Central Hall (V)
321. Buckingham Palace & Queen Victoria Memorial—Guards Band passing
322. Queen Victoria Memorial
323. Queen Victoria Memorial (V)
324. Buckingham Palace & Queen Victoria Memorial (V)
328. Buckingham Palace—The Throne (V)
338. London—Buckingham Palace—The Yellow Drawing Room (V)
347. Kensington Gardens—Peter Pin (*sic*) (V)
354. Kew Gardens—Japanese Temple Gates
355. Kew Gardens—The Rock Garden
369. Marble Arch
371. Fleet Street & St. Pauls
373. Savoy & Cecil Hotels
387. Piccadilly Circus
397. Rotten Row (C)
407. Whitehall
420. Trafalgar Sq. & St. Martin's Church

Valuations: the highest prices apply to *London Types* and then to active street scenes with clear detail of people/transport.

Period 2 pictures, published in Period 2
.. .. £2/**£4**/£8
Period 2 pictures, published in Period 4
.. .. £1/**£1.50**/£2

Notes
(V) = vertical design.
(C) = exists in coloured version only.
(+C) = exists both b & w and coloured.
Dates of PU cards where known are given.

176

■176a

Pub. 'LL'. London—The Royal Exchange and Bank of England. No. 78 .. .. .. £3

■176b

Pub. 'LL'. London EC—Holborn Viaduct. No. 123 .. .. £3

■176c

Pub. 'LL'. London Types—The Pavement Artist. No. 302 .. .. £8

RAILWAYS

It is more than 150 years since the opening of the Liverpool and Manchester Railway—the first passenger and goods carrying inter-city line. In that century and a half the lore and language of the railways have become the property of the specialist historian and collector. It is only recently that through books, like those by Reginald Silvester, the importance of the picture postcard in recording the changing fortunes of the iron roads is beginning to be appreciated.

Official cards, that is cards published for sale or use by the railways themselves, first appeared at the end of Period 1, generally as gratis hotel or on-board-ship stationery, and often court size (*qv*). Although full size picture cards were allowed from 1 November 1899, the railways sometimes used an intermediate size (130 mm × 80 mm) carrying views associated with a particular line and providing timetable information.

The first company to sell its own cards is generally supposed to be the Furness, and by the time of the great re-organisation in 1923 over 70 companies had followed suit, including the Central London Railway in 1902/3, the first Underground railway to do so. One railway, the London and North Western, whose earliest cards were printed by Tuck, out-produced all others, selling over 11 million cards between 1904 and 1914. Following the First World War and the rapid development of road transport, the railways were forced to re-organise to meet this new challenge, and in 1923 most of Britain's lines merged into the Big Four—the LMS, LNER, GWR and the SR. They too produced cards, but never on the same scale as in Period 2, when the railways were at the height of their development.

The growth of excursion travel to the Continent and the opening of new luxury hotels devoted to sport and relaxation, gave rise to advertising cards during Period 4 whose function was to proclaim the virtues of new, 'undiscovered' destinations. Sadly the cheapness of 'real photographic' and sepia photogravure printing meant that the beautifully coloured advertising cards of Period 2 did not reappear in any quantity. In 1947, Period 6, the railways were nationalised and little use was made of the postcard by British Rail, other than as an item of commercial stationery. Period 7, however, has seen some British Rail enterprise and cards have been produced to commemorate such services as High Speed Trains and Cross-Channel Hovercraft.

The most dramatic development in recent years had been the proliferation of railway preservation societies, many of which issue and sell their own postcards in order to raise funds. This restoration and protection of much-loved local lines has spurred the production of many modern cards. Reginald Silvester estimates that 500 new railway cards were issued during 1980 (*see* MODERN), helped by the 'Rocket 150' celebrations at Liverpool and Manchester.

Many collectors of postcards imagine railway cards to be just pictures of engines, rolling stock or stations. That is not so. There are superb local views, system maps, motor buses, well-appointed hotels, elegant ships and magnificent coloured posters and poster-type advertisement cards. In Period 2 the Furness, Great Western and Midland Railways all published many reproductions of their posters, each a gem of Edwardian advertising. The most prolific series of poster reproductions was that printed by Photochrom and published by the North Eastern Railway, which consisted of 20 different designs by many different artists. It would be difficult to find a more breathtaking display of colour and design in any category. This set is listed in full below, under the title '*A Railway Classic*', at the beginning of this section.

There are 3 major groupings here—firstly non-official cards are gathered under *Thematic headings* ('Accidents' to 'Mountain Railways') and then the official issues divide into *Pre-1923 Companies* ('Barry to Wirral') and *Post-1923* ('GWR' to 'Underground').

A Railway Classic
The North Eastern Railway issued 20 numbered cards, all vertical, reproducing their advertising posters. They were published by Photochrom, all beautifully coloured and printed and carry details of the area or location shown. They are:
1. Summer Holidays; 2. Yorkshire Coast; 3. Circular Tours; 4. The Yorkshire Coast; 5. Northumbria; 6. Historic York; 7. The Land of Castles & Abbeys (Whitby Abbey); 8. Holidays on the Yorkshire Moors; 9. Holidays in the Yorkshire Dales (Aysgarth Falls); 10. Golf in North-East England; 11. The Yorkshire Coast; 12. The Land of Lore and Legend (Warkworth Castle); 13. Angling; 14. The Yorkshire Coast (Cliffs); 15. The Gateway (York); 16. Hotels; 17. Holiday in Picturesque Holland; 18. The Roman

Wall; 19. Yorkshire's Enchanting Dales; 20. The Yorkshire Moors—Tranquil Solitude

Price range .. .. £50/**£55**/£60

Non-Official Cards—Thematic Listing

Accidents

Gothard, W.—photographic series £15/**£19**/£25
Other photographic/halftone/collotype cards. ■187a. (Much of the value of these cards depends on their picture content and publisher interest) .. .. .. £6/**£10**/£12

Advertisements

Reproductions of posters (see official cards)
.. .. £25/**£35**/£50
French poster series. With/without references to railways in the British Isles .. .. £6/**£10**/£15
Poster type advertising (artistic cards from many countries) .. .. £4/**£6**/£10

Artists

Although the railway companies employed many capable and well known artists to design their posters, brochures and holiday literature, very few of the designs were transferred to the medium of the postcard. A small number of notable exceptions occur and some of these are listed under 'official' cards. A selection of artists used by railways and postcard publishers is given here to stimulate interest in this aspect of the picture postcard. A. Anderson, F. Barton, Cyrus Cuneo, Hamilton Ellis, Alec Fraser, John Hassall, A. Heaton-Cooper, J. Heyermans, C. T. Howard, Fortunio Matania, R. Mayes, Chas. Mayo, F. Moore, G. Parsons Norman, Eric Oldham, C. E. Turner, Bernard Way, N. Wilkinson

Foreign Railways (those other than in the British Isles).

Official cards (those issued with company crests or titles), e.g. America & Canada (various), Cape, Japan, Natal, Russia, Tasmania. ■178a .. .. .. £4/**£6**/£10
.. .. £4/**£6**/£10
Engines .. .. £1/**£2**/£3
General views of track etc. .. .. £1/**£2**/£3
Rolling stock, inside/external views
.. .. £1/**£1.50**/£2
Stations .. .. £2/**£3**/£4

Funicular & Cliff Railways/Lifts

Great Britain .. .. £2/**£3**/£4
Foreign .. .. £1/**£2**/£3

Locomotives & Rolling Stock—Pre-1923

Fleury, Paris—a series of many hundred cards of locomotives of French Railways. Two different printings.

Red captions .. .. £1.50/**£2**/£4
Black captions. ■188a .. .. .. £1/**£1.50**/£2
Hartmann (Series 3061) .. .. £1/**£2**/£3
JWB (Commercial series No. 312–12 No.)
.. .. £1/**£1.50**/£2
Knight series .. .. £1/**£2**/£3
Locomotive magazine .. .. .. £1/**£1.50**/£2
Locomotive Publishing Co. (Early vignettes, both single and multi-col.) .. £15/**£20**/£25
Locomotive Publishing Co.—collotypes/half tone .. .. £1.50/**£2**/£3
Locomotive Publishing Co.—photographic issues .. .. £1.50/**£2**/£3
Locomotive Publishing Co.—col. series (Goffey 4–291) (F. Moore paintings)
.. .. £1.50/**£2**/£3
Misch & Co.—'Noted Trains' series 331 and 332 .. .. £3/**£4**/£6
Parsons, F. J. .. .. £1/**£2**/£3
Pictorial Centre, Brighton (24 cards)
.. .. £1/**£2**/£3
Pouteau—half-tone/photographic £1/**£1.50**/£2
Railway photographs (photographic cards, no specific publishers) .. .. £1/**£1.50**/£3
Smith, G. .. .. £1/**£2**/£3
Smith, W. H.—'Kingsway series' £1.50/**£2**/£3
Tuck, R. & Sons. 'Oilette' and other similar series (1904–1923). (6493, 9040, 9150, 9226, 9274, 9316, 9329, 9161, 9662, 9972, 9637, 8619, 9715, 9760)
.. .. £2/**£3**/£5
Tuck R. & Sons—Kerr Stuart series (4983, 4984) .. .. £1.50/**£2.50**/£4
By Train (9186) and Villes de France (123, 124) .. .. £2/**£4**/£6
Tuck, R. & Sons. LCC Reward cards (12 No.) .. .. £2/**£3**/£4

■178a

Period 2. Deutscher-Eisenbahn. 'Greetings from the Buffet Car'. Col. £10

Valentines series .. .. £1.50/**£2**/£3
Wildt & Kray (Series 1814, 1834)
.. .. £1/**£2**/£3
Wrench series—uncol. (2280–2291, 4185–4193 & 4500–4512) .. .. £1.50/**£2**/£3
Wrench Red Bordered series (10,089–10,106) .. .. £2/**£3**/£4
Locomotives and rolling stock were also well depicted on 'official' issued cards of the following pre-grouping British railways: Great Western, Lancashire & Yorkshire, London & North Western, Midland, & South Eastern & Chatham Railways

Locomotives & Rolling Stock—1923 Onwards
Allan, Ian—col./photogravure .. 50p/**75p**/£1
Chadwick views .. .. 50p/**75p**/£1
Dennis, E. T. W. .. .. 50p/**75p**/£1
Dixon, J. A. (col.) .. .. .. 50p/**75p**/£1
Judges (col.) .. .. 50p/**75p**/£1
Lake, G. H. (Eric Oldham paintings—10 cards) .. .. £1/**£2**/£3
Locomotive Publishing Co.—col. series (Goffey 292–328) .. .. £2/**£3**/£4
Mack, W. E.—(tinted cards) .. £1.50/**£2**/£3
Photochrom Co. .. .. .. £1.50/**£2**-£3
Pike .. .. £1/**£1.50**/£2
Regent—photographic series .. £1/**£1.50**/£2
Salmon, J. (col.). ■188b .. £1/**£1.50**/£2
Tuck, R. & Sons. 'Oilette' and other similar series (1923–1936). (3541, 3547, 3569, 3570, 3593, 5303, 5304.) Model Railway Engines (3404) .. .. £2/**£3**/£4
Valentines series. ■179a .. £1/**£2**/£3
Locomotives and rolling stock were also well depicted on 'official' issued cards of the following post grouping 'Big Four' British railways: Great Western, London, Midland & Scottish, London & North Eastern and Southern Railways.

Local Lines (Standard & Narrow Gauge)
Branch lines owned or operated by major railway companies, or small independent companies promoted by Parliament or Light Railway Acts. A number of superb local published cards exist of these railways, but with a publisher, social history or topographical interest they are often rated even higher in value than for their railway interest alone.
Bridges/Viaducts/Tunnels .. .. 50p/**75p**/£1
Level crossings and general trackside views
.. .. £1/**£1.50**/£3
Motor buses/road vehicles (railway owned)
.. .. £5/**£7**/£10

Official cards (see this heading)
Railway staff. Uniformed/groups .. £1.50/**£2**/£3
Rolling stock .. .. £1.50/**£2**/£3
Stations, Town (interior/platform views)
.. .. £3/**£5**/£7
Stations, Town (exterior) .. .. £2/**£4**/£6
Stations, Village (interior/platform views)
.. .. £3/**£5**/£7
Stations, Village (exterior) .. .. £2/**£4**/£6

Main Lines (Standard Gauge)
Main trunk railways (Periods 1 to 3) connecting major towns and cities such as London, Liverpool, Manchester & Glasgow. Within the British Isles, these railways became grouped together into four major concerns in 1923 (Periods 4, 5) and became State owned in 1948 (Periods 6, 7).
Bridges/Viaducts/Tunnels .. .. 50p/**75p**/£1
Level crossings/trackside views .. £1/**£1.50**/£3
Motor buses/road vehicles (railway owned).
■179b .. .. £5/**£7**/£16
Official cards (see this heading)
Railway staff. Uniformed/groups .. £1.50/**£2**/£3
Rolling stock .. .. £1.50/**£2**/£3
Stations, City (interior) .. .. £3/**£5**/£7
Stations, City (exterior) .. .. £2/**£4**/£6

■179a

Period 4. 'George Bennie' Railplane, Glasgow. Pub. Valentine's. RP. £3

■179b

Period 2. G.W.R. Delivery of Painswick-Stroud motorbus by rail. Pub. W. F. Lee. RP £16

Stations, Town (interior/platform views)
.. .. £3/**£5**/£7
Stations, Town (exterior) .. .. £2/**£4**/£6

Miniature/Pleasure/Beach Railways—(Up to 38 cm Gauge)
Ravenglass & Eskdale. Photographic/col./
collotype .. .. £1/**£3**/£5
Romney, Hythe & Dymchurch. Photo-
graphic/col. .. .. £1/**£1.50**/£2
Various pleasure/Beach railways .. £1/**£2**/£3

Mountain Railways
Snowdon Mountain railway (non-official)
.. .. £1.50/**£2.50**/£4
Foreign locations .. .. £2/**£3**/£4

■180a

Period 2. Marylebone Station. Pub. Charles Martin. Photo-origin £7

Official Cards—Pre-1923 Companies

'Official cards' is a term used to describe postcards issued/sold by railway companies to gain revenue and to promote all aspects of their business incl. hotels, ships and buses. Not to be confused with 'official' postcards issued by Postal Authorities. Official cards have been issued from Periods 1 to 7 and are still being issued, although in ever reducing numbers.

Barry
Correspondence/view cards (plain/col.)
.. .. £25/**£30**/£35

Belfast & County Down
Hotel ('Jotter') .. .. £4/**£6**/£10

Caledonian
Vignette/multi-view (early Period 2)
.. .. £10/**£15**/£25

Views (Glosso) .. .. £3/**£4**/£6
Views (col.) (National, Valentine) £4/**£5**/£6
Engines/Rolling stock (col.) .. .. £4/**£6**/£8
Engines/Rolling stock (Glosso) .. £3/**£4**/£5
Clyde steamers/Clyde views (Reliable)
.. .. £4/**£5**/£6
Hotels—court size (Periods 1, 2) £10/**£15**/£20
Hotels (plain/col.) .. .. .. £2/**£5**/£8
Hotel advertising .. .. .. £10/**£15**/£20
Poster reproductions (col. photographic)
.. .. £40/**£50**/£60
Tartan-bordered views .. .. .. £5/**£6**/£8
Ambulance train .. .. £2/**£3**/£4
Sleeping Car—Reservation card .. £10/**£15**/£20

Callander & Oban
Hotel view .. .. £6/**£8**/£10

Cambrian
Vignette-intermediate (Picture Postcard
Company). ■188c .. .. .. £15/**£20**/£25
Views—col. (Cambrian railways, Valentine,
Photochrom) .. .. £4/**£5**/£6
Correspondence/holiday advertising £6/**£8**/£10
Maps .. .. £15/**£20**/£25

Cheshire Lines
Views/correspondence .. .. £15/**£18**/£25

Cork, Bandon & South Coast
Views—col. (Tuck 'Oilette', Sunnyside of
Ireland) .. .. £2/**£4**/£6

Cork Blackrock & Passage
Paddle steamer *Audrey*/Correspondence
.. .. £25/**£30**/£35

Dublin & South Eastern
Correspondence/views .. .. .. £25/**£30**/£35

Dublin, Wicklow & Wexford
Views—vignetted .. .. .. £25/**£30**/£35
Celesque series .. .. .. £20/**£25**/£30

Dumbarton & Balloch Joint Lines
Views .. .. £12/**£16**/£20

East Coast Route (Great Northern, North Eastern, North British Railways)
'Write-away' type Vignette (Andrew Reid)
.. .. £12/**£15**/£18

Rolling stock/stations/views—col. £8/**£12**/£16
Flying Scotsman (Hildersheimer) £3/**£4**/£5

Furness
English 'Gruss Aus'—(chromo) (McCorquodale) .. .. £10/**£15**/£20
Views—col. (McCorquodale) £2/**£3**/£4
Views—col. (Heaton-Cooper paintings) (Tuck) .. .. £1.50/**£2**/£3
Engines/Rolling stock (photographic) (Tuck) .. .. £4/**£5**/£6
Lake steamers (photographic) (Tuck) .. .. £2/**£3**/£4
Barrow and Fleetwood steamers (photographic) (Tuck) .. .. .. £4/**£6**/£8
Hotel (col. photographic) .. .. £2/**£4**/£6
Poster reproductions—col. .. £50/**£55**/£60
Furness Abbey/Hotel (photographic) (Tuck) .. .. £2/**£3**/£4
Art studies—George Romney paintings (photographic) (James Atkinson) .. .. £4/**£6**/£8
Exhibitions .. .. .. £10/**£12**/£14

■181a
Period 3. Glasgow & South Western Rly. WW1 Ambulances £8

Glasgow & South Western
Vignette—col. (McCorquodale/Maclure MacDonald) .. .. £15/**£20**/£25
Views—col. (Tuck 'Oilette') .. £3/**£4**/£5
Steamers—col. (McCorquodale) £1/**£1.50**/£2
Hotels—(chromo) (Tuck) .. £10/**£12**/£15
Hotels—col. .. .. .. £2/**£3**/£4
Poster reproductions .. .. £50/**£55**/£60
Turnberry Golf Course/Hotel (col. art studies) .. .. .. £4/**£6**/£8
Ambulances—WW1. ■181a .. £4/**£6**/£8

Great Central
Vignette—intermediate (Picture Postcard Company) .. .. .. £15/**£20**/£25

Views—col. (Faulkner series) .. £4/**£5**/£6
Views—photographic (HHH series) .. .. £6/**£8**/£10
Engines/Rolling stock .. .. .. £6/**£8**/£10
Ships—col. (C. E. Turner paintings) .. .. .. £10/**£12**/£15
Ships—'Great Central series' (Tuck) .. .. £15/**£20**/£25
Hotels .. .. .. £3/**£5**/£8
Poster .. .. £50/**£55**/£60
Immingham Docks—col. (Fortunio Matania paintings) .. .. £1.50/**£2**/£3
Perforated engine card—col. (Central Advertising Co.) £75/**£80**/£100
Restaurant car—'En Route' .. £6/**£8**/£15

Great Eastern
Views/correspondence/advertising £6/**£8**/£10
View/correspondence/advertising (col.) .. .. £10/**£12**/£15
View correspondence/advertising (Jarrolds series col. and plain) .. .. £6/**£8**/£10
Views—col. (Tuck 'Oilette') .. £1.50/**£2**/£2.50
Cathedrals (chromo) (Tuck) .. £20/**£25**/£30
Cathedrals—col./plain (Faulkner) £20/**£25**/£30
Trains/Stations—col. (Locomotive Publishing Co.) .. .. .. £2/**£3**/£4
Ships—(Continental published cards, incl. moonlight series) .. .. £6/**£8**/£10
Ships (col., plain) .. .. £4/**£5**/£6
Hotels .. .. .. £3/**£4**/£5
Poster reproductions—(plain, col. incl. those by J. Hassall) .. .. £50/**£55**/£60
Collotype series with crest—various subjects incl. locomotivess, steamers, Southwold bus and views) .. £1.50/**£2**/£2.50
Motor bus .. .. .. £7/**£8**/£9
Duty paid cards/SS *Dresden* .. £4/**£6**/£8
Underground Railway Maps of London (incl. GER advertising) .. .. £5/**£8**/£10

Great Northern
Vignette—intermediate (Picture Postcard Company) .. .. .. £15/**£20**/£25
Vignette—London views (Picture Postcard Company) .. .. .. £8/**£12**/£16
Views—col. (Photochrom) .. £1/**£1.50**/£2
Engines—col. (Photochrom) £1.50/**£2**/£2.50
Engines/Trains—col. (Locomotive Publishing Co.) .. .. .. £2/**£3**/£4
Hotels .. .. .. £4/**£5**/£6
Poster reproductions—col. (including Hassall's 'Skegness is so Bracing') £50/**£55**/£60

Poster type advertising—Panoramic
.. .. £12/**£15**/£18
Correspondence/view cards .. .. £6/**£8**/£10

Great Northern (*Ireland*)
Views/Correspondence .. .. £10/**£12**/£15
Hotelss—multiview (Lawrence) .. £15/**£20**/£25
Shamrock—hotel advertising .. £15/**£20**/£25
Motor bus to Mulroy Bay (advertising)
.. .. £30/**£35**/£40

Great North of Scotland
Views (Porter, Aberdeen) .. .. £6/**£7**/£8
Hotels—multiview (Periods 1, 2) £14/**£16**/£18
Hotels—multiview .. .. £16/**£18**/£20
Palace Hotel series .. .. £6/**£8**/£10
Cruden Bay Golf Tournament .. £8/**£10**/£12

Great Southern & Western
Views—col. (Tuck 'Oilette', Sunnyside of
Ireland) .. .. £3/**£4**/£5
Great Southern Hotel—court card
(Lawrence) .. .. .. £16/**£18**/£20
Great Southern Hotel—multiview £12/**£15**/£18
Hotels in the Kingdom of Kerry—multi-
view .. .. £20/**£25**/£30
Hotel views/correspondence (Lawrence)
.. .. £6/**£8**/£10
Hotel views ('Jotter') .. .. £4/**£5**/£6
Parknasilla Hotel—Motor bus/Stage Coach
tours .. .. £8/**£10**/£12

Great Western
Vignette—intermediate (Picture Postcard
Co.) .. .. £15/**£20**/£25
Vignette—London views (court size)
.. .. £15/**£20**/£25
Views—sepia collotype/gravure/photo-
graphic .. .. £2/**£3**/£4
Views—col. .. .. £2/**£3**/£4
Engines/Rolling stock—collotype/gravure/
photographic .. .. .. £2/**£3**/£4
'Fishguard Harbour as a Port of Call'
.. .. £4/**£5**/£6
Docks series (Autotype Co.) .. .. £4/**£5**/£6
Fishguard route .. .. .. £4/**£5**/£6
Hotels—vignette/write away .. £2/**£4**/£6
Hotels, other .. .. £2/**£3**/£4
Poster reproductions—Series 3, col. (many
are the work of Alec Fraser). ■183a
.. .. £50/**£55**/£60
Poster reproductions—col. (Acme Press,
Andrew Reid) .. .. .. £45/**£50**/£55

General interest—bridges, tunnels, stations
etc. .. .. £2/**£3**/£4
Motor bus (Slough service) .. .. £6/**£7**/£8
Restaurant cars—'En Route' .. £12/**£15**/£20
Cathedral series .. .. £2/**£3**/£4
Correspondence/view cards (single colour)
.. .. £4/**£6**/£8
Wyndams series—correspondence cards (4
varieties) .. .. £4/**£6**/£8

Highland
Views—Railway title in red (Valentines)
.. .. £6/**£7**/£8
Views—Railway crest in colour (Valen-
tines) .. .. £4/**£5**/£6
Views—col. (Valentines) .. .. £5/**£6**/£7
Views—photographic (Valentines) £4/**£5**/£6
Hotel .. .. £3/**£4**/£5

Hull & Barnsley
Views/correspondence .. .. .. £8/**£12**/£15

Lancashire & Yorkshire
Vignette (Picture Postcard Co.) .. £15/**£20**/£25
Views—plain .. .. £2/**£3**/£4
Views—col. .. .. £2/**£3**/£4
Engines/Rolling stock—plain .. £2/**£3**/£4
Engines/Rolling stock—col. .. £2/**£3**/£4
Ships—plain .. .. £4/**£5**/£6
Ships—col. .. .. £4/**£5**/£6

Note: Many of these cards (probably all) were
overprinted in French in 1910 and 1913 with
advertisements for holidays in England, Isle of
Man and Ireland. Cards having these overprints
should have their prices increased to twice the
prices given here.

Ships—col./plain (joint cards with other
companies) .. .. £8/**£10**/£12
Liverpool & Drogheda steamers—'on
board' .. .. £15/**£20**/£25
Wyre Dock/correspondence .. £15/**£20**/£25

London, Brighton & South Coast
Vignette—including London views (Picture
Postcard Co.) .. .. .. £15/**£20**/£25
Views/general interest (Waterlow) £2/**£3**/£4
Bridges (Waterflow) .. .. .. £3/**£4**/£5
Poster reproductions—(single colour)
.. .. £50/**£55**/£60
Correspondence .. .. .. £4/**£6**/£8

■183a

Period 2. G.W.R. Series 3. Artist Alec Fraser.
Col. £60

■183b

Period 1. London, Chatham & Dover Rly.
Pre-January 1899. Col. Court size £30

London, Chatham & Dover
Vignette—col. (court size) (Pictorial Post-
card Syndicate). ■183b .. .. £20/**£25**/£30
Vignette—single colour (court size) (Pic-
torial Postcard Syndicate) .. £20/**£25**/£30
Vignette—single colour (court size) (Picture
Postcard Company) .. .. £20/**£25**/£30
Note: This railway ceased to exist on January 1st
1899 when it was joined by an Act of Parliament
to the South Eastern to become the South Eastern
and Chatham and Dover, soon changed to South
Eastern and Chatham.

London & North Western
St. Louis exposition .. .. .. £6/**£7**/£8

Tuck Cards
Engines/Rolling stock/Railway business
.. .. £1/**£2**/£3
Views .. .. £1/**£2**/£3
Ships .. .. £2/**£3**/£4
Hotels .. .. £2/**£3**/£4

McCorquodale Cards
Views—plain/col. .. .. £1/**£2**/£3
Engines/Rolling stock—plain/col. £1/**£2**/£3

Ships—plain/col. .. .. £2/**£3**/£4
Buses and motor transport .. .. £8/**£10**/£12
Miscellaneous—plain/col. .. .. £4/**£6**/£8
Hotels—plain/col. .. .. £1/**£2**/£3
Poster reproductions—plain/col. .. £50/**£55**/£60
Maps—col. .. .. £50/**£55**/£60

For full and detailed listing of all London & North
Western Railway postcards see 'Official Railway
Postcards of the British Isles' by R. Silvester.

London & South Western
Vignette—(court size) (single colour) (Pic-
torial Postcard Syndicate) .. £20/**£25**/£30
Vignette—intermediate (col.) (Pictorial
Postcard Syndicate) .. .. £20/**£25**/£30
Vignette—intermediate (Picture Postcard
Co.) .. .. £15/**£20**/£25
Vignette—London views (Picture Postcard
Co.) .. .. £10/**£15**/£20
Ships—'on board' (col.) .. .. £12/**£15**/£18
Southampton Hotel .. .. £15/**£18**/£20
Poster reproductions .. .. £50/**£55**/£60
Correspondence/view .. .. £8/**£10**/£12
Orphanage (Locomotive Publishing Co.)
.. .. £3/**£4**/£5

Londonderry & Lough Swilly
Map .. .. £40/**£45**/£50

Maryport & Carlisle
Map .. .. £40/**£45**/£50

Midland
Vignette (Picture Postcard Co., British and
Colonial Auto. Trading Co., Automatic
General Stores—same views) .. £15/**£20**/£25
Vignette—London views (Picture Postcard
Co.) .. .. £10/**£15**/£20
Vignette—col. (Route to Scotland) (Andrew
Reid) .. .. £12/**£15**/£18
'Nearest Station'—views—col. .. £6/**£8**/£10
Views—col. (Photochrom, with/without
'bear' trademark) .. .. .. £2/**£3**/£4
Rolling stock—col. .. .. .. £4/**£6**/£8
Engines—plain .. .. .. £2/**£3**/£4
Ships—col. .. .. £4/**£6**/£8
Hotel—(court size) .. .. .. £16/**£18**/£20
Hotels—'Travel and Entertainment
.. .. £16/**£18**/£20
Hotels—vignettes (col.) .. .. £5/**£6**/£7
Hotels—col. .. .. £2/**£3**/£4

Hotels—restaurants/public rooms (plain, col.) .. .. £2/**£3**/£4
Poster reproductions—Series (col.) £50/**£55**/£60
Poster reproductions (col.) .. .. £40/**£45**/£50
Maps (col.) .. .. £10/**£12**/£14
Heysham—Morecambe Electric Train (col.) .. .. £20/**£25**/£30
Midland Grand Hotel—Business lunches .. .. £40/**£45**/£50
Exhibitions .. .. £15/**£18**/£20

■184a

Period 4. L. & N.E.R. Hotel Poster ad. col. .. £40

Midland (Northern Counties Committee)
View .. .. £15/**£20**/£25

Midland & Great Northern
Correspondence/view .. .. .. £5/**£10**/£15

Midland & Great Western
Hotels—col. ('Jotter') .. .. £2/**£3**/£4
Hotels—col./photographic (Lawrence) £3/**£4**/£5
Wembley Exhibition Trade Stand (with GS & WR) .. .. £10/**£15**/£20

North British
Views—plain with crest on front .. £6/**£8**/£10
Views—plain, col., tinted .. .. £3/**£4**/£5
Views—Edinburgh (col.) (Caledonian 129 series) .. .. £2/**£3**/£4
Ships—plain/col. .. .. .. £3/**£4**/£5
Hotels—plain .. .. £3/**£4**/£5
Hotels—col. advertisements .. £10/**£12**/£15

North Eastern
Views—photo Panoramic (series of 40) £6/**£7**/£8

Views—photo Panoramic (with map overprints) .. .. £10/**£12**/£15
Newcastle Electric trains (col./plain) .. .. £4/**£5**/£6
Ships (plain/col.) .. .. .. £4/**£5**/£6
Hotels (plain/col.) .. .. .. £2/**£3**/£4
Poster reproductions (series of 20) (col.) (Photochrom). ■184a .. .. £50/**£55**/£60
Industrial poster reproductions (series of 4) (col.) .. .. £55/**£60**/£75
Riverside Quay, Hull (col.) .. .. £6/**£8**/£10
North Eastern railway houses—(col.) .. .. £2/**£4**/£6
Exhibition .. .. £4/**£5**/£6

North Staffordshire
Views—collotype, gravure, col. enamelled, platemarked .. .. .. £4/**£5**/£6
Views—as above (including scenes on the Leek and Manifold railway) .. £4/**£6**/£8

Portpatrick & Wigtownshire Joint
Views—single/multi-view, numbered series .. .. £15/**£20**/£25
Ships .. .. £12/**£16**/£20
Correspondence/views .. .. £20/**£25**/£30

South-Eastern & Chatham & Dover
Vignette—intermediate (col.) (Pictorial Postcard Syndicate) .. .. £20/**£25**/£30
Vignette—intermediate (Picture Postcard Co.) .. .. £15/**£20**/£25
Vignette—London views (Picture Postcard Co./Automatic General Stores) £10/**£15**/£20
Engines/Rolling Stock—col. (McCorquodale) .. .. £2/**£3**/£4
Trains/Stations—col. (McCorquodale) £2/**£3**/£4
Ships—col. (McCorquodale) .. £2/**£3**/£4
Ships/correspondence—(plain/col.) £4/**£6**/£8
South Eastern Hotel (plain) .. .. £4/**£6**/£8
Poster reproduction (col.) .. .. £50/**£55**/£60
Maps (col.) .. .. £16/**£18**/£20
Maps/engines and trains (plain) .. £16/**£18**/£20
Correspondence/views (Photochrom) .. .. £10/**£12**/£15
Exhibition .. .. £4/**£6**/£8
Bologne views—col. (Stevenard edit with overprints) .. .. .. £4/**£6**/£8

Stratford-on-Avon & Midland Junction
Poster reproduction—col. .. £50/**£75**/£100

West Clare
View .. .. £16/**£18**/£20

West Coast Route (Caledonian and London & North Western)
Views—(plain/col.) .. .. .. £6/**£8**/£10
Rolling Stock (plain/col.) .. .. £12/**£14**/£16

West Highland
Views—col. (National) .. .. .. £8/**£10**/£12

Wirral
Pictorial route map .. .. .. £40/**£45**/£50

Official Cards—Post-1923 Companies

1. Main Railways
Great Western Railway
Views—col. (L. Richmond paintings) £2/**£3**/£4
Engines—gravure/photographic .. £1/**£2**/£3
Engines—col. .. .. £1/**£2**/£3
Hotels—gravure/Chas. Mayo series.
 ■187b .. .. £2/**£3**/£4
Poster reproductions .. .. £45/**£50**/£55
'King George V'—folded col. locomotive
 card .. .. £20/**£25**/£30

London Midland & Scottish Railway
Engines—col. .. .. £1/**£2**/£3
Ships—col./plain .. .. .. £2/**£3**/£4
Hotels—col./plain .. .. .. £1/**£2**/£3
Holiday tickets/views—photographic with
 overprints .. .. £3/**£4**/£5
Poster reproductions .. .. £30/**£35**/£40
Container services advertising .. £20/**£25**/£30

London & North Eastern Railway
Engines/Trains—photographic .. £2/**£3**/£4
Ships—photographic .. .. .. £2/**£3**/£4
Hotels—gravure/photographic etc. £1/**£2**/£3
Poster reproductions .. .. £30/**£35**/£40

Southern Railway
Engines—gravure/photographic .. £1/**£2**/£3
Engines/trains—col. ■185a .. £1/**£2**/£3
Ships—photographic .. .. .. £1/**£2**/£3
Poster reproductions .. .. £30/**£35**/£40

Correspondence .. .. £2/**£3**/£4
Harbours/West Country scenes (paintings
 by L. Richmond) .. .. .. £2/**£3**/£4

Official Cards—Post-1947 (British Railways)
Trains—col. ■185b .. .. .. £1/**£2**/£3
Ships—photographic/col. .. .. 50p/**75p**/£1
Hotels—photographic/col. .. .. 50p/**75p**/£1
Poster reproduction (HST Services—
 Western Region) .. .. .. £1/**£2**/£3
Seaspeed—Hovercraft .. .. 50p/**75p**/£1
Gleneagles/Turnberry Golf Courses—col.
 .. .. 50p/**75p**/£1
Birmingham 'New Street Station'—photo-
 graphic (London, Midland Region)
 .. .. £1/**£1.50**/£2
Kyle of Lochalsh Station (Scottish Region)
 .. .. £1/**£2**/£3
Correspondence .. .. £1/**£2**/£3

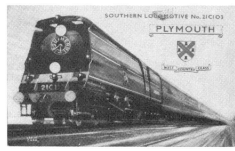
■185a
Period 6. Southern Rly. Plymouth—*West Country Class locomotive. Col.* £3

■185b
Period 7. B.R. Western Region. Inter-City 125. c. 1977. Out of print £3

2. Minor Railways

Bideford, Westward Ho! & Appledore
Views/trains .. .. £6/**£8**/£10

Campbeltown & Macrihanish
Advertising—col. .. .. £40/**£45**/£50

Corris
Views—photographic (George's series)
.. .. £6/**£7**/£8

Festiniog
Poster reproduction .. .. ..£50/**£75**/£100

Freshwater, Yarmouth & Newport
Vignettes (Picture Postcard Co.) .. £20/**£25**/£30

Invergary & Fort Augustus
Views (Highland Railway series) .. £10/**£12**/£15

Isle of Wight
Vignettes (Picture Postcard Co.) .. £15/**£20**/£25

Isle of Wight Central
Vignettes (Picture Postcard Co.) .. £20/**£25**/£30

Joint South Western & Brighton
Vignettes (Picture Postcard Co.) .. £15/**£20**/£25

Kent & East Sussex
Views/train .. .. £6/**£7**/£8
Engine/correspondence .. .. .. £5/**£6**/£7
Correspondence .. .. £12/**£15**/£18

Lynton & Barnstaple
Views/stations/trains (Peacocks & P. & Mc.
series) .. .. £4/**£6**/£8

Newport, Godshill & St. Lawrence
Vignettes (Picture Postcard Co.) .. £15/**£20**/£25

Vale of Rheidol
Views—col./plain .. .. £6/**£8**/£10

Wick & Lybster
Views (Highland Railway series) .. £6/**£8**/£10

3. Electric Railways

Central London
Station/train views (plate-marked)
(Wrench) .. .. £5/**£6**/£8
Stations/trains (Hartmann) .. .. £5/**£6**/£8
Stations/trains—photographic (Rotophot)
.. .. £5/**£6**/£8
Views—(col.) (Photochrom Celesque)
.. .. £4/**£6**/£8
Maps/rolling stock etc. .. .. .. £10/**£12**/£15
Exhibitions—'Pillar Box Pull-Out' £10/**£15**/£20
Exhibitions—'Blow Card' .. .. £30/**£35**/£40

District/Metropolitan District
Vignette—intermediate (col.) (Pictorial
Postcard Syndicate) .. .. .. £20/**£25**/£30
Vignette—London views (single colour)
(Pictorial Postcard Syndicate) £15/**£20**/£25
Vignette—London views (single colour)
(Picture Postcard Co.) .. .. £15/**£20**/£25
Engines/Rolling stock exhibition (photo-
graphic) .. .. £5/**£6**/£7
Poster type advertising .. .. .. £15/**£20**/£25

Great Northern & City
Views .. .. £5/**£6**/£7
Poster type advertising .. .. .. £30/**£35**/£40

Great Northern, Piccadilly & Brompton
Views—stations/trains/construction (col.)
(Locomotive Publishing Co.) .. £4/**£6**/£8
Map—col. (Locomotive Publishing Co.)
.. .. £15/**£20**/£25

Hampstead Tube
'Last Link' views (col.) .. .. .. £4/**£6**/£8

Liverpool Overhead
Correspondence/view .. .. .. £4/**£6**/£8

London Underground Electric
Poster reproductions—London's Nooks &
Corners (col.) .. .. £30/**£35**/£40
Advertising—multiview (Bakerloo, Pic-
cadilly & Hampstead Tubes) (col.)
.. .. £12/**£15**/£18
'The Link of London Lines' (panoramic
maps/train views etc.) (col.) (W. H.
Smith) .. .. £8/**£10**/£12
Underground maps—advertisement over-
prints (col./plain) .. .. .. £8/**£10**/£12

Mersey
Views—stations/lifts/trains (Wrench) £6/**£8**/£10

Metropolitan
Views—sepia (series of 30) .. .. £4/**£6**/£8
Correspondence .. .. .. £8/**£10**/£12
Maps .. .. £16/**£18**/£20

■187a
Period 2. G.W.R. Yeovil accident. RP £12

Preservation Societies/Museums
A growing number of railway lines are now in the hands of preservation societies, and rolling stock is preserved by many museums both National (York) or local. Many cards listed are still on sale, but they are changed frequently and only printed in relatively small quantities, and can soon become unobtainable.
York Museum
Centenary Celebrations (1925)
Clapham/National Railway Museum
London Transport Museum
Industrial Railways/Engines
Narrow Gauge. ■187c
Preserved Engines
Preserved Railways. ■187d
Rail 150 (Stockton–Darlington)
Rocket 150 (Liverpool–Manchester)
Price range 15p/**30p**/50p

■187b
Period 5. G.W.R. Hotel ad. 1942. Ronotone on buff £4

■187c
Period 7. Ravenglass & Eskdale Rly. RP .. 25p

Snowdon Mountain Railway
Views (Snowdon/Festiniog & Welsh Highland Railways) (photographic) £4/**£5**/£6
Hotel/railway advertising (court size) (Periods 1, 2) .. .. .. £15/**£20**/£25
Poster reproductions—col./plain .. £15/**£20**/£25
Map—col. .. .. £15/**£18**/£20

Underground Railways
London Transport .. .. £1/**£2**/£3
Foreign U. Bahnes/Metro's .. .. £2/**£3**/£5

■187d
Period 6. Welshpool & Llanfair Rly. The Countess. RP 25p

187

■188a

*Pub. F. Fleury. French. Periods 2, 3. Engine No.
220-501. Card No. 148 .. .. £2*

■188b

*Pub. Salmon. Periods 4, 5. Artist C. T. Howard.
'LNER The East Anglian'. No. 4698 .. £1.50*

■188c

*Pub. Picture Postcard Co. Periods 1, 2. Small
size,* UB. *Green design. Cambrian Railway. Pandy
Mill, Dolgelly £15*

---

*The Stanley Gibbons Postcard Department
is at 391 Strand, London WC2. Open
Mon–Fri. 9 a.m.–5.30 p.m.; Sat. 9.30
a.m.–12.30 p.m.*

RELIGION

It is the Roman Catholic countries, especially Italy, which provide the most colourful and the greatest number of postcards—through all the 7 periods. Also included in the section are missions and associations like the YMCA and the Salvation Army. For Jewish cards, *see also* SOCIAL HISTORY/TOPOGRAPHICAL.

ANGLICAN CHURCH
Cathedrals, churches—*see* 'Buildings' under
  SOCIAL HISTORY. Pictures of Biblical
  characters, Jesus, etc. **50p**
Portraits of clergy **50p**
Others **50p**

CHRISTIAN SCIENCE
Churches **50p**
Personalities .. ..   –/**50p**/75p

COLPORTAGE
Distributors of Bibles, religious tracts. RPs
  of travelling vans, preaching platforms.
  Period 2 .. .. 50p/**£1**/£1.50

GENERAL RELIGIOUS THEMES
Angels, Christmas and Easter Themes (*see also* GREETINGS), Old Testament Texts, Reproductions of Religious Old Masters (*see* ART REPRODUCTION) etc. Many of these postcards are beautifully produced, often embossed and/or gilded. Publishers include Birn Bros. (especially 'Guardian Angel' series), Ettlinger, Tuck, Wildt & Kray.
Price range .. .. 50p/**75p**/£2

HINDUISM
Many beautiful coloured series of Indian cards showing Hindu legends exist.
Hindu Myths. Artist Evelyn, Paul £1/**£1.50**/£2
Pub. Ravi-Varma Press. ■189a .. £1/**£1.50**/£3
Others .. .. 50p/**75p**/£1.50

MISSIONS/SOCIETIES
Church Lads' Brigade. ■189b 50p/**75p**/£1.50
Church Mission to Jews. Personalities
  .. .. 50p/**75p**/£1
Ditto. Special overprints by Photochrom
  .. ..   **50p**
International Society of the Apocrypha.
  Subscription reminders, etc. ..   **50p**

London Society for Promoting Christianity
  to the Jews. Personalities .. .. 50p/**75p**/£1
Ditto. Special overprints by Photochrom
  .. ..   **50p**
Scripture Gift Mission. Various issues
  .. ..   **50p**
St. John's League of Mercy. Outings, etc.
  .. .. –/**50p**/75p
Society for the Propagation of the Gospel.
  Photographic origin issues showing good
  ethnic detail .. .. .. 50p/**75p**/£1
Ditto. Others **50p**
South American Missionary Soc. Various
  issues **50p**
Universities Mission to Central Africa.
  Various issues **50p**
YMCA/YWCA (*see also* WAR). Various
  issues .. .. –/**50p**/75p

■189a

Pub. Ravi-Varma Press. Artist Ravi-Varma. 'Vishan with his two wives'. Period 2   ..   £1.50

■189b

Pub. Johnson, Riddle & Co. Church Lads' Brigade Camp. PU *1912* £1.50

NONCONFORMISM

Chapels—*see* 'Buildings' under SOCIAL HISTORY.
Outings—cards of photographic origin
.. .. 50p/**75p**/£1.50
Personalities .. .. –/**50p**/75p

PASSION PLAYS

Oberammergau: every ten years incl. 1980.
 Photographs of actors/stills 50p/**75p**/£1.50
 General views .. .. –/**25p**/50p
USA Pubs. Periods 2 to 4 incl. Bruckmann
 Trant, Commercial Color-type, Conwell,
 Crocker, Leo Schweyer .. .. 50p/**75p**/£1
Others 25p/**50p**/75p

PRAYERS

Lord's Prayer

Ger. series of 6. Period 2. chromo-litho. Per
 set .. .. £4/**£6**/£8
USA Pub. Taggart. Series of 8. Per set
.. .. £3/**£5**/£15
Others. Per card .. .. 25p/**50p**/£1

RELIGIOUS ECCENTRICS

Dervishes, fakirs, etc. .. .. 50p/**75p**/£1.50
Meva, Apostle of Natural Life. ■190a
.. .. 50p/**75p**/£1
Others .. .. –/**50p**/75p

ROMAN CATHOLICISM

Anti-Catholicism

Various Protestant crusades (incl. 'anti-
 Popery in Birmingham Streets' series)
 and publications/others .. .. 50p/**75p**/£1

Events

The following list does not claim to be comprehensive, but gives a typical selection of religious
events for which postcards are known, in chronological order, in Periods 1 to 7.
1897. It. 19th Eucharist Congress, Venice
1898. It. Exhibition of Sacred Art
 It. 20th Anniversary of Pope Leo XIII
1899. It. 800th Anniversary of St. John Baptist
1900. It. Celebrations of Holy Year
1903. It. Death of Pope Leo XIII
 It. Accession of Pope Pius X
1908. Fr. Lourdes Jubilee
1914. It. Accession of Pope Benedict XV
1922. Pope Pius XI
1925. It. Celebrations of Holy Year
1939. Accession of Pope Pius XII
1958. Accession of Pope John XXIII

Price range (the highest valuation is for
 Period 1 cards and cards PU on day of
 issue) .. .. £2/**£4**/£10

 Period 7 cards include:
1976. 41st International Eucharist. Vatican
 'Maxi' Series
1978. John Paul I. Vatican Maxi series and other
 issues
 John Paul II. Various issues
1979. Voyages of John Paul II to Ireland, Monte
 Cassino and other Italian locations, Poland,
 USA
 Various Vatican 'Maxi' series
Price range .. ..50p/**£1.50**/£3

Fund-Raising/Recruiting

Recruiting posters for priests/Vatican fund-
 raising. Others. ■190b .. .. 50p/**75p**/£3

■190a

Pub. Anon. 'Meva. The Apostle of Natural Life'.
PU *Brighton* (*where he was appearing*) (*1906*)
.. ..75p

■190b

*Pub. La Press Ouvrière, Brussels. Proceeds of sale
to 'Radio Vatican'. Pope Pius XII. Period 6* 75p

General

Artist/sculpture Mastroianni religious subjects
Hospice of St. Bernard (incl. dogs). ■191a
Lourdes. Various issues
Monks (incl. liqueur making)
Pictures of angels, Biblical characters, saints
Portraits of clergy/Popes
Swiss Guard
Views of Vatican
Others
Price range   ..   ..   –/**50p**/75p

SALVATION ARMY

Gen. Booth. Various   ..   ..   ..75p/**£1**/£1.50
Gen. Booth memoriam card Pub. Rotary
  1912   ..   ..   £1/**£3**/£6
Mrs. Booth/other members of the Booth
  family ..   ..   50p/**75p**/£1.50
Various   groups/meetings.   ■191b
  ..   ..   50p/**75p**/£1.50

TEN COMMANDMENTS

Ger. Co. Period 2. Set of 10. Per set
  ..   ..   £7/**£10**/£12
Pub. Tuck. 2 versions: Catholic and Protestant (Nos. 163c and 163p). Per set
  ..   ..   £6/**£8**/£10
USA Pub. P.F.B. Per set   ..   ..   £3/**£5**/£8

OTHER RELIGIONS/PERSONALITIES

Various issues   ..   ..   –/**50p**/£2

■191b

Pub. Salvation Army Publishing Offices. Inter-national Staff Songsters. PU *1904. Message about 'the dear General' on reverse* £1.50

■191c

Period 4. Charabanc £1.50

■191a

Pub. Jullien Frères, Geneva. Father Clavendier and his favourite dog, Barry, at the Hospice of St. Bernard. PU *1923* 50p

■191d

Period 4. Vienna motorcycle road race. 1936. Official card issued by the German Motoring Association £12

191

ROAD TRANSPORT

The postcard and the techniques of photographic and lithographic reproduction developed rapidly during a period in which the varieties of public transport were also changing—and competing. Railway engines, ships and aeroplanes have always had their collecting aficionados, and they quickly realised that the postcard was a rich source of information and history. There are separate sections in this catalogue for those highly specialised fields (*see* AVIATION; RAILWAYS; SHIPPING). But the postcard also recorded the battle between the horse and the internal combustion engine, and where a specialist category can be found with both horsedrawn and motorised examples, the former is usually considered to be more valuable. There is inevitable overlapping with SOCIAL HISTORY/TOPOGRAPHICAL, but here we have set out to list those themes which are more concerned with 'transporting', e.g. 'Omnibuses', than with 'activity', e.g. 'ploughing'. The valuations given apply to the broad mass of collectable cards and the highest values should be attached to RP cards with close-up detail. However, this is a field in which particularly good RP close-up examples can command prices beyond the valuations quoted here, especially if there is a strong social history connection. Values apply to Periods 1, 2 unless otherwise stated.

Accidents
Periods 1, 2. All Transport categories. Value much the same or perhaps slightly less than the non-accident entries below.
Other periods. General .. .. .. £1/**£1.50**/£2

Ambulances
Horse	..	..	..	..	..	£4/**£6**/£11
Motor	..	..	..	..	..	£4/**£5**/£9

Buses
Horse	..	..	..	..	..	£7/**£12**/£25
Motor	..	..	..	..	..	£5/**£11**/£25
Steam	..	..	..	..	..	£9/**£15**/£28

Charabancs
Periods 1, 2. ■191c .. .. .. £1/**£2**/£3.50

Commercial Carts
(Incl. ponies and traps) .. .. .. £2/**£3**/£5

Fire Engines
Horse	..	..	..	..	..	£4/**£7**/£15
Motor	..	..	..	..	..	£4/**£6**/£15

Horse and Rider .. .. .. 75p/**£1**/£1.50

Lorries
Motor	..	..	..	..	..	£4/**£5**/£9
Steam	..	..	..	..	..	£6/**£8**/£17

Motor Cars
Periods 1, 2	..	..	..	..	..	£1/**£2.50**/£5
Periods 3 to 5	..	..	..	..	..	50p/**£1**/£2
Period 6	..	..	..	..	..	50p/**75p**/£1

Motor Cycles
General	..	..	..	..	..	£1.50/**£3**/£5
Racing ads. ■191d			..	..	..	£6/**£12**/£15

Motor Racing
The first formal international motor races were sponsored by American newspaper publisher James Gordon Bennett and began in 1900, running each year until 1905, when they finished. In 1906 the French introduced the Grand Prix racing events. On the European mainland, cards showing drivers and their pioneering motor cars are valued higher than in this country, although with the recent popularity of RP social history cards, there has been a quickening of interest here. Clear close-up RP examples of car and driver rate the higher valuations.

Famous Cars
Bluebird (Malcolm Campbell)	..	£2/**£2.50**/£5
Golden Arrow (Major Seagrave)		
.. ..		£2.50/**£3**/£5
Others ..	..	.. .. .. £1.50/**£2**/£4

Fernel Series
Fernand Fernel, one of the 'Collection des Cent' artists, drew a series of 10 cards around 1903 called 'Courses Automobiles' (Car Races). Different cards represent different races.
'Car Races'. ■193a		£3/**£4**/£5
Hill Climbs. RP. Periods 5, 6	..	£1.50/**£2**/£3
Motor Magazine. Portrait series	..	75p/**£1.50**/£3

Personalities (with their machines in brackets)
Allietz	..	..	..	£5/**£8**/£10
Baras (Brasier)	..	..	..	£3/**£4**/£5
Bariller (Brasier)	..	..	..	£2/**£4**/£5
Boegge (Mercedes)	..	..	..	£3/**£5**/£6
Bonnier, Joakim	..	..	..	75p/**£1**/£1.50

Brabham, Jack	..	..	£2/**£2.50**/£5
Brooks, Tony	..	..	50p/**75p**/£1.50
Cagno (Itala)	..	..	£2/**£4**/£5
Duchene	..	..	£5/**£8**/£10
Fabry (Itala)	..	..	£3/**£5**/£6
Fangio, Juan	..	..	£1/**£2**/£2.50
Gabriel (Bayard-Clement)	..	£2/**£4**/£5
Gregory, Masten	..	..	.50p/**75p**/£1.50
Hawthorne, Mike	..	..	£1/**£1.50**/£3
Lancia (Fiat)	..	..	£5/**£8**/£10
Landon (Mors)	..	..	£2/**£4**/£5
Moss, Stirling	..	..	.50p/**75p**/£1.50
Nazzaro (Fiat)	..	..	£3/**£5**/£6
Porsche	..	..	£5/**£8**/£10
Salvadori, Roy	..	..	.50p/**75p**/£1.50
Salzer (Mercedes)	..	..	£3/**£5**/£6
Seagrave, Major H. O. D.	..	£2/**£3**/£4
Sisz (Renault)	..	..	£2/**£3**/£5

Artist Fernand Fernel. Period 2. Impression of the third Gordon Bennett Cup Race (1902) .. £4

Races

Gordon Bennett chromo-litho	..	£10/**£12**/£14
Gordon Bennett photo-origin (highest for RP)	£3/**£5**/£8
Indianapolis (1910)	£5/**£10**/£15
Nurburg Ring	£2/**£4**/£6
Rennen (1907). 'Kaiser Prize'	£4/**£6**/£8
Periods 1, 2 others	£3/**£5**/£8
Periods 3 to 6 others	..50p/**£1.50**/£3

Valentine's Autocar series
Period 6. ■193b .. .. ..75p/**£1.50**/£3

Pub. Valentine. Period 6. Autocar series. Mike Hawthorn in a BRM £1

Motor Shows *See* ADVERTISING

Pedal Cycles, *see* BICYCLING

Royal Mail
Buses (*see also* PHILATELIC) and Vans
.. .. £4/**£8**/£10
Carts .. .. £2/**£3**/£5

Traction Engines .. .. £4/**£8**/£15

Trams (the higher values for close-up RPs)
Electric .. .. £3/**£8**/£10
Horse .. .. £5/**£12**/£18
Steam .. .. £5/**£10**/£15

Trolley Buses (the higher value for close-up
RPs) .. .. £3/**£4**/£9

1896. Fr. Visit of Czar and Czarina to Paris £15

ROYALTY

This is a section which is inextricably bound with several others, notably:

COMMEMORATIVE (Many Royal events were the subject of superb commemorative postcards. They will be listed under ROYALTY.)

POLITICAL (In Victorian and Edwardian times Royal personages—especially abroad—were often politically influential.)

SOCIAL HISTORY/TOPOGRAPHICAL (Royal visits were important events to the towns and cities where they took place.)

WAR (In Victorian and Edwardian times Royal personages often led their countries' war efforts, at least as figureheads.)

Royal cards are ideal for building up a collection throughout the 7 periods as they were amongst the first picture cards and are still being produced today.

This is a vast field and FOREIGN and GB cards are listed separately, in chronological order.

FOREIGN

Period 1. Royal Commemorative Postcards

Royal events postcards before the turn of the century vary from official issues (which are virtually non-pictorial) to coloured, elaborate and beautifully printed vignettes. Because of their rarity and interest, they command high prices on the Continent. They have not so far appeared in sufficient quantity to set a precise valuation for each item in this country. Therefore the main Foreign Royal events before 1900 are listed here in chronological order, with a price range for the whole list. What the earlier issues lack in pictorial interest they make up for in value because of their rarity factor.

1888
Ger. Mourning card for William I.
Ger. Mourning card for Frederick III.
Price range .. .. £5/**£10**/£30

1891
Ger. Marriage of Prinz F. Augustus, Dresden. .. .. £4/**£8**/£20

1896
Bulg. Baptism of Prince Boris into Russian Orthodox Church.
Fr. Visit of Czar Nicholas II and the Czarina to Paris during their coronation year journey. Several versions. ■193c
Ger. Visit of Czar and Czarina to the Kaiser and Kaiserin in Germany.
Ger. 70th birthday of Grand Duke Friedrich of Baden.
It. Official card to celebrate marriage of the Prince of Naples and Princess Elena of Montenegro (5 diff. cols. exist). ■194a.
It. Semi-official ditto.
Price range .. .. £5/**£10**/£25

1897
Russ. Czar with Pres. Fauré of France during the latter's visit to St. Petersburg.
Ger. Visit of King Chulalongkorn of Siam to Germany.
Fr. Later version of Czar and Czarina's visit to Paris.
Price range .. .. £5/**£10**/£25

1898
Aust. Mourning card for Empress Elisabeth of Austria–Hungary, assassinated in Geneva.
Aust. Golden Jubilee of Emperor Franz Josef of Austria–Hungary.
Ger. Visit of Kaiser Wilhelm II and the Kaiserin to Jerusalem.
Price range .. .. £3/**£15**/£25

1899
Crete. Visit of Prince George of Greece to Crete.
Ger. Visit of Kaiser to Remscheid
Price range .. .. £3/**£10**/£15

■194a

1896. It. Official card to celebrate marriage of the Prince of Naples and Princess Elena of Montenegro. PU £5

Periods 2, 4. Royal Commemorative
Postcards (*see also* WAR for Periods 3, 5)
The higher valuation is for UB chromolithographed items or particularly rare items.

1900
It. Mourning cards for King Umberto I,
assassinated Monza (several versions) (Rare).
It. Accession of King Victor Emmanuel III.
Price range .. .. £5/**£10**/£20

1901
Fr. Visit of Czar and Czarina to France.
Ger. 200 years of Prussian Kings.
It. Semi-official mourning card for Q. Victoria
(Rare).
It. Accession of Edward VII.
It. Semi-official card to celebrate birth of Princess
Yolande. Illus. by Artist R. Tafuri.
Ger. Mourning card for Kaiserin Friedrich.
Price range .. .. £8/**£20**/£30

1902
Belg. Visit of Shah of Persia (Rare).
.. .. £10/**£15**/£20

1905
Ger. Marriage of Crown Prince Wilhelm.
Marriage of Prince Gustavus Adolphus of
Sweden.
Visit of King Alfonso XIII of Spain to Paris.
Visit of King Alfonso of Spain to Britain.
Visit of Prince & Princess of Wales to India. Pub.
Tuck. Chromo-litho
Price range .. .. £2/**£3**/£8

1906
Bavarian. 100 years of Bavarian kings.
Ger. Silver Wedding of Kaiser and Kaiserin.
Marriage of King Alfonso of Spain and Princess
Ena of Battenburg.
Price range .. .. £1/**£1.50**/£3

1907
Ger. Marriage of Prinz August Wilhelm and
Princess Alexandra Victoria.
Christening of heir to Spanish Throne.
Price range .. .. 75p/**£1**/£2

1908
Aust. Diamond Jubilee of Emperor Franz Josef I
of Austria–Hungary. Superb design by
Koloman Moser. ■195a

Memoriam cards for assassinated King and
Crown Prince of Portugal.
Accession of King Manoel of Portugal.
Price range .. .. £3/**£5**/£8

1911
Ger. 90th birthday of Prinz Regent Rupert of
Bavaria.
Ger. Silver wedding of Royal Couple,
Wurttemberg.
Bulg. Coming of age of Prince Boris of Bulgaria.
Price range .. .. £2/**£5**/£10

1912
Ger. Mourning card for Prince Leopold of
Bavaria .. .. £1/**£3**/£5

1913
Ger. Silver Jubilee of Kaiser Wilhelm II.
Ger. Marriage of Prussian Princess Victoria
Louise to Duke of Brunswick.
Price range .. .. £1/**£1.50**/£3

■195a
*1908. Diamond Jubilee of Emperor Franz Josef of
Austria Hungary. Superb design by Koloman
Moser (very much in* Wiener Werkstätte *style)* £5

■195b
*1922. Gathering of Royalty, Bucharest, for the
marriage of King Alexander of Yugoslavia and
Princess Marie of Rumania. Our own Prince
Albert competes in the fancy uniform stakes (4th
from left standing). Photographed by Julietta,
Court Photographer to the Royal Court at
Bucharest* £5

1914
Aus. Reissue of 1908 Emperor Franz-Josef Jubilee card with 'United in Strength' overprint .. .. 75p/**£1**/£2

1921
Rum. Marriage of Crown Prince Carol of Rumania and Princess Helen of Greece (Rare) .. .. £1/**£1.50**/£2

1922
Rum. Marriage of King Alexander of Yugo-slavia and Princess Marie of Rumania and Royal gathering. ■195b (Rare) .. .. £1/**£1.50**/£5

1935
Mourning card for Queen Astrid of Belgium (Rare) .. .. £2/**£4**/£6

Foreign Royalty Portraits of Periods 1–6
Posed photographic portraits. Highest value for Russian and obscure Balkan Royal families. .. ..50p/**£1.50**/£5

Hohenzollern—Gallerie
Rare Ger. series of 20 cards of monarchs up to Kaiser Wilhelm II. Period 1. Vignette. The set .. .. £30/**£45**/£60

GREAT BRITAIN

Periods 1, 2, 4, 6, 7. Royal Commemorative Postcards (*see* War for Periods 3, 5)

1897. Q. Victoria's Diamond Jubilee
Pub. Dederich. Highest value for PU .. .. £65/**£150**/£250
Pub. Preston Guardian .. .. £15/**£20**/£25
Others .. .. £10/**£15**/£20
Other Pre-1900 GB Royal events £10/**£15**/£20

1900
Pub. Tuck. 'Empire' postcards Souvenir of 1900 with Q. Victoria oval portrait .. .. £3/**£5**/£7.50
Pub. Tuck. 'Royal' postcard, ditto £3/**£5**/£7.50

1901. Q. Victoria's Death
Pub. Faulkner, C. W. In Memoriam card produced within 15 hours of her death .. .. £6/**£8**/£10

Ed. VII Accession commemoration £2/**£4**/£6
Pub. Tuck. 'Empire' postcards Memoriam .. £6/**£8**/£15
Pub. Wrench. Memoriam cards published in Saxony and a week late in shops. ■196a .. .. £6/**£8**/£15
Other Victoria mourning cards ..£5/**£7.50**/£10

1901. Voyage of the Duke and Duchess of Cornwall and York
Pub. Martin, B., Melbourne. 3 cards. Portraits of Ed. VII, The Duke, The Duchess .. .. £3/**£5**/£8
Other Australian publishers .. .. £2/**£4**/£6
Pub. Tuck. 'Empire' Series 1649. ■196b .. .. £4/**£6**/£8
Pub. Wrench. 'Links of Empire' cards to commemorate the Royal voyage in the *Ophir*. Postcards taken on board and posted at ports of call. Series a. Ten cards. Portsmouth to Australia via Gibraltar, Malta and Port Said.

■196a
1901. Queen Victoria mourning card. Pub. Wrench. Printed in Saxony, therefore a week late £8

■196b
1901. Pub. Tuck. Empire Postcard 1649 Souvenir of Royal Tour £6

Series b. Ten cards. South Africa, Canada and return to England

Mint	£8/**£10**/£12
PU from ports	£10/**£12**/£15

The complete set postally used would be very valuable.

1902. Coronation of Edward VII

Set for 26 June 1902, postponed because of the King's illness and reset for 9 August. Cards to commemorate the coronation were published by:

Bird, Alfred & Sons (4 custard ads, UB vignettes) .. .. £10/**£15**/£25
Blum & Degen; Dobbs; Downey; Galyons; Mansell; Pascalis Moss; Rotary; Russell; Others .. .. £1.50/**£3**/£5
Stead, W. T. Current Event postcards. Four designs (incl. postponement) .. £5/**£8**/£10
Stewart & Woolf. Set of 10 col., embossed showing V.I.P.s at the coronation (note mistake 'H.R.H. Princess of Wales' on Prince of Wales card) .. .. £2/**£4**/£6
Tuck. Kings & Queens of England (*see also* COLLECTIONS). Six cards of Edward with diff. Shakespeare quote. (Date erased when coronation postponed) .. £4/**£6**/£8
Tuck. 'Coronation' series. Embossed, gilded, circular design .. .. .. £3/**£5**/£8
Tuck. 'Empire' postcards 1462, 1451/ 1453 .. .. £3/**£5**/£8
Tuck. Other designs .. .. £1.50/**£3**/£5

1902–1910. Reign of Edward VII

Many cards showing the Royal Family visiting towns, cities, seaside, races, etc. to open public buildings, review the fleet or inspect troops, sail or attend the races, etc., etc. *See also* SOCIAL HISTORY. ■197a.

Price range .. ..75p/**£1.50**/£6

1903

Tuck. Series of 10 cards to commemorate King's visit to Paris, issued in France
.. .. £2/**£3**/£4
Voisey, Chas. Set of 15 cards to commemorate King's visit to Paris £2/**£3**/£4
Others .. .. £1/**£2**/£3

1907

Historic meeting of Crowned Heads, Windsor Castle. Several Pubs. 75p/**£1.50**/£2

1908

Pub. Southwood. Empire Day 'Greeting from the Motherland'. Artist E. J. Walker .. ..75p/**£1.50**/£3

1910. Edward VII's Death

Memoriam cards, many silvered, in purple or in plain black/Coronation Souvenirs/Procession/Q. Alexandra's Message. Publishers include Beagles; Downing; East London Printing Co.; Faulkner, C. W.; Hutson Bros.; Millar & Lang; Louis Levy; Lillywhite; Philco; Ritchie; Rotary; Tuck; others.
Price range .. ..75p/**£1.50**/£5

1910. Proclamation of George V

Pub. Mark Cook of Chester; Judges; others
.. ..75p/**£1.50**/£2

1910. George V's First Court

Pub. Tuck. Artist Harry Payne .. £2/**£4**/£6

1911. Coronation of George V and Queen Mary

The event was covered almost as thoroughly as his father's by the following publishers Davidson Bros.; Inter-Art (incl. Spurgin designs); Louis Levy; Vivian Mansell; McKenzie; Rotary; Russell; Schwerdtfeger; Taylor; Tuck ■197b; others
.. ..75p/**£1.50**/£3

First UK Aerial Post—the most original Coronation celebration. *See* AVIATION.

■197a
King Edward VII and his nephew, Kaiser Wilhelm II, in Berlin. Mid-Period 2 .. .. .. £2.50

■197b
1911. Pub. Tuck. 'Coronation' series. King George V and Queen Mary £4

1911. Investiture of Prince of Wales at Caernarvon
Various Pubs. ■198a .. .. .. £1/**£1.50**/£3

1911. Crowning of King George V as Emperor of India at Delhi Durbar 75p/**£1**/£2

1923. Marriage of Duke and Duchess of York
Price range .. ..75p/**£1.50**/£2

1935. Silver Jubilee of King George V and Queen Mary
Various Pubs. ■198b .. .. .. £1/**£2**/£3

1936. George V's Death
Mourning and Memoriam cards by various
pubs. .. .. £1/**£2**/£3

1936. Edward VIII
Unveiling of Vimy Memorial. Pub. Beagles. RP.
Various other designs.
Price range .. .. £1.50/**£2**/£4

1937. Coronation of King George VI and Queen Elizabeth
Various designs .. ..75p/**£1.50**/£3

1938. Visit of George VI and Queen Elizabeth to France
Various designs .. ..75p/**£1.50**/£2

1947. Betrothal of Princess Elizabeth and Philip Mountbatten
Various designs .. .. 50p/**75p**/£1

1947. Marriage of Princess Elizabeth and Prince Philip
Various designs .. .. 50p/**75p**/£1

1952. George VI's Death
Mourning cards by various pubs. 50p/**£1**/£2

1953. Coronation of Queen Elizabeth II
Various Pubs. .. .. 50p/**75p**/£1

1960. Marriage of Princess Margaret and Antony Armstrong-Jones
Various Pubs. .. .. 50p/**75p**/£1

1969. Investiture of Prince Charles as Prince of Wales at Caernarvon
Various Pubs. .. .. .. 50p/**75p**/£1

1972. Silver Wedding of Queen Elizabeth and Prince Philip
Various Pubs. .. .. –/**50p**/75p

1973. Marriage of Princess Anne and Capt. Mark Phillips
Various Pubs. .. .. –/**50p**/75p
Post Office PHQ card. ■198c .. –/**£3.50**/–

■198a
1911. Investiture of Prince of Wales (later Edward VIII) £3

■198b
1935. Royal gathering for the silver jubilee of King George V and Queen Mary—with the Kents, the Lascelles and the future George VI and his family (including the future Elizabeth II) .. £2

■198c
Post Office PHQ3. Wedding of Princess Anne and Capt. Mark Phillips 1973 .. .. .. £3.50

1977. Silver Jubilee of Queen Elizabeth II
Post Office PHQ cards. Set of 5 .. **£5**
Pub. Carousel. City of Portsmouth Souvenir
    Postcard HMS *Victory* **60p**
Pub. Postcard Association of Great Britain.
    col. ■199a **40p**
Others 25p/**50p**/75p

*1980. 80th Birthday of Queen Elizabeth, the
    Queen Mother*
Post Office PHQ card. **25p**
Others—*see* MODERN

*1981. Wedding of Prince of Wales & Lady Diana
    Spencer*
Post Office PHQ card(s) **50p**
Others incl. Pubs. Carousel, Dixon, Salmon,
    TVH Current Event. ■199b .. 15p/**35p**/£1

Adverts/Charities featuring Royalty (*see also* WAR)
Companies who used Royalty to endorse
    their products incl. Gossage's Soap,
    C. & E. White (tailors using Prince of
    Wales, Period 4) .. .. .. £2/**£3**/£5
Pub. 'The Gentlewoman'. Royal Artists
    postcard series for the benefit of con-
    sumption sufferers .. .. .. 75p/**£1**/£1.50

G.B. Royalty Portraits. All Periods
Posed photographic portraits incl. '3
    Generations'; '4 Generations'; 'The
    Crown and its Jewels'; 'Five Royal
    Georges', etc. Highest valuation for
    obscure or short-lived Royals (like Prince
    John) for Edward VIII and for 'topical'
    Royal personages, e.g. Lord Louis Mount-
    batten (assassinated in 1979) and
    Princess Alice of Athlone, Queen Vic-
    toria's longest surviving grandchild who
    died in 1981. ■199c
Price range .. .. 50p/**75p**/£3

Novelty Postcards of Royalty (*see also* NOVELTY)
Bas Relief. Various Pubs. .. .. 75p/**£1**/£1.50
'Frictograph' cards. Pub. Hartmann (1902)
    .. .. £1/**£1.50**/£2
Woven silk portraits by Grant, Neyret
    Frères, Stevens .. .. £20/**£30**/£40

■199a

*1977. Silver Jubilee of Queen Elizabeth II. Pub.
Postcard Association of Gt. Britain 40p*

■199b

*Engagement of Prince Charles and Lady Diana
Spencer February 1981. Pub. Salmons. .. 25p*

■199c

*Princess Alexander of Teck (Princess Alice of
Athlone, 1883–1981). Pub. Beagles. Period 2 £1*

SHIPPING

Many of the Period 1 and early Period 2 advertising cards were produced for shipping lines and carried chromo-litho vignettes of their ships. Sometimes these cards were sold—say at 2*d.* for 6 cards—sometimes they were given away. They often carried details of on-board menus. One publisher in particular who specialised in producing high quality chromos for shipping lines was Andrew Reid & Co. of Newcastle-on-Tyne. Equally beautiful poster type cards were drawn by the Belgian artist, Cassiers, for the Red Star Line, and many printed by O de Rycker & Mendel of Brussels carry both identification letters and numbers. These coloured cards generally show the ship's name and the correct line flag or funnel. For example, the names of White Star Liners usually end in the letters '-ic', e.g. *Oceanic, Cedric, Celtic*, and the funnels should be yellow with black tops. Similarly Cunard names usually ended with the letters 'ia', e.g. *Ivernia, Lusitania*, and the ships had red funnels with black tops. However, the rule is not foolproof! Not all postcards are concerned with the mighty transatlantic lines. Shipping lines abounded around the British coastline, plying from resort to resort and from the mainland to islands. Cards showing paddle steamers that were popular during the early part of Period 2 are becoming most collectable, particularly the RP versions. There is overlapping here with SOCIAL HISTORY/TOPOGRAPHICAL and, as in that category, valuations can be augmented by close-up details, RP printing and local interest. To some collectors additional value attaches to cards with railway or island connections. Postmarks too can be important, particularly the *Paquebot* or *Posted at Sea* strikes. A specialist work of reference should be consulted on that subject. *See also* RAILWAYS and WAR for Periods 3, 5.

Advertising

Many early cards showing liners (in particular) are advertising cards produced by the Line concerned. General valuations are given here with more specific information on noted publishers, e.g. Andrew Reid, or artists given below.

Period 1 and early Period 2, chromo-litho vignettes, UB .. .. £3/**£6**/£8

Period 2, 3. Col. art, not vignettes, e.g. White Star, Cunard, Canadian Pacific, Blue Funnel. ■200a .. .. .. 50p/**£1**/£2

Poster types .. .. £2/**£5**/£10
Other periods .. .. 50p/**£1**/£2

Artists

Bannister, A. F. D.
Period 4 steamers, e.g. *Isle of Guernsey, Isle of Jersey*, etc. .. .. .. 50p/**75p**/£1
Sailing Ships. *Cutty Sark*, etc. .. 25p/**50p**/75p

Burgess, Arthur
Cammel Laird col. ships. HMS *Birkenhead*, HMS *Chester*, MS *La Playa*, MS *La Perla*, MS *La Marea*, etc. .. £1/**£1.50**/£2

Cassiers, H.†
Red Star Poster type ads. UB .. £3/**£4**/£10
Red Star ads. UB .. .. .. £2/**£3**/£5

Chilley, A.
Sailing ships. *Cutty Sark, Golden Hind*, etc. 25p/**50p**/75p

Dixon, Chas.
Belfast Steam Ship Co., Red Star Line, Royal Mail Steam Packet, etc. £1/**£1.50**/£2

Eckenbrecker, T. von
Chromo detachable menu cards, e.g. Nord-Deutscher Lloyd .. .. .. £3/**£4**/£4.50

Forrest, A. S.
Booth Line. 'Picturesque Portugal' series .. .. 50p/**75p**/£1

Mason, Frank
Merchant ships. Pub. F. T. Everard .. .. 25p/**50p**/£1

Shoesmith, Kenneth
Norwegian views .. .. .. £1/**£1.50**/£2

■200a

SS Laurentic. White Star Liner Period 2. Col. art £1

Harbour/Shipyard Scenes

Good general detail .. .. ..75p/**£1.50**/£3	
Launchings .. .. £1/**£2**/£4	

Hovercraft

Period 6 only **25p**

Japanese Ship Advertising ■201a

Price range .. .. £1/**£2**/£3

■201a
Period 2. Japanese SS Kashima Maru .. £3

Life at Sea/Sailors

Oilette types, e.g. 'Britain's Bulwarks'
.. .. 50p/**75p**/£1
Pub. Gale & Polden 25p/**50p**/75p
Others, e.g. Pub. John Walker .. –/**25p**/50p

Menu Cards (not chromo-litho)

Periods 1 to 4. ■201b 25p/**50p**/75p

■201b
Period 2. Menu. White Star Line. SS Megantic
.. ..50p

Naval Ships (*see also* WAR)

Period 1. Chromo-litho .. .. .. £5/**£6**/£8
Gale & Polden 'Wellington' series. Col. art.
  battleships .. .. 50p/**75p**/£1
Tuck 'Empire' series .. .. .. £2/**£5**/£8
Tuck Oilettes. Our Navy, e.g. HMS
  Australia, HMS *Queen Mary*, HMAS
  Sydney, etc. .. ..75p/**£1**/£1.25

Paddle Steamers

This section is concerned with photographic origin and real photographs. RP types are most highly valued, particularly with close-up people detail. Artist-drawn cards should be valued under the *Passenger and Merchant Ships* heading.
Albert Victor; Albion; Alexandra; Balmoral; Barry; Bickerstaffe ■*201c; Bilsdale; Boudicea; Bournemouth Queen; Brighton Queen; Cambria; City of Rochester; Clacton Belle; Columba; Consul; Crested Eagle; Devonia; Duchess of Hamilton; Duchess of York; Duke of Devonshire; Eagle; Eagle III; Empress; Essex; Essex Queen; Galatea; Glen Avon; Glen Gower; Glen Rosa; Golden Eagle; Grenadier; Greyhound; Isle of Arran; Jeanie Deans; Juno; Kenilworth; King Edward; La Marguerite; Lady Evelyn; Lady Moyra; Lord of the Isles; Lorna Doon; Minden; Monarch; Mona's Queen; Prince of Wales; Queen; Ravenswood; Royal Sovereign; St. Elvies; Sannox; Southend Belle; Suffolk; Talisman; Viking Manxman; Waverley.*
Price range .. .. £1/**£1.50**/£3

■201c
Period 2. Paddle Steamer Bickerstaffe .. £1.50

■201d
Pub. M. Sternberg, Hong Kong. HMS Phoenix *wrecked at Kowloon. September 1906* .. £1.50

Passenger & Merchant Ships

This section overlaps with SOCIAL HISTORY/TOPO-GRAPHICAL and covers a broad spectrum of passenger and merchant vessels, e.g. ferries, trawlers, tugs, etc. Higher values are associated with clear RP cards, or where appropriate, fine chromo-litho UB examples, and local interest can raise values beyond these bands.

General Period 2	.. 50p/**£2**/£2.50
General Periods 3, 4	..50p/**£1.50**/£2
Sailing ships	..50p/**£1**/£1.50
Others	.. 25p/**50p**/75p

Piccadilly Hotel (Ship Cards)

Price range .. .. 50p/**75p**/£1

Publishers

David MacBrayne
Glasgow & Highland Royal Mail Steamers. chromo-litho vignette. Printer McQuor-quodale. UB .. .. .. £5/**£8**/£10

Andrew Reid
Chromo-litho vignettes for The America Line; Belfast Steam Ship Co.; P. & O.; Pacific Steam Navigation Co. (Orient Line); Pacific Line; Ullswater Navigation & Transit Co., etc. Ships include:
SS Arabia; SS Graphic; SS Heroic; SS Himalaya; SS India; SS Macedonia; SS Magic; SS Malwa; SS Marmord; SS Mongolia; SS Moolton; SS Moormond; SS Oravia; SS Orcana; SS Orellana; SS Oropesa, ■202a; *SS Oroya; SS Raven; SS Sardinia; SS Simla; SS St. Louis.*
Price range. UB .. .. .. £4/**£8**/£14
Sepia art, e.g. Pacific Line. UB .. £1/**£1.50**/£2
Sailing ships. UB .. .. .. £3/**£6**/£8

F. G. O. Stuart
Ships series, e.g. RMS *Adriatic*, RMS *Amazon*, RMS *Aragon*, RMS *Briton*, SS *Armdale Castle*, SS *Avondale Castle*, SS *Durham*, SS *Goorkha*, SS *Kenilworth Castle*. Price range .. .. £1/**£2**/£2.50

Shipwrecks

Ship Names

Abertay (Cornwall, 1912) ..	.. £1/**£2**/£2.50
Alaska	.50p/**75p**/£1.50
Bardic (Lizard, 1924) RP ..	£1/**£1.50**/£2

Berlin (Holland, 1907). Pub. Hartmann.
  Set of 12 .. .. £1/**£2**/£2.50
Cecile Herzogin (Salcombe, 1936)
  .. ..75p/**£1**/£1.50
Coopland .. .. .. 50p/**75p**/£1.50
Crescent City .. .. .. 50p/**75p**/£1.50
Gladiator, HMS (1908). Pub. Broderick
  .. .. £1/**£2**/£2.50
Hilda (St. Malo, 1905) 50p/**75p**/£1.25
La Gascogne (St. Nazaire) .. ..75p/**£1**/£1.50
Le Chili (Bordeaux) .. ..75p/**£1**/£1.25
Mahratta, SS (on Goodwins, 1909). Pub. Glencairn Craik, Deal .. .. 75p/**£1**/£2
Mermaris (River Tigris) .. 50p/**75p**/£1.50
Montagu, HMS (Lundy, 1906). Pub. Twiss Bros., Ilfracombe .. .. 50p/**75p**/£1.50
Phoenix, HMS (Kowloon, 1908). Pub. M. Sternberg. ■201d .. .. £1/**£1.50**/£2
Pisagna (Dover, 1912) .. .. £1/**£1.25**/£2
Queen Elizabeth (Steamboat) (Kew, 1904). Pub. Walter Pearce, Brentford 75p/**£1**/£1.50
Scotia (1909). Photo S. Thorn, Bude
  .. .. £1/**£1.25**/£2
Thyra (Duncan's Bay, 1914) RP £2/**£2.50**/£3
Others .. ..50p/**£1.50**/£3

Silks

Woven types, incl. Grant & Stevens, e.g. RMS *Adriatic*, RMS *Edinburgh Castle*, RMS *Empress of Britain*, RMS *Carmania*, RMS *Ivernia*, RMS *Mauretania*, RMS *Royal George*, RMS *Titanic*, SS *Haverford*, etc. (*see also* NOVELTY). Price range .. .. £12/**£20**/£25

Titanic

At least 50 different cards exist (*see also* SILKS).

Artistic
e.g. Artist W. Fred Mitchell. Pub. Salmon
  .. .. £1.50/**£2**/£3

■202a

Period 2. Pacific Line RMS Oropesa. *Chromo-litho* UB £8

Memoriam

Bamforth. 'Nearer my God' types	75p/**£2**/£3
Goodred, Cyril. Black border ..	£2.50/**£3**/£5
Millar & Lang. Verse, ship and captain	
.. ..	£3/**£5**/£8
Rotary. 'Nearer my God' types ..	£2/**£3.50**/£5
Valentine's. 'Among the Icebergs'	£1/**£1.50**/£2

RP Types

Price range	£4/**£8**/£10

Tuck Celebrated Liners

Tuck produced at least 20 Oilette series under this title, all or most of which contain six cards. The identified series are:

3592
6228 White Star Line
6229 Orient Pacific
6230
9106 Cunard
9112 P & O
9121 Canadian Pacific
9124 N. D. Lloyd Line
9125 Hamburg American Line
9126 Atlantic Transport
9133 Union Castle Line
9140 American Line
9151 Royal Mail SS Co.
9155 Dominion Line
9213 Allan Line
9215 White Star Line
9268 Cunard
9503 White Star Line
9682 Canadian Pacific
9898 White Star Line
Valuations per card .. . . £1/**£2**/£2.50

Three Band Pricing System

Left Hand Band.	*The lowest price you will probably be asked to pay for this card.*
Middle Band.	*What you will normally be asked to pay for this card; its average, reasonable price.*
Right Hand Band.	*The highest price you will probably be asked to pay for this card.*

For a full explanation of the System, see page viii.

SOCIAL HISTORY/ TOPOGRAPHICAL

This section is mainly concerned with viewcards of Britain, probably the biggest category of all. The publishers Blum & Degen alone had issued over 7000 different views by 1905, and Tucks claimed double that number. Yet neither was the largest producer. That honour lay with Valentine's, the photographic kings.

The old photographic picture postcard is often today's only source of accurate pictorial information concerning places and people of the years between 1900 and 1914. The same is true to a lesser extent of times up to just a few years ago. The postcard recorded scenes that no other medium found interesting enough, and the postcard was 'collected' and thus saved for posterity. The importance of these cards is increasing as larger numbers of people become interested in the history of their localities, and the popularity of the pictures is such that many local libraries are now selling reprints of old postcards.

Postcard collectors have referred variously to the picture content of such old cards as 'Social History' (meaning 'people') and/or Topographical (meaning 'places'). We believe that separate listing makes analysis too complex. The categories are inextricably entwined. Therefore, we have put them together.

Many local postcard clubs have produced check lists of cards connected with their area. This identification of cards sometimes leads to local competition over a supposedly scarce example, and prices can escalate well beyond the ranges given here. Interest in a Period 2 RP card of an empty High Street in, say Canterbury, is likely to be confined to collectors living in and around that City, but if a solitary traction engine were to be trundling down that same road, collectors throughout the country would take notice. The value of SOCIAL HISTORY/TOPOGRAPHICAL cards, therefore, tends to be a very subjective matter, and this point should always be taken into account.

We have included a small special section on Hop Cards in order to illustrate the extraordinary scope of the hobby. The number of different publishers of Kent Hop Picking Cards so far identified can almost certainly be matched by the number of publishers who produced cards showing 'fish gutters', 'shop fronts' and a vast range of fascinating subjects.

Since the term 'Social History' is infinitely flexible, it can be made to cover every human activity. There is, therefore, overlapping with just about every other category in this catalogue. The key word for this section is 'Local'; but before settling upon a valuation for a card it would be wise to consult the Index for other references e.g. 'traction engines'. Higher valuations of a given subject relate to RP cards with close up detail, particularly if people are clearly visible and are engaged in activities associated with Period 1 or 2 —or using old fashioned equipment or machinery.

The following sub-divisions have been used:

AGRICULTURE/FISHING/RURAL
AMUSEMENT PARKS
ARCADES
ARTISTS
ASSOCIATIONS/ORGANISATIONS
BUILDINGS/STRUCTURES
COMMERCIAL/INDUSTRIAL
COURT CARDS
CRAFTS/OCCUPATIONS/SERVICES/TRADES
CRESTS/HERALDIC DEVICES/TARTANS
DISASTERS
ETHNIC ACTIVITIES/CHARACTERS/GROUPS
HARBOURS/PORTS
INLAND WATERWAYS
LEGEND AND LORE
LOCAL EVENTS/GATHERINGS
LONDON
MAP CARDS
POLAR AND EVEREST EXPLORATION
SEASIDE
STREET SCENES
STRIKES
UNIFORMED PUBLIC SERVICES
VIEWS

AGRICULTURE/FISHING/RURAL

As with many categories of postcards, cards in this section could overlap with ANIMALS and ROAD TRANSPORT. We will describe here cards which show rural and fishing occupations, especially those which no longer exist (or which modern technology has completely altered), agricultural machinery and fish processing.

In all sections of this category the higher price range applies to clear RP cards showing active scenes with good detail of people and equipment.

Agricultural Shows

RP	..	..	..	..	..	..	75p/£1/£2
Others	..	..	..	..	..	..	50p/75p/£1

Equipment/Machinery (Periods 2 to 4)

Horsedrawn carts/ploughs. RP ..	£1/**£2**/£3
Others	50p/**75p**/£1.50
Other machinery. RP	£2/**£4**/£8
Others	75p/**£1.50**/£3

Shire series—*see* MODERN CARDS.

Occupations

Period 1 examples of all occupations
.. .. £1/**£3**/£5

Animal-Tenders (Periods 2 to 4)
Cowherds/Pigmen/Shepherds, etc.

RP	75p/**£1.50**/£2
Others	25p/**50p**/75p

Arts/Cottage Industries/Crafts (Periods 2 to 4)
E.g. Blacksmiths/Forges/Watercarriers
Dairy industries/Lace-making/Spinners/Weavers/
Wheelwrights, etc. ■205a

RP	£1/**£2**/£3
Others	25p/**50p**/75p

Fisher Folk (Periods 2 to 4)
Scenes at markets, ■205b/fish halls/on board/
landing the catch, coracle or Curragh fisher men,
etc.

RP	£1.50/**£2**/£2.50
Others	50p/**75p**/£1
'LL'	£1/**£1.50**/£2

Pictorial Stationery Co. series	50p/**75p**/£1
Valentine's series	50p/**75p**/£1.50
Wrench series	75p/**£1**/£2

■205b

*Pub. Anon. Period 3. B & w card of photographic
origin. Scotch girls gutting herring at Gorleston
.. .. £1.50*

■205c

*Pub. Anon. Period 2. B & w photo of Tobacco
Harvest at Church Crookham, Hants.* PU *1914
.. .. £1.50*

■205d

*Pub. Young & Cooper, Maidstone. Period 2.
Coloured card of photographic origin. London Hop
Pickers Homeward Bound.* PU *1905 .. £1.50*

■205a

*Pub. Frith & Co. Period 2. B & w photomontage
Honiton Lacemaker and Lace* PU *1905 .. 75p*

205

Harvesters (People) (Periods 2 to 4)
E.g. Grain/Tobacco Foreign/Tobacco GB (higher valuation). ■205c

RP	..75p/**£1.50**/£2
Others	25p/**50p**/75p

Pickers (Periods 2 to 4)
E.g. Flowers (e.g. lavender)/Fruit (e.g. plums, strawberries)/Hops—*see below*/vegetables (e.g. potatoes)

RP	£1/**£1.50**/£3
Others	50p/**75p**/£1

Hops—Special Entry
In order to illustrate the general collecting potential of what might at first seem to be modest themes, we have chosen to list as an example, publishers of Period 2 cards that depict Kent hop fields. This listing is likely to be typical of any number of country themes and we would be pleased to receive information from collectors for future entries. Many hop card publishers cannot be identified, but taking differences in style as indicators there are at least 40 separate publishers. These include:
T. W. Barber (Faversham) (b & w); H. Camburn (Tunbridge Wells) (b & w); G. A. Cooper (Maidstone) (col.); Daniell Bros. (Lewisham) (col.); De'ath (Ashford) (b & w); De'ath & Dunk (b & w); Earle (Bromley) (col.); File & Sons (Boughton) (col.); Filmers (Faversham) (col.); T. A. Flemans (Tonbridge) (b & w); H. J. Goulden (Canterbury) (b & w and col.); Goulden & Wind (Ashford) (b & w); A. N. Hanbrook (Snodland) (col.); F. Hartmann (London) (col.); Judges (Hastings) (b & w); L & NWR series (b & w); Lane (Faversham) (b & w); Millar & Lang (Glasgow) (col.); Miller & Jarvis (Ashford) (b & w); Mockford (Tonbridge) (b & w); Moore, Fisk (Canterbury) (b & w); Pettit & Son (Canterbury) (b & w); Photochrom (London & Tunbridge Wells) (b & w and col.); Pictorial Postcard Co. (London) (col.); Ridley (Tenterden) (b & w); Salmon (Sevenoaks) (col.); A. Shrubsall (Sittingbourne) (col.); E. A. Sweetman & Son (b & w); Tester, Massy & Co. (London) (col.); Thornton Bros. (New Brompton) (col.); Valentine's (Dundee) (col.); H. Waters (Cranbrook) (b & w); H. & J. West (Ramsgate) (b & w); Whitbread (b & w); Young & Cooper (Maidstone) (The major Kent publisher).

Young & Cooper cards
    Lettered cards, A to K. b & w
    Numbered cards, 1 to 25. col. ■205d

Price range. RP	£1/**£2**/£3.50
Others	50p/**£1**/£2

Rural Scenes (Periods 2 to 4)

Grazing herds/landscapes/views ..	–/**25p**/50p
Scenes of Village Life. RP. ■206a	£1/**£1.50**/£3
Others	25p/**50p**/75p
Tuck named series, e.g. 'Rapholette glossy'	25p/**50p**/75p

Tuck Oilettes
Series titles include 'Cottage Gardens', 'Country Charms', 'Rural England', 'The Simple Life', etc. *See* ARTISTS below
.. .. 25p/**50p**/75p

AMUSEMENT PARKS

RP. ■206b	£1/**£2**/£3
Others	..75p/**£1**/£1.50

■206a
Pub. Anon. Period 2. B&w photo of Newborough Small Holdings Harvest (1912) £1.50

■206b
Period 2. Flying Machine at Blackpool £2

ARCADES

RP. ■207a	.. ..	£1.50/**£2.50**/£5
Others	.. ..	50p/**75p**/£1.50

ARTISTS

We consider here artists who produced scenic views of the 'Oilette type'—a genre produced by most of the major publishing houses during Periods 2 to 4. Unsigned, or indecipherable signatures will normally be valued less than named artist cards. We indicate a general price range and at least one publisher (in brackets) for whom the artist has drawn or for whom his or her drawings were reprinted.

(† = *see* ARTISTS for more details.)

Austen, Alex (Regal Art Co.—Rapco)
Barrow, W. H. (Water Col. P.C. Co.)
Beni, F. (Worth of Exeter)
Boyne, Tom (J. W. Ruddock)
Bréanski, A. de (Faulkner)
Bridgeman, A. W. (Tuck Oilette)
Clarke, S. (Faulkner)
Cole, Edwin (Wilding)
Corke, C. Essenhigh (Salmon)
Cubley, Hadfield (Tuck)
Endacott, S.† (Frith, Worth)
Fletcher-Watson, P. (Tuck)
Flower, Charles E.† (Tuck)
Fulleylove, John† (Regal Art Co.; Robert Peel of Oxford; Tuck)
Gaston, R. (Hildesheimer)
Gretty, G. (Tuck)
Hayes, F. W.† (Meissner & Buch; Tuck)
Heyermans, John A. (Tuck)
Jackson, Helen (Tuck)
Longstaffe, E. (Hildesheimer)
Lugg, R. J. (Frith)
Matthison, W.† (Robert Peel of Oxford; Tuck)
McIntyre, R. F. (Tuck)
Minns, Fanny M. (J. W. Ruddock; George Stewart & Co.)
Morris, M. (Tuck)
Newton, G. E. (Tuck)
Parr, F. (Worth)
Payne, Arthur† (Hildesheimer; J. W. Ruddock; Tuck)
Payne, Harry† (Hildesheimer; Tuck)
Penley, Edwin E. (Tuck)
Percival, E. D. (Regal Art Co.; Tuck)
Perry, Arthur W. (Worth)
Phillimore, R. P.† (Phillimore)
Pressland, A. L. (Salmon)
Quatremain, W. W. (Salmon)

Quinton, A. R.† (Salmon; Tuck)
Ramsay, George S. (Childeric of Buxton, 'Peakland series')
Richards, Frank (Nister, chromo-litho)
Richardson, F. Esdaile (Tuck)
Severn, Walter (Tuck)
Smith, T. (Tuck)
Stannard, Henry (Boots Cash Chemists; Tuck)
Stanton, Charles R. (Frith)
Thors, Joseph (Regal Art Co.)
Van Hier, Professor (Boots Cash Chemists; Davidson Bros.; Tuck)
Vaughan, E. H. (Tuck)
Warrington, Ellen (Tuck)
Welbourne, Ernest (C. W. Faulkner)
Wimbush, Henry B. (A. & C. Black; Tuck)
Young, A. (Faulkner; Wildt & Kray)
Young, Walter Hayward—'Jotter'† (Boots Cash Chemists; Ettlinger; Frith; Hartmann; Misch & Co.; Pictorial Stationary Co.; Robert Peel of Oxford; Tuck; Wildt & Kray)

Price range .. ..50p/**£1.50**/£3

■207a
Period 2. Great Western Arcade, Birmingham
.. .. £1.50

■207b
Pub. Schwerdtfeger. Period 2. 'A British Scout'
.. .. £1.50

ASSOCIATIONS/ORGANISATIONS

See also RELIGION.

Bands	50p/**75p**/£1
Church Army	.. 75p/**£1**/£1.25
Dr. Barnado	−/**50p**/75p
Evangelism	£1.50/**£2**/£3
Guiding	£1.50/**£3**/£4
Jewish	£2/**£3**/£4
Political	£2/**£5**/£8
Red Cross	50p/**75p**/£1
St. John Ambulance	50p/**75p**/£1
Salvation Army	£1/**£1.50**/£3
Scouting. ■207b	£1.50/**£3**/£4
Strikes	£4/**£7**/£10
YMCA	25p/**50p**/75p
YWCA	25p/**50p**/75p
Others	25p/**50p**/£1

BUILDINGS/STRUCTURES

Until recently there has been little interest in this category. Growing attention to local history has led collectors to seek picture records, particularly where demolition and other great changes have taken place. Cards in this section are essentially Period 2 with the higher values reserved for RP examples, and where appropriate, internal views with activity. Clearly there is overlapping with other sections. References are given below. Valuations are based upon the major thematic identification of the cards being to do with 'buildings' rather than 'people' although of course in some cases the presence of people identifies the building, e.g. a school as in ■208a. See also 'Commercial/Industrial' which follows this section.

Bandstands	.. 50p/**£1**/£1.50
Barracks	−/**50p**/£1
Casinos	£1/**£2**/£4
Cinemas (*see also* CINEMA)	£4/**£7**/£10
Crystal Palace. Pub. Beagles, Rotary, etc.	50p/**75p**/£1
Crystal Palace. Pub. Excelsior Fine Arts (E.F.A.)	.. 75p/**£1**/£1.50
Crystal Palace. Pub. Russell & Sons	75p/**£1.50**/£2.50
Crystal Palace. Pub. Schwerdtfeger	50p/**75p**/£1
Other cards of Crystal Palace ..	−/**50p**/75p
Factories	.. 50p/**£1**/£1.50
Fire stations (*see also* 'Uniformed Public Services' below)	£1/**£1.50**/£2
Historical buildings/structures ..	**50p**
Hospitals (*see also* 'Uniformed Public Services' below)	−/**50p**/75p
Hotels	£1/**£1.50**/£2
Municipal buildings	−/**50p**/75p

Police stations	£1/**£1.50**/£2
Post offices (*see also* 'Uniformed Public Services' below)	£2/**£4**/£6
Public houses	£1.50/**£2**/£3
Railway stations (*see also* RAILWAYS)	£2/**£4**/£7
Religious buildings	**50p**
Restaurants	£1/**£1.50**/£2
Royal Mint	.. 25p/**50p**/75p
Schools. ■208a	..50p/**£1**/£1.50
Skyscrapers. Chrysler Building, Flat Iron Building, New York.	−/**50p**/75p
Theatres (*see also* THEATRE)	75p/**£1**/£2
Village halls	50p/**75p**/£1
Others	**50p**

■208a
Period 3. Allison Road School. Group II. 2nd Sept. 1914. Location unknown 50p

COMMERCIAL/INDUSTRIAL

This section deals with picture cards which can readily be associated with a particular commercial or industrial enterprise. The highest valuations are for clear RP with good people activity.

Bridges	50p/**75p**/£1
Chimneys	−/**50p**/75p
Coalmines. Surface scenes	£1/**£2**/£3
Coalmines. Underground scenes. ■209a	£1.50/**£2**/£4
Engineering activities	£2/**£4**/£8
Mills. Water	..50p/**£1**/£1.50
Mills. Wind	£1/**£2**/£3
Shop fronts	£2.50/**£4**/£6
Shop interiors	£2/**£4**/£5
Tin mines	£2/**£3**/£5
Workshop scenes	£2/**£4**/£6

CRAFTS/OCCUPATIONS/SERVICES/ TRADES

This section covers all forms of work except those included in 'Uniformed Public Services' below. All cards must have a subject contemporary to the period in which they were published, i.e. 'historical' types are not included. The major interest lies in skills or activities now out of date. *See also* 'Agriculture/Fishing/Rural' above. Cards showing individuals in trade situations are sometimes depicted in series as 'Types', e.g. 'London Types' published by Photochrom. *See also* 'London'. We have listed a selection of the crafts/occupations/trades/'Types' that may be found and provide two broad band valuations— one for artist drawn cards and one for those of photographic origin. As the growing interest in these cards unearths additional information, more detailed listings will become possible, e.g.

Artist L. J. Kipper. Pub. E. Nister. Series
190. ■209b   ..   ..   £2/**£3**/£5
Pub. EFA (Excelsior Fine Arts). Series 533.
■209c   ..   ..   £1/**£2**/£3

The following list of types does not pretend to be exhaustive but only indicative of what may be found. Readers are invited to send in detailed information.

Barber. ■210a
Cabbie
Chauffeur
Chimney Sweep
Clerk. ■210b
Deliveryman
Dentist
Doctor
Egg Seller
Errand Girl. ■209b
Flower Girl
Horn Blower
Match Girl
Message Boy
Milkman. ■210c
Newsvendor
Rat Catcher
Road Sweeper
Sandwichboard Man
Servants
Shoeblack. ■209c
Shopkeeper
Snake Catcher
Street Trader
Town crier.
Waiter

Foreign—French example. Key Cutter. ■210d
Artist drawn examples of above   ..   £1/**£2**/£4
Photo-origin examples of above. RP examples command the highest prices. *See also* 'London Types'   ..   ..   £2/**£5**/£8

■209a
Pub. J. Starr. Wigan. Period 2. Miners working a seam of coal £4

■209b
Pub. Ernest Nister. Artist L. J. Kipper. The Errand Girl. Series 190 No. 1   ..   ..   ..   £4

■209c
Pub. Excelsior Fine Arts (EFA). Period 2. The Shoeblack. Series 533   ..   ..   £2.50

■210a
Pub. Tuck. Artist Gunning King. Period 2.
Gossips. Oilette 'Life in our Village'. Series
1393 .. .. £1

■210d
Pub. E. Le Deley (Fr). Period 2. The Key Cutter.
Maggi 'Paris' series. No. 903 .. .. .. £12

■210b
Period 2. Clerks sitting on high stools £2

■210e
Pub. Byers (W.E.B. & Co.). Period 2. 'Favourite
series'. Eastbourne. No. 1204 .. .. £1.25

■210c
Period 2. Milkman. Malvern. Good pony and
cart £3

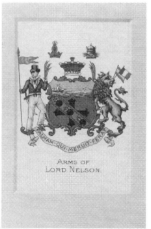

■210f
Pub. Faulkner. Period 2. Heraldic. Framed. Arms
of Lord Nelson £1.50

CRESTS/HERALDIC DEVICES/TARTANS

The intricate designs and bold colours of heraldic devices were natural for transfer to the picture postcard as the rotary printing processes came into full production early in Period 2. Most Period 1 examples are of foreign designs often used on commemorative issues. Here we are concerned with British designs only, of which there are vast numbers. For example, Stoddard & Co. issued over 1000 different versions of their well known Ja-Ja series. The listing is by publisher.

Brown & Rawcliffe (B. & R.)
Heraldic/view. Camera series .. **50p**

Byers, W. E. (W.E.B. & Co.)
'Favourite' series. Heraldic/multi-view.
■210e .. .. 50p/**£1**/£1.25

Cambridge Picture Postcard Co.
Cambridge colleges	—/**50p**/75p
Oxford colleges	—/**50p**/75p
Public schools	50p/**75p**/£1

Cynicus
Tartans .. .. —/**50p**/75p

Davis, A. M.
Heraldic .. .. 50p/**75p**/£1

Faulkner
Crests	..50p/**£1**/£1.50
Heraldic. Framed. ■210f	£1/**£1.50**/£2
Heraldic. Unframed	£1.50/**£2**/£2.50

Highland Clan Postcard
Scottish Clans .. .. —/**50p**/75p

Jarrold
Heraldic .. .. —/**50p**/75p

Johnston, W. & A. K.
Scottish Clans (about 100 cards) **50p**

Millar & Lang
Heraldic. National series. .. .. 50p/**75p**/£1

Peel, Robert
Cambridge colleges	—/**50p**/75p
Oxford colleges	—/**50p**/75p
Public schools	50p/**75p**/£1

Ritchie, William (W. R. & S.)
City Arms. Reliable series .. .. 50p/**75p**/£1

Stoddart (Ja-Ja)
Heraldic series (about 1000 cards).
.. .. 50p/**75p**/£1

Tuck
Heraldic. Embossed. View. Unframed. UB.	
.. ..	£5/**£6**/£8
Heraldic. Framed. UB	£4/**£5**/£6
Scottish clans	£1/**£1.50**/£2

Valentine
Multi-shields .. .. 50p/**75p**/£1

DISASTERS

This section deals with 'Acts of God' such as epidemics, fires, floods, landslides and storms rather than obviously man-made catastrophes like rail or road accidents, except where the latter assumed disaster proportions. Probably every area of the country has had its own disaster.

Bristol. Fire (1905). Pub. Pincock Bros. RP	£1/**£1.50**/£2
Clapham. Fire. Arding & Hobbs (1909)	£1/**£1.25**/£1.50
Hampstead Colliery (1908). Pub. Nightingale.	£4/**£6**/£8
Handcross Motor Bus Fatality.	
Pub. Kerhhohn & others. RP ..	£1/**£1.50**/£2
Pub. Ingram Clark	£2/**£4**/£6
Lincoln Typhoid outbreak (1905).	£10/**£12**/£15
Louth Floods (1920). Pub. Benton, Harrison, *Yorkshire Observer* ..	£1/**£2**/£3
Lynmouth Floods (1952). Photo cards pub. by H. Barton	50p/**£1**/£2
Messina Earthquake. It (1908). Incl. 'Before & After' Novelty cards	25p/**50p**/75p
Norwich Floods (1912). Pub. Pioneer RP	£1.25/**£2**/£2.50
Paris Floods (Inondations) (1910). Over 40 pubs. Over 3000 cards.	50p/**£1**/£3

Pub. Warner Gothard of Barnsley. About 25 different disasters (1905–14). Photo-montage type, e.g. HMS *Tiger*, HMS *Berwick* (1908); Saddleworth Railway Smash (1909); HMS *Gladiator*/HMS *Paul* (1908); Hampstead Colliery (1908); Woodhouse Junction Railway Smash (1908); Tonbridge Railway Disaster (1909); Cromer Express Wreck (1913) .. .. £15/**£19**/£25

Rescue operations	£1.50/**£3**/£4
San Francisco Earthquake (1906)	25p/**50p**/75p
Stalybridge floods (1906). Pub. Hallas	£1/**£2**/£3
Others	25p/**£1**/£5

ETHNIC ACTIVITIES/CHARACTERS/ GROUPS

As before the most highly valued cards are those of photographic origin, although certain artists, like John Innes of Canada, are attracting attention. By 'ethnic' we mean that the subject matter is directly concerned with a particular race. The reference may be humorous (the endless Irish/ Scottish/Welsh jokes are of little value) or observant of activity or dress.

Artist Drawn Cards

This section includes cards showing national costumes, ethnic humour and general 'artistic' records of ethnic activities.

Africa	–/50p/75p

Britain. Typical examples in this category are the Irish, Scots and Welsh costume cards (Welsh ladies in tall hats, etc.) and humorous cards such as those teasing the Scots about their supposed meanness. ■212a **50p**

European Mainland. Continental collectors value these cards more highly than the equivalent cards are valued in Britain, but there are more chromo-litho examples to be found for this sub-section and hence the upper valuation is higher than average. ■212b .. .. 50p/**£1**/£1.50

Far East. Early in Period 2 there was a European vogue for things Japanese and some fine artistic cards were produced such as Tucks 'Real Japanese' in the Connoisseur series 2514.

Japanese	50p/**£2**/£8
Others	50p/**75p**/£1
Gypsies	50p/**75p**/£1

India, e.g. Tuck 'Native Life in India' Series
7408	–/50p/75p

Jewish. The internationality of the Jewish race makes this a more than averagely popular theme. ■212c .. .. £1/**£2**/£5

Middle East. ■213a .. .. .. –/50p/75p

North America. American and Canadian interest in this artist drawn category is strong, and to an extent their interest is reflected in British valuations of their cards.

Artist John Innes (Can.). ■213b	
.. ..	£1/**£1.50**/£2
Cowboys	50p/**75p**/£1
Indians. ■213c	50p/**£1**/£1.50
General	–/**50p**/£1
South America	50p/**75p**/£1

Photo Origin Cards (Highest valuations for RP)

Africa. ■213d .. .. 50p/**£1**/£1.50

■212a
Pub. Photochrom. Period 2. Welsh lady in National Costume. 'Celesque' series No. C.45192 .. .. 50p

■212b
Artist A. Esposito (It). Pub. Tuck. Period 2. Children in Naples. 'Connoisseur' series. No. 2526 UB *.. .. ..* £1.50

■212c
Artist Donald McGill. Pub. E. S. London. Period 2. Caption reads 'Rube: "'Ave a cigar, Solly?" Solly: "Vat's der matter vid it?"' £3

Britain	–/**50p**/75p
European Mainland	£1/**£3**/£5
Far East. ■213e	£1/**£1.50**/£2

Gypsies. ■213f	£1/**£1.50**/£2
India. ■213g	50p/**75p**/£1
Jewish	£2/**£3**/£5
Middle East	50p/**75p**/£1
North America	..75p/**£1.50**/£2
South America	50p/**75p**/£1

■213a

Artist Abdul Hafez A. Rassi. Pub. Technografica, Milan. Period 2. A lemonade seller, Cairo 75p

■213b

Artist John Innes (Can). Pub. M. G. Macfarlane. Period 2. 'Roping a Steer'. 'Troilene' Ranching series. UB £2

■213c

Pub. Tuck. Period 2. An American Indian. 'Art' series. No. 1360 .. .. £1.50

■213d

Pub. J. Barnett. South Africa. Period 2. 'Sunday on the Mines' No. 213 .. .. £1.50

■213e

Pub. G. R. Lambert, Singapore. Period 2. Chinese barber and ear cleaner. UB £2

■213f

Pub. J. G. Short. Period 2. A Gypsy camp. New Forest £1.50

■213g

Pub. Moorli Dhur & Sons, India. A Bearer .. £1

HARBOURS/PORTS
See also SHIPPING.

Close-up detail landward. ■214a ..	50p/**£1**/£2
General views	–/**50p**/75p

INLAND WATERWAYS

Bridges
Artist drawn	–/**50p**/75p
Photo-origin with traffic detail. ■214b	
.. ..	50p/**75p**/£1

Canals
British
Close-up RP views of barge life are well thought of.
Artist drawn	25p/**50p**/75p
Barge life	£2/**£3.50**/£5
Photo-origin. General	£1/**£2**/£3

Foreign
Photo-origin	–/**50p**/75p

Dams/Weirs ■214c
Price range	–/**50p**/75p

Ferries (*see also* SHIPPING)
Price range	75p/**£1.50**/£2

Lakes
Photo-origin with boats	–/**50p**/75p

Rivers. General Scenes with River Traffic
Artist drawn	–/**50p**/£1
Photo-origin	50p/**75p**/£1.50

LEGEND & LORE
Many areas have their own folk history and often tales are based on historical events. Therefore, there may be some overlapping with HISTORICAL. These cards are of non-photographic origin. However, sometimes local pageants and processions may re-enact a legend and photographic cards of that event were published. Such photographic origin examples should be valued under 'Local Events/Gatherings' below.
Customs generally	**50p**

Folk dances, Maypoles, Morris men, etc.
.. ..	–/**50p**/£1
Ghosts	50p/**75p**/£1
Gretna Green	–/**50p**/75p
Lady Godiva (not silk)	–/**50p**/75p

Local Legends:
Wiltshire Moonrakers. ■214d ..	50p/**75p**/£1
Others	–/**50p**/75p

■214a

Pub. Blinko's Book Shop, Ramsgate. Period 2. The repairing slip Ramsgate harbour. No. 130 .. .. £1.50

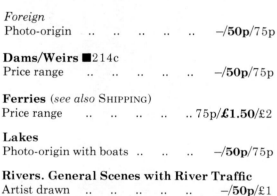

■214b

Pub. Western Mail, Cardiff. Period 2. Clarence Bridge Cardiff. 'The Camera' series 75p

■214c

Pub. Valentine. Period 2. Bell Weir Lock, Egham, Surrey £1

■214d

Pub. Barrett, Swindon. The Wiltshire Moonrakers. Period 2 .. .. 75p

LOCAL EVENTS/GATHERINGS

The cards in this section are of photographic origin, and it includes all those Edwardian activities which attracted the attention of the professional or amateur photographer. Very many splendid 'posed groups' may be found—amateur theatrics, families, nurses and just people gathered together for some special occasion—and while, frequently, neither place nor person can be identified the card can be a valuable social record. Such cards are covered by the general heading 'Edwardian Life' below.

Auctions .. .. £1/**£1.50**/£2
Beating bounds/Crying marches .. £1/**£1.50**/£2
Carnivals (mostly Continental) .. 75p/**£1**/£2
Edwardian life. ■215a .. .. .. £1/**£1.50**/£2
Elections .. .. £1/**£2**/£4
Fairs. ■215b .. .. £5/**£8**/£10
Fêtes .. .. £1/**£2**/£3
Flower Festivals (e.g. Nice, Ger 'Rosenfests') .. .. 50p/**£1**/£2
Fund-raising. ■215c .. .. .. £1/**£2**/£4
Goose fairs, e.g. Nottingham, Tavistock, etc. .. .. £2/**£3**/£4
Inaugurations, e.g. hospitals, libraries, etc. .. .. £1/**£2**/£3
Markets .. .. £1.50/**£2**/£4
Oktoberfest (Ger Munich Bierfest) 75p/**£1**/£2
Ox Roasts .. .. £2/**£3**/£4
Rag days .. .. £3/**£4**/£5
Regattas .. .. £1/**£2**/£3
Sommerfest (Ger) .. .. 50p/**75p**/£1
Unusual, e.g. Airship Beta's forced landing in Little Park, Andover in 1910. Pub. The Andover *Bazaar* .. .. £3/**£4**/£5
Works outings. ■215d .. .. .. £2/**£3**/£4

LONDON

In London, of course, can be found all the categories which are present in the rest of the country, and generally London cards may be valued via the body of the catalogue. However, London attracts special attention as our capital city, and the home of so many postcard entrepreneurs, and provides a popular collecting theme. We are concerned in this section only with early cards, important artists and series, or cards which have a particular reason for being singled out, e.g. a London view drawn by Tom Browne, an acknowledged and well collected comic artist. Cards issued by London schools as rewards for good marks or attendance by pupils (known as Reward Cards) are not normally postcards. They are not included here.

■215a

Pub. A. & G. Colwell, Worcester. Fine Edwardian gathering. Period 2 .. .. £2

■215b

Travelling Fair, Worcester. Showboards can be read (1905) £10

■215c

Fund-raising for Aldershot hospital. Good shop window at rear (1906) £3

■215d

Works outing, Devon. Added interest from coach and horses (1905) £4

Artist Drawn

One of, if not the most, prolific publishers in this field was Tuck, who used dozens of artists. This section deals only with artists who were also well known outside of this special theme.

(† = *See also* ARTISTS for more details.)

Browne, Tom.† Davidson series 2543. £2/**£3**/£4
Valentine's 'London Street Scene series'
.. .. £2/**£3**/£4
Cassiers, H.† P. G. Huardel London views
.. .. £2/**£3**/£4
Colls, H. Faulkner's first series. London
views (12 cards) .. .. .. £1/**£2**/£3
King, Edward. Tuck Oilettes, e.g. 'The
Pavement Artist' .. .. 75p/**£1**/£1.25
Kyd. Pictorial Stationery Co. Peacock series.
Types .. .. £2/**£3**/£5
Sauber, R.† Pictorial Stationery Co.
Familiar figures of London (12 cards).
.. .. £4/**£5**/£6
Ward, Dudley, E. T. W. Dennis. London
characters .. .. £1/**£2**/£3
Wheatley, F. Set of 13 'Cries of London'
after originals by the artist. Various pubs.
incl. Faulkner, Giesen Bros., J. J.
Samuels & Rotophot .. .. 50p/**75p**/£1.50

Composite Sets

Pub. F. G. O. Stuart. Albert Memorial (15
cards). Complete set is valued at card
total plus 10% .. ..50p/**£1**/£1.50
Pub. Tuck. Map of London. Series 9352 (6
cards). Value set as above .. £2/**£2.50**/£3
'LL'. 24 cards perforated booklets. Per
booklet .. .. £4/**£5**/£8

Court Size Cards

Pub. Beechings. 'Every Day' London scenes,
e.g. Bootblack, City Bus, Policeman,
Sandwich Men, etc. Period 1 .. £30/**£45**/PA
Pub. Pictorial Stationery Co. Col. vignette
views. Capital letters in red. Period
1 .. .. £5/**£6**/£10
Others .. .. £1.50/**£4**/£8

London Life

The majority of London cards may be valued under the appropriate general category. There were literally hundreds of publishers who issued cards showing London and many of them produced thousands of different examples. Both Charles Martin and E. Gordon Smith are each credited with over 3000 numbered views of Greater London. Sepia bromide prints of street scenes are a good source of detailed information as they have less tendency to fade than their black and white equivalents. Companies (Period 2 unless indicated) that produced such sepia cards include:

Degen, C.
E.A.S. (Schwerdtfeger)
Hammond
Hunt. Glossy Real Photo series
Judges (Periods 2 to 4)
Lewis, R. & A. G. 'Robin Hood' and 'Colonial' series
Rapid Photo
Regent
Scott, Walter (Period 4)
Stengel & Co.

In this section we have listed photo-origin cards that currently attract particular attention and concern ourselves with the subject of 'London Life'. The higher values are for close-up RP pictures of events, street scenes, 'types' or views that no longer exist. However, in this category, as in the SOCIAL HISTORY/TOPOGRAPHICAL section as a whole, collectors will often pay more than is indicated here for an RP card that has a particular meaning for them.

Pub. Aristophot .. .. £1/**£2**/£4
Pub. Beagles 'Real Photo' series .. £1/**£2**/£3.50
Pub. 'LL'. Particular attention should be
paid to the address side of 'LL' cards.
Those that do not carry instructions
concerning the message or the address,
and where the stamp box is not drawn in,
are almost certainly reprints from the
original printing plates. These were done
in France during Period 4 and are very
black and very clear.
Period 2 published. London Types
.. .. £2/**£4**/£8
Period 2 pictures. Period 4 published
.. .. £1/**£1.50**/£2
Pub. Martin, Charles .. .. £1.50/**£3**/£5
Pub. Photochrom. Celesque series. 'London
Types'. ■217a .. .. £3/**£4**/£5
Pub. Skilton. London Life .. .. £3/**£4**/£5
Pub. Rotary
Photo series 10513 (over 80 cards)
.. .. £6/**£8**/£12
Other photo series, incl. 10514, (over 40
cards), 10167, 10482, 10484 £2/**£3**/£5
Pub. Smith, Gordon .. .. ..50p/**£1.50**/£3
Sidney Street Siege (Higher value for cards
showing Winston Churchill) .. £1/**£2**/£5
Others .. .. £1.50/**£2**/£3

St. Paul's Hospital Postcard Competition
   (12 cards) *see also* COMPETITIONS

Complete with coupon	£2/**£4**/£5
Without coupon	50p/**£1**/£2

Tuck

Raphael Tuck & Sons probably produced more postcards than any other company in the world. London took a lot of their attention. Indeed, when they started publishing postcards on 1 November 1899, the first day that British publishers were allowed the same freedom as their Continental counterparts, their first cards were of London. It is extremely likely that only 48 Tuck cards were published in Period 1, and that these cards are those undivided backs numbered from No. 1 to No. 48. All four dozen concern London, or the area surrounding the city or bordering the River Thames. Their first 12 cards were called 'View' cards and they were chromo-litho vignettes. Later, in the splendid Aquarette and Oilette series, were many more views of London and its types—the 'London' series, 'the District Messengers of London', 'Old London Gateways'; 'Old London Churches'; 'Westminster Abbey'; 'The Houses of Parliament'; Grays Inn series and so on. Artists like Chas. E. Flower and Wimbush produced minor works of art.

Aquarette/Oilette series. ■217b ..	£1/**£2**/£3
London Life. Series 9015. ■217c	£1/**£2**/£4
Period 1. 'View' series. Card nos. 1—12.	
Chromo-litho vignettes UB. ■218a	
.. ..	£8/**£10**/£12

MAP CARDS

Specialist map cards such as those for wars and railways may be more appropriately valued as propaganda or advertising respectively under WARS and RAILWAYS. The earlier the war the more sought after the maps, while the railway cards are valued according to the issuing company. Map vignettes were often combined with crests and multi-views during Period 2 so there can be overlapping with 'Crests/Heraldic Devices/Tartans', above. Non-war map cards were introduced into Britain around 1903. The engravers J. Bartholomew produced cards for publishers John Walker who set out to cover the country. By 1904 Walkers had issued over 400 different cards. This section deals with cards that are more 'map' than anything else.

■217a

Pub. Photochrom. Period 2. Smithfield Market Porter. 'Celesque London Types' series £5

■217b

Pub. Tuck. Artist Charles E. Flower. Period 2. Bow Church, Cheapside. Oilette 'Old London Churches' series. No. 6259 .. .. £2

■217c

Pub. Tuck. Period 2. Controlling the Traffic. Oilette 'London Life' series. No. 9015 .. .. £3

217

Cyclists' Touring Club. All numbered, prob-
ably 20 in set .. .. £2/**£2.50**/£3
Foreign map cards. Period 1, early Period 2.
UB .. .. £1/**£2**/£3
Pub. Bacon 'Excelsior' series .. £1/**£2**/£3
Pub. Ettlinger .. .. £3/**£4**/£5
Pub. John Walker 'Geographical' series.
■218b .. .. £2/**£3**/£4
Pub. John Walker. Gordon Bennett Race
Course. Autocar overprint .. £5/**£6**/£7
Ger. *Liebes Rathsel* (Love puzzles) set.
Men and women concealed in map design.
Early Period 2 (10 cards). ■218c.
Per card .. .. £4/**£4.50**/£5
Per set .. .. £45/**£50**/£60
Others .. .. 50p/**75p**/£1

POLAR AND EVEREST EXPLORATION

Amundsen
1911. S. Pole Expedition .. .. £10/**£12**/£15
1918. Attempted drift in the dirigible Maud
across the N. Pole .. .. .. £8/**£12**/£15

Bruce, Gen. the Hon. C. G.
1924. Everest Expedition. ■218d £15/**£20**/£25

Nansen
1893. Expedition to N. Pole. Four card composite set. Per set .. .. £75/**£100**/£150

Nobile, Gen.
1925. Airship Expedition to the N. Pole
.. .. £15/**£20**/£25

Scott, Capt.
1901. Expedition. Wrench. Links of the Empire.
Series of 4 cards. Value per card:
Posted from ports of call .. £50/**£75**/£100
Unposted .. .. .. £15/**£35**/£50
1910. Expedition:
Expedition scenes .. .. .. £3/**£4**/£5
In Memoriam cards. ■219a .. £6/**£8**/£10
Portraits .. .. £2/**£3**/£4

Others
Price range .. .. £2/**£4**/£6

■218a
*Pub. Tuck. Period 1. Cleopatra's Needle and St.
Pauls. 'View' series. No. 2.* UB. *Posted Period
2 .. .. £10*

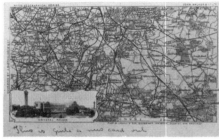

■218b
*Pub. John Walker. Engraver J. Bartholomew.
Period 2. 'Geographical' series. No. 720 .. £3*

■218c
*Geographische Liebes–Rathsel (Love Puzzle).
Early Period 2. Col.* UB £4

■218d
*Everest Expedition of Gen. Bruce 1924.
(Collection Percy R. Oliver) £25*

SEASIDE

This section deals with the landed aspects of the seaside; for water activities *see* BATHING section. Photographic origin cards with close-up detail are the most highly rated.

Lifeboats. Being launched	£2/**£4**/£7
Lifeboats. On shore	£1/**£2**/£5
Lifeboats. RNLI ads	£2/**£3**/£3.50
Lighthouses	25p/**50p**/75p
Piers. ■219b	50p/**75p**/£1
Promenades. ■219c	25p/**50p**/75p
Spas	..50p/**£1**/£1.50

STREET SCENES

The interest in street scenes is essentially two-fold. Streets bustling with activity are valued for their record of people, shops and transport, while empty or obscure streets such as those in small villages are collected as records of the way things used to be. Valuations are changing quickly in this category and there is an accelerating interest in Period 6 when the motor car began to be a major factor in British life. However, unless stated, valuations apply to Periods 1 and 2 and London scenes tend to be less valued than others. However, additional interest attached to particular photographers/publishers, or unusually fine pictures, can take values outside these bands.

Cities

Busy. ■219d	£2/**£3**/£4
Normal	£1/**£2**/£3
Quiet	..50p/**£1**/£1.50

Period 6

Price range	..50p/**£1**/£1.50

Towns/Villages

Busy	£1/**£3**/£5
Normal	..£1/**£1.50**/£2
Quiet	..75p/**£1**/£1.50

STRIKES

Most strikes remain local issues. The upper valuations will apply where there is good photographic origin detail which identifies strongly with the locality, e.g. names of individuals involved, readable strike notices, etc.

Belfast (1907)	£4/**£8**/£10
Black Country (1913)	£4/**£6**/£8
General Strike (1926)	£6/**£10**/£15
Ilkeston (1912)	£6/**£10**/£12
Liverpool (1910)	£5/**£8**/£10
Smethwick (1913)	£6/**£10**/£12
Thirlwall (1910/1911)	£6/**£10**/£15
Others	£3/**£5**/£7

■219a
Pub. Rotary. Memorial card for Capt. Scott. Period 2 .. .. £8

■219b
Pub. J. Welch. Period 3. Deal Pier £1

■219c
Pub. E. T. W. Dennis. Period 2. Queens Parade, Scarborough. 'Dainty' series No. R27 .. ..75p

■219d ..
Period 2. Bank of England and Royal Exchange £3

UNIFORMED PUBLIC SERVICES

This section is concerned with people, and the accoutrements and equipment needed to carry out their tasks, rather than the buildings from which they may operate. Except where indicated, higher values are for clear photographic origin cards.

Customs & Excise	£3/**£4**/£5
Fire Service. ■220a	£2/**£3**/£4
Nursing/Medical staff	£1/**£1.50**/£2
Police. ■220b	£1/**£2**/£3
Postal. Comic drawings. F.S., etc.	75p/**£1**/£1.25
Postal. Post boxes	50p/**£1**/£1.50

Postmen (*See also* ROAD TRANSPORT—Royal Mail). Periods 1, 2. Photographic origin

.. ..	£1/**£1.50**/£2
Postmen. Others	50p/**75p**/£1

Series. 'La Poste en . . .' (Postmen of the World). French text. Forty-eight cards. Premium on card total for complete set. Period 2.
1. Abyssinia; 2. Argentine Republic; 3. Australia; 4. Austria; 5. Belgium; 6. Bolivia; 7. Brazil; 8. Bulgaria; 9. Cashmere; 10. China; 11. Corea; 12. Deccan; 13. Denmark; 14. Dutch East Indies (Java); 15. Egypt; 16. England; 17. France; 18. French Guiana; 19. Germany; 20. Greece; 21. Hayti; 22. Holland; 23. Hungary; 24. India; 25. Indo-China; 26. Italy; 27. Japan; 28. Madagascar; 29. Mexico; 30. Montenegro; 31. Morocco; 32. Natal; 33. Norway (Lapland); 34. Persia; 35. Peru; 36. Portugal; 37. Roumania; 38. Russia; 39. Servia; 40. Siam; 41. Spain; 42. Sweden; 43. Switzerland; 44. Transvaal; 45. Trinidad; 46. Turkey; 47. United States of America; 48. Venezuela.

Per card valuation	£3/**4**/£6

Postmen of the British Empire. Pub. Colman's Starch. By-line often printed out. 14 cards. Premium for complete set.

    Trinidad, West India Island
    Saddle & Pack Horses for carrying Mail in Mashonaland
    The Mombasa to Uganda mail carrier
    Australia
    The Mail Coach stowed up
    Indian home. British Guiana
    Burmah, India
    London Postman (1820)
    Barbados. West India Islands
    Natal, Africa
    Night Mail Train (1904)
    Canada
    English Postman (1904)
    One unidentified

Per card valuation	£3/**£4**/£5

Prison	£1/**£2**/£3
Railway (*see also* RAILWAYS) ..	£2/**£4**/£5
Others	£1/**£1.50**/£2

■220a

Period 2. Decorated horsedrawn fire engine with fireman **£2**

■220b

Period 2. Portrait card. Two policemen   £1.50

VIEWS

Here we consider postcards which show a locality *per se*, without significant additional interest by way of people, transport or any other factor which would raise their value—the literal and original meaning of 'topographical'. Many are of little value because they are poorly printed, badly coloured and lacking contemporary detail. Some, however, have been overlooked by collectors. Many multi-view and framed cards have very fine, if small, views on them—and so too do the 'Fake Moonlight' scenes popularised by Delittle Fenwick & Co. These latter cards, based upon photos taken in daylight and then given moon shadows (frequently in the wrong direction) and lighted windows to simulate night-time, may actually be very good view cards. Artistic views such as the 'Rough Seas' types were produced in great numbers during Period 2. Tuck had over 500 designs in that one category by 1905. Currently they are not much collected today, but there are some fine chromo-litho examples. It is on the basis of their chromo-litho printing that some early view cards are collected. View cards are very difficult to value and those that are currently collected probably fit into another category in this catalogue, e.g. ARTISTS. However, we list here the factors to take into account when attempting to assess the value of a view card:

Artist—well known names may be collected. *See also* ARTISTS.

Period—Period 1 and early Period 2 may have 'Victorian/Edwardian' appeal.

Printing—chromo-litho examples may be collectable as fine products of the printer's art. *See also* EARLY CARDS. Some early view cards were printed in black, on blue card. Often the drawings are clear and well etched. These 'Blue Card' views are collectable.

Publisher—the collecting of cards by 'Publisher' is beginning to take place, e.g. Tuck and local publishers.

Subject—some view cards may fit into a subject category, e.g. 'Seaside'.

The average artistic view card without a specific thematic content is likely to be priced around 25p. Most major publishers issued such cards. Some examples are listed below. Similar Tuck Oilettes would command slightly more.

Boots
Canterbury series **50p**

Davidson Bros.
Arcadia series **50p**
Marlborough series **50p**

Eyre & Spottiswoode
Woodbury series **50p**

Hildesheimer
Norfolk Broads series **50p**
Warwickshire series **50p**

Misch & Stock
Nature Miniatures series **50p**

Philco
Bournemouth series **50p**

Photochrom
Bournemouth series **50p**

Regal Art Publishing Co. (RAPCO)
Delightful Devonshire series **50p**
Picturesque Hampshire series   ..   **50p**

Ruddock, J. W.
The Artist series **50p**

Salmon
Artist—Essenhigh Corke   ..   ..   –/**50p**/75p
Artist—Quatremain   ..   ..   ..   –/**50p**/75p
Artist—Quinton   ..   ..   ..   50p/**75p**/£1

Wrench
Rambler series **50p**

Unusual Types

Blue Cards
Various sizes. Period 1 and early Period 2.
   Pub. Blum & Degen, Valentines. ■221a
   ..   ..   £1/**£2**/£3

■221a

Pub. Blum & Degen. Period 2. 'Blue Card'. Gallowtree Gate, Leicester. UB. No. 2173   ..   **£2**

Fake Moonlight
Published by Delittle Fenwick & Co.; Tuck;
   Woolstone Bros.; Valentine and others.
■222a .. .. –/**50p**/75p

Multi-Views ■222b
Price range .. .. –/**50p**/75p

■222c

Pub. Ullman. Baseball Player. Harvard. PU
1907 .. .. £2

■222a

Pub. Delittle Fenwick & Co. 'Fake Moonlight'
Kings Road, Brighton 50p

■222b

Pub. Jackson & Son 'Multi-view'. Skegness. Jay
Em Jay series. No. 388 .. .. 50p

■222d

Pub. Grange Publishing. Period 2. Billiards room
in London Transport's Convalesent Home £1.50

Three Band Pricing System

Left Hand Band. *The lowest price you will probably be asked to pay for this card.*

Middle Band. *What you will normally be asked to pay for this card; its average, reasonable price.*

Right Hand Band. *The highest price you will probably be asked to pay for this card.*

For a full explanation of the System, see page viii.

■222e

Pub. Gottschalk, Drefus & Davis. Period 2.
B. J. T. Bosanquet, Middlesex £3

SPORTS/PASTIMES

The sporting theme is found in most postcard categories and there is particular overlap with COMIC and SOCIAL HISTORY/TOPOGRAPHICAL. This section deals with cards whose *raison d'être* is predominantly due to a sport or pastime, but in order to illustrate the width of the subject we have listed some comic examples under 'Comic Artists' below.

Angling
Price range .. .. 50p/**75p**/£2.50

Archery
Price range .. .. 50p/**75p**/£1

Athletics
Athletes .. .. 50p/**75p**/£1.50
Meetings (photo origin) .. .. .. £1/**£1.50**/£2

Badminton
Price range .. ..75p/**£1**/£1.50

Ballooning
Artist drawn—*see also* **Artist drawn** in
  this section .. .. £1/**£2**/£4
Photo-origin (higher value for RP) £3/**£5**/£8

Baseball
Comic
  Baseball Illustrated. Pub. Davidson Bros.
    Series 2618/9. Artist Tom Browne
    .. .. £4/**£6**/£8
  Baseball Kidlets. Pub. Ullman Series
    195 .. .. £2/**£3**/£4
  Others .. ..75p/**£1.50**/£2
General
  Baseball Series. Pub. The Rose Co.
    .. ..75p/**£1.50**/£2
  Baseball Terms Illustrated. Pub.
    Frederickson. Artist Dewey .. 75p/**£1.50**/£2
  Others .. .. 50p/**75p**/£2
Players
  Baseball Hall of Fame. Pub.
    Cooperstown, N. F. .. .. £1/**£2**/£3
  Baseball Players. Pub. Pomand. Chromo-
    litho .. .. £1/**£2**/£3
  Others. ■222c .. ..75p/**£1.50**/£2

Basketball/Netball
Price range .. ..75p/**£1**/£1.50

Bicycling
See BICYCLING

Billiards/Snooker
Artwork by Tuck. Pub. J. V. A. Carica-
  tures .. .. £2/**£3**/£3.50
Billiards rooms. ■222d .. .. ..75p/**£1**/£1.50
Others .. .. 50p/**75p**/£1

Board Games
Price range .. ..50p/**£1.50**/£5

Boating/Canoeing
Comic .. .. 50p/**£1**/£2
Scenes .. .. 50p/**75p**/£1

Bowls
Price range .. .. 50p/**75p**/£1

Boxing
Pub. Beagles. 'Famous Boxers' series
  .. ..75p/**£1**/£1.50
Pub. Lilywhite 1919. Carpentier versus Joe
  Beckett. Twelve cards in set
  .. .. £1.50/**£2**/£2.50
Others .. ..50p/**£1.50**/£3

Bullfighting
Price range .. .. 50p/**75p**/£1.50

Camping
Comic .. .. 50p/**75p**/£1
Photo-origin .. .. 50p/**75p**/£1

Card Games
Price range .. .. –/**50p**/£1

Comic Artists
Probably every comic artist did at least one sketch related to sports and pastimes. Valuations should be made first according to the artist and then according to the sport. Here are six examples.

Browne, Tom†
Billiards Made Easy. Davidson series 2578
  .. .. £3/**£4**/£5
Footballers. Davidson series 2546 £2/**£2.50**/£3
Illustrated Sports. Davidson series 2602.
  .. .. £2/**£3**/£3.50

Carter, Reg.†
Sporting Chinamen. Chromo series 364
  .. .. £2/**£3**/£3.50

Kinsella, E. P.†
Boy Cricketer. Langsdorf series 675
  .. .. £1/**£1.50**/£2
Girl Tennis Player. Langsdorf series 695.
  ■63b .. .. £1.50/**£2**/£2.50

Sager, Xavier†
Bowling at Bal Tabarin .. .. .. £6/**£7**/£8

Thackerary, Lance†
Bridge Illustrated. Tuck series 9062
.. .. £2/**£3**/£3.50
Ping Pong. Tuck series 624 .. .. £3/**£4**/£5

Thiele, Arthur†
Bowling Alley. Faulkner series 1375
.. .. £2/**£4**/£5

Cricket
Postcards of cricket teams and personalities were often produced in book form (e.g. Gottschalk, Dreyfus and Davis—G.D. & D. cards) and sold on the grounds. Higher valuations are for clear photo-origin cards.

Comic   50p/**£1.50**/£5

Personalities
G.D. & D. series. Hawkins photo.
B. J. T. Bosanquet. ■222e .. .. £2/**£3**/£4
Dr. W. G. Grace .. .. .. £2/**£3**/£4
Others .. .. 50p/**£1**/£2

Tuck. 'In the Open' series (Period 3)
Famous Batsmen, 6450 .. .. .. £1/**£2**/£3
Famous Bowlers, 6451 .. .. .. £1/**£2**/£3
Famous Fielders, 6452 .. .. .. £1/**£2**/£3
Others .. .. £1/**£2**/£2.50

Teams
County .. .. 75p/**£2**/£5
Local. ■224a .. .. 50p/**£1**/£4
Touring. ■224b .. .. .. £1/**£3**/£6

Croquet
Comic .. .. 50p/**75p**/£1
Scenes .. .. 75p/**£1**/£1.50

Curling
Artist drawn 25p/**50p**/75p
Photo-origin .. .. 75p/**£1**/£1.50

Cycling—*see* Bicycling

Dancing
Many famous artists, e.g. Mela Koehler, Thiele, Usaba, etc. did 'Dance' series.
Value according to Artist .. .. £1/**£3**/£15
Others .. .. 50p/**75p**/£1

Diabolo—*see* Crazes, etc.

Fencing
Comic .. ..75p/**£1**/£1.50
Photo-origin .. .. 50p/**75p**/£1

Football—Association
Comic—general .. .. 50p/**75p**/£1
Comic—named artists .. .. ..50p/**£1.50**/£4
Commemoratives .. .. .. £1.50/**£3**/£4
Crowd scenes .. ..75p/**£1**/£1.50
Grounds/scenes .. ..75p/**£1**/£1.50
Players—amateur .. .. 50p/**75p**/£1
professional .. .. .. £1/**£2**/£3
Teams—amateur .. .. .. £1/**£2**/£3
military .. .. ..50p/**75p**/£1
professional pre-1939 .. £2/**£3**/£4
professional post-1939 .. 75p/**£1**/£2

Football—Rugby League
Players .. .. £1/**£2**/£3
Teams—amateur .. .. .. £1/**£2**/£3
professional .. .. £2/**£3**/£5
touring .. .. £2/**£3**/£5

Football—Rugby Union
Comic .. ..75p/**£1**/£1.50
Grounds, scenes .. ..75p/**£1**/£1.50
Pub. Tuck. Oilette .. .. ..75p/**£1**/£1.50
Teams—city .. .. .. £1/**£2**/£2.50
touring .. .. .. £1/**£2.50**/£4
town/village .. .. .. £1.50/**£3**/£4

■224a
Period 2. Minster (Kent) cricket team .. £1.50

■224b
Pub. T. Holland. Period 2. The 12th Australian touring team (1905) £4

Foxhunting—*see* ANIMALS: Horses

Gambling/Playing Cards—*see* CURIOUS/
MISCELLANEOUS

Golf
Comic—general	..75p/**£1**/£2.50
Comic—named artists	50p/**£2**/£5
Courses/Club houses	..50p/**£1.50**/£3

Gymnastics
Price range	50p/**75p**/£1

Hockey
Comic	50p/**75p**/£1
Teams	..£1/**£1.50**/£2
Others	..25p/**50p**/75p

Horse racing—*see* ANIMALS: Horses

Motor Racing—*see* ROAD TRANSPORT

Mountaineering
Artist drawn. Period 1/Early Period 2
.. ..	£1/**£2**/£4
Comic	50p/**75p**/£1
Pub. Abrahams, Keswick	50p/**75p**/£1
Others	25p/**50p**/75p

Olympic Games
Anniversary (20th) of re-establishment of the Games (1914)	£6/**£10**/£12

Moscow (1980). ■225a. Official cards.
Artist drawn. Garish colour. Printed
1978	25p/**50p**/75p
Nazi. Berlin (1936). Col. designs ..	£12/**£15**/£20
Monotone officials	£1.50/**£3**/£5

Garmish Partenkirchen (Winter Games)
(1936)	..£7/**£10**/£12
Paris (1924). Artist Pauteuberge ..	£8/**£10**/£12
Others. Period 4	£4/**£7**/£10
Period 6	50p/**75p**/£1

Polo
Price range	..75p/**£1**/£1.50

Roller Skating—*see* COMPETITIONS: Rinking

Rowing
Price range	25p/**75p**/£3

Sailing/Yachting
Crews, races, regattas, sailing ships
.. ..	£1/**£3**/£6

Shooting
Game	..50p/**£1**/£1.25
Target	..50p/**£1**/£1.50

Show-jumping (Horse Shows)
General scenes	..75p/**£1**/£1.25
Olympia Horse Show. General ..	£1/**£2**/£4
Poster ads.	£5/**£10**/£15

Skating
Comic	50p/**75p**/£1
Others	25p/**50p**/75p

Sports Days & Events
Price range	50p/**75p**/£1

Swimming
Price range	25p/**£1**/£2

■225a
Pub. Varantsoff. Moscow Olympics 1980. Printed 1978 .. ..75p

■225b
Pub. The Sportsman *magazine. Period 2. Cross channel swimming cup displayed at the Coronation Exhibition* £1.25

Table tennis (Ping Pong)
Comic—general .. ..75p/**£1**/£1.50
Comic—named artist. *see* **Artists**
Others .. .. 75p/**£1**/£2

Tennis
Artist drawn (value according to artist)
.. .. £1/**£3**/£5
Comic (value according to artists) 50p/**75p**/£3
General scenes 25p/**50p**/75p
Wimbledon players, pre-1939 .. £1/**£2**/£3
    post-1939 .. .. ..75p/**£1**/£1.50

Tobogganing
Price range .. .. 50p/**75p**/£1

Trophies ■225b
Price range .. ..50p/**£1**/£1.50

Walking
Racing .. .. £1/**£1.50**/£3
Round the World .. .. .. £1.50/**£2.50**/£3

Water Polo
Price range .. ..75p/**£1**/£1.50

Winter Sports
Chromo-litho. ■226a .. .. £1/**£1.50**/£2
Others **50p**

Wrestling—*see also* GLAMOUR
Price range .. .. £1/**£1.50**/£3

■226b

Pub. John Waddington. Poster advertisement for Joy Bells at London Hippodrome. Artist unsigned, but style reminiscent of Barribal. Period 2 ..£12

■226c

Pub. HMSO for Victoria & Albert Museum. Programme cover of Farewell Performance at the Windmill Theatre, 31 October 1964 .. ..75p

■226a
Artist R. Mahn. Period 2. Chromo-litho. Skiers. No. 174 .. ..£2

■226d
Photographer 'LL'. Punch & Judy in the Champs Elysées. 'Benches reserved for children'. PU 1907 .. ..£3

THEATRE/WIRELESS

This section describes actors, actresses, advertising, theatre buildings and stills from theatrical productions. It also includes cards dealing with WIRELESS (Radio) and 'fringe theatre' acts like Punch and Judy, etc. Freaks, and other strange phenomena who entertained the public in circus or fair side shows and theatres are described under CURIOUS.

ACTORS AND ACTRESSES

Literally hundreds of thousands of portrait postcards were published. Listed below are the artists most reproduced on the postcard. It is virtually impossible to separate the 'straight' actors/actresses from the musical comedy/music hall/pantomime artistes, as many popular stars performed in several types of theatre (e.g. pantomime during the winter, music hall during the spring and summer; dramatic artistes sometimes played roles that required them to sing or dance, etc.).

Where an artist was predominantly famous in a particular field or fields, the initials D (for Dramatic roles); MC (Musical Comedy); MH (Music Hall) and P (Pantomime) will appear after their name.

Perhaps because they were more photogenic, perhaps because they needed the publicity more, many minor stars (sometimes virtually chorus girls) appeared on a large number of postcards, whereas the great stars often prove more elusive to find on the postcard. This contributes to the fact that their postcard portraits command a premium and they are featured in a separate list.

Female
Allan, Maud (D/MH)
Arundel, Sybil (MC/P)
Ash, Maie (MC)
Ashwell, Lena (D)
Augarde, Adrienne (MC)
Baird, Dorothea (Mrs. H. B. Irving) (D)
Bateman, Jessie (D)
Braithwaite, Lilian (D)
Brayton, Lily (D)
Boucicault, Nina (D)
Burke, Billie (also a film star) (MC)
Campbell, Mrs. Patrick (friend of G. B. Shaw) (D)

Chase, Pauline (MC)
Clifford, Camille (model for the Gibson girl) (MC)
Compton, Fay (sister of Compton McKenzie)
Cooper, Gladys (most photographed in Period 4) (D/MC)
Courtneidge, Cecily (*see also* CINEMA) (MC)
Crichton, Madge (MC)
Dainton, Marie (MC)
Dare Sisters (Phyllis and Zena) (MC/P)
Deslys, Gaby (recipient of King of Portugal's fabulous pearls) (MC)
Elliott, Gertrude (D)
Elsie, Lily (MC)
Fealy, Maude (D)
George, Marie (MC/P)
Gordon, Kitty (MC)
Green, Mabel (MC)
Greene, Evie (MC)
Hare, Winifred (P)
Jay, Isabel (MC)
King, Hettie (male impersonator) (MH)
Langtry, Mrs. (The Jersey Lily) (D)
Leighton, Queenie (MC/P)
Lessing, Madge (MC)
Love, Mabel (MC)
Loftus, Cissy (D/MH)
May, Edna (MC)
May, Maggie (MC)
Millar, Gertie (MC)
Millard, Evelyn (D)
Monkman, Phyllis (MC)
Moore, Carrie (MC/P)
Moore, Eva (D)
Nielson, Julia (D)
Potter, Mrs. Brown- (D)
Price, Nancy (D)
Ray, Gabrielle (MC)
Ray, Ruby (MC)
Reeve, Ada (MH/P)
Rowlands, Gaynor (MC)
Sevening, Nina (MC)
Studholme, Marie (MC)
Tempest, Marie (D/MC)
Terriss, Ellaline (MC)
Terry, Ellen (D)
Tilly, Vesta (male impersonator) (MC/P)
Vanbrugh, Violet (D)
Waller, Mrs. Lewis (D)
Price range .. ..   25p/**75p**/£1.25

Male
Ainsley, Henry (D)
Alexander, Geo. (D)
Asche, Oscar (D)
Benson, F. R. (D)

227

Bouchier, Arthur (the first 'Old Bill' on stage) (MC)
Bradfield, Louis (MC)
Coffin, Hayden (MC)
Coyne, Joseph (MC)
Gill, Basil (D)
Graves, George (MC/P)
Hicks Seymour (husband of Ellaline Terris) (D/MC)
Huntley, G. P. (MC)
Irving, H. B. (son of Sir H. and husband of Dorothea Baird) (D)
Lang, Matheson (D)
Robertson, Forbes (of the admirable profile) (D)
Terry, Fred (D)
Waller, Lewis (D)
Wright, Huntley (MC)
Price range .. .. 50p/**75p**/£1.50

As well as the straight portraits, many series of the stars in their homes, with their bicycles, children, parents, pets and spouses were produced.

Add a premium for hand autographed, *Art Nouveau* borders, Large Letters, photomontage, etc., and early UB's.

ADVERTISING

Poster Types
See also ARTISTS for details of theatrical work by Tom Browne (the 'Arcadians'), Raphael Kirchner (Geisha, Mikado, San Toy).

Pub. David Allen & Sons Ltd., Belfast & Harrow. The largest publishers of theatre posters who reproduced many of their full size posters as postcards from about 1903. Artists (*see also* ARTISTS for individual valuations and play titles) include:
Bairnsfather, Bruce
Barribal, W.
Hassall, J. ■59c
Kinsella, E. P. ■63b
Owen, Will.
Thackeray, Lance
Wood, Lawson.
Price range .. .. £2/**£10**/£25

Pub. John Waddington, Leeds & London. A company which produced some fine poster adverts during Periods 2 to 4. Play titles include:
'Extra Special'
'Flying Colours' (Artist Bairnsfather)
'Joy Bells'. ■226b
Price range .. .. £5/**£15**/£30+

Other Publishers of theatrical posters.
Price range .. .. £3/**£8**/£15

Advertising on Reverse/Play Stills

Pub. David Allen
Reproductions for *Answers* magazine
.. .. £1/**£2**/£4
Photographic scenes from plays (e.g. Bad Girl of the Family, Beggar Girl's Wedding, Girl Who Took the Wrong Turning)
.. .. 75p/**£2**/£4

Pub. James Henderson & Sons
Period 2 Toy Model Series of Pantomimes with 1 card to cut out as theatre: Aladdin, Cinderella, Harlequinade, Red Riding Hood, Robinson Crusoe. Per set £6/**£10**/£15

Photographer Foulsham & Banfield. Pub. Rotary. Dorothea Baird & H. B. Irving in 'The Bells' and other plays in The Assembly Rooms, Malvern. Period 2
.. .. 50p/**75p**/£1.50

Pub. Rotary: Real Photographic
1903 onwards. Several sets of contemporary productions like Beauty of Bath, Kitty Grey, Mother Goose, Three Little Maids.
1905. Beerbohm Tree's Much Ado About Nothing, Lewis Waller's Henry V.
1907. Antony & Cleopatra, Romeo and Juliet.
Price range .. .. 75p/**£1**/£2

Pub. Tuck
Large number in 'Play Pictorial' series
.. .. 75p/**£1**/£2
Others .. .. 50p/**75p**/£1.50

Pub. Victoria & Albert Museum
Period 6 series to commemorate Farewell Performance at the Windmill Theatre. ■226c .. .. −/**50p**/75p

Pub. Wrench
Several productions, incl. Country Mouse, Princess of Kensington, by photographer Bassano .. .. £1/**£1.25**/£2.25

DANCERS

Ballet
Dolin, Anton
Genée, Dame Adeline
Karsavina, Tamara
Markova, Alicia
Massine
Nijinski
Pavlova
Price range .. .. £2.50/**£5**/£10
Hand autographed cards will always attract a premium.

Other Types of Dancer
Duncan, Isadora
Fuller, Loi
Graham, Martha
Goulue, La
Hari, Mata (Mrs. McLeod)
Price range .. .. £3.50/**£8**/£15
Hand autographed cards will always attract a premium.

FRINGE THEATRE/SPECIALITY ACTS
Clear photographs with good detail only.

Amateur Dramatics
Usually by local photographers/publishers. Productions of schools, societies in towns and villages .. .. –/**50p**/75p

Concert Parties
Geo. Hall's Merry Japs
Holiday Camp Groups
Kitty Denton's Little Rays of Sunshine
Others
Price range .. .. 50p/**75p**/£1.50

Magicians
Price range .. .. £1/**£1.25**/£2

Pierrots
See also BATHING for seaside Pierrots. Artist drawn Harlequins and Pierrots: a favourite theme which includes chromo-litho UB and Period 4 *Art Deco* versions
.. .. £2/**£4**/£10

Punch & Judy
Seaside shows—*see also* BATHING. Others, incl. Fr photographs by 'LL'. ■226d
.. .. 75p/**£1.50**/£3

Seldoms
Stage act simulating classic sculpture—*see* ART REPRODUCTIONS.

Ventriloquists
Price range .. .. £1/**£3**/£5

Others .. ..50p/**£1.50**/£3

PRESTIGE PERFORMERS
Performers whose postcards command a premium for the eminence of the subject and/or the rarity of examples.
Baker, Josephine (US col.) (Fr cabaret artist)
Bernhardt, Sarah. ■229a (D)
Bruant, Aristide (Fr cabaret)
Chevalier, Albert (MH)
Chevalier, Maurice (Fr MH)
'Casque d'Or' (Fr MH clairvoyant)
Chirgwin ('the White-Eyed Kaffir') (MH)
Colette (Fr author with stage act) (*see also* LITERARY)
Coward, Noel (D. Cabaret)
Duse, Eleonora (Fr D)
Elliott, G. H. ('The Chocolate-Coloured Coon') (MH)
Ford, Florrie (MH)
Fragson, Harry (P)
Gillette, William (D)
Guilbert, Yvette (MH)
Guitry, Sacha (Fr D)
Irving, Sir Henry (D) (*see also* COMMEMORATIVE)
Lauder, Harry (MH)
Leno, Dan (P)
Lloyd, Marie (MH)
Miller, Max (MH)
Mistinguett (Fr MH)
Réjane (Fr D)
Stratton, Eugene (MH)
Tate, Harry (MH)

■229a

Pub. Rotary, photographer Reutlinger, Paris. The Divine Sarah Bernhardt, Period 2. .. £2.50

229

Tich, Little (MH)
Vernon, Harriet (MH)
Price range .. .. £3/**£6**/£12
The higher band applies to the rare early French cabaret stars, to autographed cards, and to cards of the stars in elusive roles.

PUBLISHERS OF ACTORS/ACTRESSES

Productions vary from matt photographic to highly glossy, ornate borders and frames, photo-montages, etc.

Aristophot; Davidson Bros.; Dennis; Faulkner; Hartmann; Lillywhite; Knight Bros.; Philco; Rapid Photo; Rotary; Tuck; Valentine; Wrench.
Price range .. .. –/**50p**/£1.50
Pub. Rotary. Real photo stamp postcards with adhesive backs. ■230a .. £1/**£1.50**/£3
Pub. Silberer & Bros. Leading artists of the American stage .. .. .. 50p/**75p**/£1.50

THEATRE BUILDINGS

Good close ups of photographic origin of opera houses, theatres on piers and in towns. Publishers include: Excelsior Fine Art Co., Knight Bros., Local Publishers, Rotary, Valentine.
Exteriors .. ..75p/**£1.50**/£4
Interiors .. .. 50p/**£1**/£2

WIRELESS

Broadcasters: Groups & Portraits

Periods 2 (■230b), 3, 4
Often showing groups of musicians for the days of early broadcasting with the station number ('2LO', etc.), some showing good detail of microphones, equipment, etc.
Price range .. ..75p/**£1.50**/£5

Period 5
Stars from the popular war-time shows, like Arthur Askey, Tommy Handley, etc.
Price range .. .. 50p/**£1**/£2

Comic Wireless Cards

Periods 2 to 4
Various artists, value according to artist and period .. .. 50p/**75p**/£1.50

Period 5
Incl. 'ITMA' jokes by Bert Thomas (*see also* WAR) and others .. .. .. 50p/**£1**/£2

Other Wireless Subjects
Price range .. .. 50p/**75p**/£1.50

■230a
Pub. Rotary. Real photostamp Postcard Gladys Cooper. Period 4 .. .. £2.50

■230b
Pub. Redpath-Vawter Chautauqua System. Broadcasters for the station in 1909 .. .. £5

■230c
Artist Dudley Hardy. Pub. Davidson. Period 2. Russo–Japanese War. Series 3015 .. .. £5

■230d
Ramsgate Air Raid. 17 May 1915. Damage at Albion Place £2

WARS

The range of activities featured on postcards during wartime is at least as large as it is in peacetime. However, the ulterior motive of propaganda influences much of the supposedly factual material produced—sometimes doing so unbeknown to the card publishers—thus adding additional interest to what might otherwise be nondescript cards. This is particularly true of wartime comic cards. National pride and spirit in adversity adds its slant to every topic, from humour to sentiment, and then there is the other dimension represented by the messages on the cards. Such messages from those at 'The Front' to those 'At Home' and vice versa, are truly the stuff of history, and war cards should always be closely examined on both sides. German cards of WW1 and WW2 should be carefully scrutinised as many modern reprints are coming into circulation from that country that are not marked as reprints.

The greatest number of wartime cards were produced in Period 3 from 1914 to 1918, although Period 5 covering the Second World War, was by no means fallow. Nevertheless, the general values of Second World War cards are considerably higher than equivalent WW1 examples, properly reflecting their relative scarcity.

The cards listed under WARS are those produced immediately before, during and after the war i.e. the contemporary records. Cards which depict previous wars or warlike activities or old uniforms, etc. are to be found under HISTORICAL/MILITARY/TRADITIONAL. Except for studies drawn by well known artists, photographic cards with close-up detail are more highly valued than artistic impressions.

Information about the cards produced during the Korean and Vietnam Wars will be gratefully received and acknowledged. The wars which we consider here are:
THE BOER WAR
THE BOXER REBELLION
THE RUSSO–JAPANESE WAR
WORLD WAR 1
THE SPANISH CIVIL WAR
WORLD WAR 2

BOER WAR (OCT. 1899–MAY 1902)
This was a struggle in South Africa between the Boers (Dutch settlers) and the British. The Boers besieged Kimberley, Ladysmith and Mafeking.

During the latter siege the town Commander Baden Powell began the Scouting movement which is now worldwide. Formal Boer resistance ended in July 1900 but guerilla warfare continued until May 1902.

The divided back card was first introduced in mid-1902 therefore all contemporary Boer War cards must be of the undivided back variety.

Anonymous/Minor Publishers
Battle scenes UB .. .. .. 50p/**£1**/£3
Commemorative UB .. .. £1.50/**£2**/£4
Personalities UB .. .. £1/**£2**/£3
Satire/Propaganda UB .. .. .. £2/**£3**/£5

Anti-British Satire
Dutch Pub. J. G. Vlieger Cartoons UB
.. .. £8/**£10**/£12
French Artist Friedello UB .. .. £5/**£7**/£10
German Pub. Antiquariat Bremen UB
.. .. £6/**£8**/£10

Collectors Publishing Co.
Personalities, photographic origin UB
.. .. £2/**£4**/£6
Personalities as above plus *The Picture Postcard* magazine title overprint
.. .. £7/**£9**/£10

Koumans, P. J. Publishers, Delft, Holland
Dutch/Boer War personalities UB. At least
10 cards in set .. .. .. £1/**£2**/£5

Peace, Memorials and Reconciliation
Divided back all types **50p**
Joseph Chamberlain Tour Memorial card showing route and full designs both sides
UB .. .. £12/**£20**/£25
Peace Conference commemorative UB
.. .. £3/**£4**/£5

Picture Postcard Co.
Artist drawn battle scenes. Caton Woodville, etc. .. .. £4/**£6**/£8
Vignettes of army commanders .. £3/**£4**/£6

Sieges
Ladysmith (2 November 1899–28 February 1900)
Natal officials printed during the siege, plus line drawn vignettes in red each side.
Used .. .. £100/**£150**/£300
Unused .. .. £25/**£40**/£50
Photo origin views of siege .. £10/**£15**/£25

Mafeking (12 October 1899–17 May 1900)

Artist drawn	£6/**£7**/£8
Photo origin	£7/**£9**/£10

Tuck Empire Series
Artist drawn. Berkeley, Payne, Teller, etc.

.. ..	£7/**£9**/£12
Photographic origin	£5/**£8**/£10

BOXER REBELLION (JUNE 1900–SEPT. 1901)

In 1899, in reaction to increasing foreign presence within China, including the activities of Christian missionaries, the Chinese government under Dowager Empress Tzu Hsi incited a secret society to violence against foreigners and Chinese converts. The organisation was called 'The Society of the Righteous Fists' from which came the name 'Boxers'.

By June 1900 the foreign nations felt impelled to land armed forces in China and before the end of the fighting the Allies had included Americans, British, Christian Chinese, French, Germans, Italians, Japanese and Russian. Early in the struggle the German Minister was murdered and this prompted the issue of German anti-Chinese cards.

German artist drawn satire	£10/**£15**/£20
Other artist drawn	£3/**£4**/£7
War scenes. Photographic origin ..	£2/**£3**/£4

RUSSO–JAPANESE WAR (FEB. 1904– SEPT. 1905)

In reaction to growing Russian influence in Manchuria and Korea the Japanese, without warning, attacked the Russian fleet at Port Arthur on 8 February 1904. There followed the siege and surrender of the Russian garrison at Port Arthur (May 1904–Jan. 1905) and the destruction of the Russian fleet in the Tsushima Straits in May 1905. Peace was signed in the USA on 6 September 1905 through the efforts of President Theodore Roosevelt. Japanese cards are relatively common, British less so and Russian and American hard to find.

Battle Scenes/War Portraits

Anonymous Publishers

Japanese—Finely drawn full picture b & w UPU UB	£1/**£1.50**/£2
Japanese—Pub. 1904. Poorly coloured photographic origin UPU UB ..	50p/**£1**/£1.25

Pub. Hildesheimer
War series 5224. Artist signed. Norman Wilkinson, HW Kockkock, Ernest Frater, Caton Woodville .. .. 50p/**£1**/£1.50

Humour/Satire

Artist Dudley Hardy. Pub. Hildesheimer. Series 3015. ■230c	£4/**£5**/£7
French. Artist E. Muller. Pub. P. L. Paris	£2/**£3**/£4
French. Pub. MM, Paris	£2/**£4**/£5
Others	£1/**£2**/£2.50

Military Review 1906
This was a review to celebrate Japanese success in the war. Special cards with photo montage battle scenes were issued in transparent envelopes in Tokyo and Kobe.

With Tokyo handstamp	£4/**£6**/£8
With Kobe handstamp	£5/**£7**/£10
Without handstamp	£2/**£3**/£5
Transparent envelope	50p/**£1**/£2

Official Japanese

Communications Department. Post War issue	£1/**£2**/£3
Post Office 1904 issue. Photo montage. Art borders UB	£3/**£4**/£5
Tuck. Real photographic series no. 5170. 1904	–/**50p**/£1
Tuck. Russo–Japanese series no. 1330	50p/**75p**/£1

Peace Conference

Pub. Knight Bros. Multi-view. ..	£2/**£3**/£5
Pub. Rotograph Co. New York (1906). 'The Portsmouth Drama'	£3/**£4**/£5

Russian Outrage on Hull Fleet

Anonymous/minor pub. artistic cards	**50p**
Photographic origin. Damage detail	50p/**£1**/£1.50
Valentines	–/**50p**/£1

WORLD WAR 1 (4 AUG. 1914–11 NOV. 1918) PERIOD 3

Following the assassination of the Archduke Ferdinand at Sarajevo on 18 June 1914, all the major nations of the world were brought into conflict with each other because of a series of interlocking defence agreements. This first 'World War' gave new life and purpose to the picture postcard which had been dying. The postcard was economical in its use of paper and, in carrying a picture that could be seen by everyone who handled it during its postal journey, it was an excellent vehicle for propaganda. It also unwittingly recorded the effect that the war had on the home front. This time, civilians were at war too and were subject to sea and air bombardment, rationing and increased governmental control. These things are often ingredients in a picture card which was designed for quite a different purpose, e.g. humour, propaganda, fund raising and so on. Therefore, we have not attempted to define a separate category for the home front, but where pictures allude *en passant* to some feature of that front they have a premium value. We have, however, included a *Women at War* section, because it was during WW1, while millions of men were away from home, that women first had a chance to prove that they could do most of the jobs that up until then had been done by men. The picture postcard records that.

This section, covering Period 3, is probably the one during which the largest number of picture postcards were produced. In order to provide an adequate frame of reference we have used the following sub-divisions:

AIR WARFARE
FUND RAISING/WELFARE
HEROES/PERSONALITIES/SOLDIERS
HUMOUR
LAND WARFARE
OFFICIAL CARDS
PATRIOTISM/PROPAGANDA/SENTIMENT
PEACE/VICTORY
PIN-UPS
QUEEN MARY'S COLLECTION
SEA WARFARE
SILKS
WOMEN AT WAR

Air Warfare

Aces/Personalities

British	..	..	..	..	.. 75p/**£1**/£1.50
French	..	..	..	..	.. 50p/**£1**/£2
USA	..	..	..	..	.. £1/**£2**/£3

Top Aces

Ball, VC	..	..	..	..	.. £1/**£2**/£3
Boelcke (Ger)	..	..	..	..	£3/**£4**/£5
Guynemer (Fr)	..	..	..	..	£3/**£4**/£5
Hawker, VC	..	..	..	..	.. £1/**£2**/£3
Immelman (Ger)	..	..	..	..	£2/**£3**/£4
Mannock, VC	..	..	..	..	£2/**£3**/£4
McCudden, VC	..	..	..	..	£1/**£2**/£3

Richthofen, Baron von (Ger)	..	£4/**£5**/£7
Rickenbacker (USA)	..	..	£3/**£4**/£5

Bomb Damage in Britain ■230d

Photographic origin only	..	..	£1/**£2**/£3

Ramsgate 17 May 1917. Zeppelin Raid

..	..	..	..	..	.. 75p/**£1.50**/£2

Combat Studies

Artistic	..	..	..	..	.. 75p/**£1**/£2.50
Crashes	..	..	..	..	.. £1.50/**£2**/£3
Photographic origin	..	..	..	£1/**£2**/£3

Deley, Le E. (Fr Pub.)

'War in the North' series. Combat scenes
.. .. £1/**£1.50**/£2
'Air War Personalities' series. Aviators in aeroplanes .. .. £2/**£3**/£5

Observation Balloons

Price range	..	..	..	..	.. 50p/**£1**/£1.50

Photochrom. Artist Algernon Black

Allied Warplanes (6 in set) .. .. £2/**£3**/£4

Tuck. Artist G. T. Clarkson

Allied warplanes 'In the Air' series £1.50/**£2**/£3
European War series. 'Notabilities'
.. .. 50p/**75p**/£1

Zeppelins

Artistic impressions .. .. .. –/**50p**/75p
German propaganda .. .. .. £4/**£5**/£6
'Zepp Slayers', e.g. Pub. Faulkner and similar, featuring Leefe-Robinson, Tempest and/or Sowrey .. .. .. –/**50p**/£1

■233a

Pub. Gale & Polden. Artist Bert Thomas. Weekly Despatch Tobacco Fund. ''Arf A Mo, Kaiser!'. No. 1293. Period 3 .. .. £2

Fund Raising/Welfare

'Arf a Mo Kaiser' Pub. Gale & Polden,
Artist Bert Thomas. ■233a .. £1/**£2**/£2.50
Bovril, Gladys Storey Fund, etc. .. –/50p/75p
Egg Fund **50p**
Evening News POW Fund. Attached stamp
type .. .. 75p/**£1**/£2

Official Organisations
Belgian cards .. .. –/50p/£1
British Ambulance Committee .. **50p**
Church Army **50p**
French cards .. .. –/50p/75p
German cards .. .. .. 50p/**75p**/£1.50
Institute for the Blind .. .. .. –/50p/75p
Italian cards .. .. 75p/**£1**/£1.50
Regimental days .. .. –/50p/75p
Relief Fund, Sir John French, etc. .. –/50p/75p
St. John Ambulance Association .. –/50p/£1
Salvation Army **50p**
Star & Garter, Jack Cornwell stamp card,
handmade .. .. £3/**£5**/£7
Submarine banks, photographic detail
.. .. 50p/**£1**/£2
Tank banks, photographic detail .. –/50p/£1
War Bonds Campaign **60p**
Welsh Troops days **50p**
YMCA Hut Fund **50p**

Red Cross
Belgian **50p**
British **60p**
Dutch Artist Louis Raemaekers £1/**£1.25**/£1.50
French .. .. –/50p/75p
Italian .. .. 50p/**75p**/£1
German .. .. £1/**£1.25**/£1.50

Religious Meetings
Price range **60p**

Tobacco Funds
Performers **50p**
Weekly Dispatch (see also 'Arf a Mo Kaiser'
above) .. .. £1/**£2**/£2.50

Heroes/Personalities/Soldiers

Particularly at the beginning of WW1 it was
believed that 'Great Leaders' would decide the
outcome. Thus statesmen, royalty, generals and
admirals feature on thousands of cards, sometimes in order to raise funds, sometimes for
propaganda and frequently because publishers
knew that such cards sold well. As the war
progressed, heroic deeds became news, and all
nations have cards describing individual actions of
gallantry, some drawn by fine artists.

The more well known the artist, e.g. Caton-
Woodville, Georges Scott, the higher the value of
the card. Then there are local and camp photographers' pictures of the soldiers themselves, which
the latter would send home. They are not highly
valued, but particularly when they have messages
on may be greatly prized. They are worth a careful
examination.

Artists
Cards signed by the following artists have higher
than average valuations. († = *see also* ARTISTS for
more details.)
Beerts, Albert (Fr) .. .. –/50p/£1
Caton-Woodville, Richard† .. .. 50p/**£1**/£1.25
Dodd, Francis .. .. £1/**£2**/£2.50
Dupuis, Emile (Fr). ■234a .. .. £1/**£2**/£3
Hoger, R. A. (Ger) .. .. 50p/**75p**/£1
Pearse, A. .. .. 50p/**75p**/£1.25
Scott, Georges (Fr) .. .. .. 50p/**£1**/£2
Wagemans, M. (Belg) .. .. .. 75p/**£1**/£1.25
Ward, Herbert .. .. .. £1.50/**£2**/£2.50
Wood, Stanley .. .. 50p/**75p**/£1

Boy Scout Movement, 'A Hero's Fate'
.. .. –/50p/£1
Churchill, Winston .. .. .. £1/**£1.50**/£2
George V & Queen Mary, Christmas card
1914, Army & Naval uniforms .. –/50p/£1

Heroic Deeds
Artists impressions (*see above also*)
.. .. –/50p/75p
Photographic origin **50p**

Kitchener Memorial cards .. .. 75p/**£1**/£2
'L' Battery Pub. ELD .. .. .. –/50p/75p

■234a
*Pub. 'Color', Paris. Artist Emile Dupuis.
Bavarian Infanteer. 'Leurs Caboches' series.
Period 3* £2

Portraits

German cards are valued about 25% higher than others.

Generals, etc.	50p/**75p**/£1
Politicians/Civilian leaders	**60p**
Soldiers	**50p**

VC's. Pub. Gale & Polden, Artist Stanley
Wood, rounded corners .. .. 75p/**£1**/£1.25

Humour

This section is concerned with postcards whose prime objective was to provide amusement. In the general field of humorous cards British production outstrips that of every other country. This holds true in wartime. Because there are so many comic British cards they are not highly valued, but careful examination will often reveal references to ration books, gas masks and other wartime paraphernalia as well as to recent military offensives. In such cases there may be a dramatic increase in value.

Some publishers, such as Inter-Art, Photochrom and H.B. (Hutson Brothers) were prolific producers of this genre, but because the great mass of war humour cards is of minimum value we have listed those artists whose signature will add a premium and have identified collectable sets and topics.

Artists

Anonymous cards rate a maximum of 50p, but signatures of the following artists will rate a valuation within the price range shown below particularly for French and German examples. († = *see also* ARTISTS for more details.)

Beerts, Albert (Fr)
Buxton, Dudley†
Cattley, R.
Carter, Reg.†
Downes, Horace
English, Archibald† (A.E.)
Heischer, A. (Ger)
Gilson, T.†
Glanville.
Hassall, John† (Pub. Jarrold) (*see also* 'Sets' below)
Ibbetson, Ernest†
Lewin, F. G.
Mackain, F.
Maurice, Reg.
McGill, Donald
Muller, E. (Fr). ■235a
Osborne, Lieutenant Frank
Shepheard, G. E.†

Spurgin, Fred.†
Tempest, D.
Thomas, Bert† (*see also* 'Fund Raising/Welfare' above)
Young, Hayward† ('Jotter')
Zahl, H. (Ger)
Price range .. .. 50p/**75p**/£4

Sets

Deutschmeister Witwen und Waisen Stiftung. (Widows and Orphans Fund). 'Action in the Field' series. Pub. C. Pietsch, Vienna. Artist R. Kristen. All cards numbered. B & w line drawn cartoons. Over 75 examples identified .. 75p/**£1**/£1.50
'Egyptian Humour'. Pub. P. Coustouldis. Artist V. Manavian (10 cards) 50p/**£1**/£1.25
'Fragments from France'. ■235b. *See* ARTISTS for complete listing.
Invasion of England. Humorous series. ■236a 25p/**50p**/75p

■235a

Artist E. Muller (Fr). 'Belgium Protests'. Period 3 .. .. £2.50

■235b

Pub. Bystander. *Artist Bruce Bairnsfather. Fragments from France. Series 3. 'Where did that one go to?'. Period 3* £1

'La Journée Du Poilu'. Artist Saul
   Chambry .. ..   –/**50p**/75p
'More News by Liarless From Berlin'. Pub.
   Jarrold. Artist Hassall (two series)
   .. .. £3/**£3.50**/£4
'Our Sailors'. Pub. Raffaelli, Toulon. Artist
   H. Gervèse. ■236b (at least 30 cards
   repeated with French titles) .. £1/**£1.50**/£2
Silhouettes. Pub. Photochrom. 'American
   Silhouettes', 'Camp Silhouettes' & 'Jack
   Ashore' (each set probably 6 cards)
   .. .. 75p/**£1**/£1.50

Topics
Conscientious Objectors .. £1/**£1.25**/£1.50
DORA (Defence of the Realm Act) £1/**£1.50**/£2
Rationing .. .. 75p/**£1**/£1.25
Recruiting .. .. 50p/**£1**/£1.25
Submarines .. .. 50p/**75p**/£1
Women's Suffrage .. .. .. £1/**£1.50**/£1.75
Zeppelins .. .. –/**50p**/£1

■236a
'Invasion of England'. Kaiser Bill and von Tirpitz
No. 73. Period 3 .. .. 60p

■236b
Pub. Raffaelli. Artist Gervèse (Fr). Our Sailors
series. 'Fascination'. No. 30. Period 3 .. £1.50

Land Warfare

The main interest in the cards which record the
fighting, centres upon the details of clothing,
equipment, conditions and general environment
which characterised the conflict. Thus busy cards
of photographic origin tend to be more prized than
artistic impressions, although there are some
exceptions such as works by the French artist
Georges Scott (*see also* 'Heroes/Personalities/
Soldiers' and 'Patriotism/Propaganda/Senti-
ment'). Since most of the fighting took place on
French soil the majority of cards are French,
particularly those showing the damage to towns
and villages. There is little interest in those in
Britain although close-up scenes of front line life
by the French photographic publishers Lévy Fils
& E. Le Deley are collected.

The major British series was published by the
Daily Mail and has a separate entry below. Other
publishers are listed together since the values
placed upon their cards result more from the
subject matter than the publishing house.
Combat scenes .. .. 50p/**75p**/£1
Daily Mail series. ■237a. The contract to
   reproduce battle pictures from the front
   was won by the *Daily Mail* who guaran-
   teed a minimum payment of £5000 to
   military charities. The first seven sets of
   cards, numbers IV to X went on sale on 6
   September 1916. By April 1917, twenty-
   two sets, each of 8 cards, had been issued.
   Some pictures are repeated in black and
   white and colour, and by different printing processes. (A special album was
   issued to contain all the cards—*see also*
   ACCESSORIES).

Series I (col.)
1. Wounded Tommy to the Photographer:
   'I'm Not a German'
2. Highlanders pipe themselves back from
   the trenches
3. Church Service before battle
4. British heavy gun in action
5. Helping an ambulance through the mud
6. Sir D. Haig introducing Sir Pertab Singh
   to Gen. Joffre
7. Army Chaplain tending British graves
8. Thirsty German prisoners in their barbed
   wire cage.

Series II (col.)
9. Ypres after two years of War
10. RAMC picking up wounded
11. A 'fag' after a fight.

12. Tommy's look-out in a captured trench at Ovillers
13. British mine exploding at Beaumont Hamel
14. Crawling to the German trenches under fire
15. British machine gunners wearing gas helmets
16. A gallant rescue under fire

Series III (col.)
17. Tommy finds shell holes comfortable to sleep in
18. After the first cavalry charge, July 1916
19. Firing a heavy howitzer in France
20. Tommy at home in German dug-outs
21. Black Watch Pipers playing to the captors of Longueval
22. Gordons bringing in a wounded German
23. Burial of 2 British soldiers on the battlefield.
24. Hero—saving a wounded comrade under fire.

Series IV (photogravure—sepia)
25. Decorating a Canadian on the field of battle
26. London Scottish going into their trenches.
27. Happy Tommies wearing Hun helmets
28. Loyal North Lancs. Regiment cheering when ordered to the trenches
29. Tommy at home in German dug-outs. ■237a
30. A Gallant Rescue under fire
31.. A 'fag' after a fight
32. Firing a heavy howitzer in France

Series V (photogravure—sepia)
33. Worcesters going into action
34. *as* 10
35. *as* 23
36. *as* 4
37. *as* 2
38. *as* 8
39. British Infantry practising an attack
40. Australians parading for the trenches

Series VI (photogravure-sepia)
41. *as* 3
42. Wiltshires cheering during the Great Advance
43. Glorious First of July, 1916—our first prisoners
44. *as* 1

45. Helping an ambulance through the mud
46. 'Fighting Fifth' (Northumberland Fusiliers)
47. *as* 9
48. Taking prisoners during the Great Advance

Series VII (b & w)
49. *as* 6
50. *as* 25
51. Star Shell bursting near British Lines
52. *as* 7
53. 'Fighting Fifth'
54. *as* 12
55. *as* 26
56. *as* 43

Series VIII (b & w)
57. *as* 1 and 44
58. 'Black Watch' pipers playing to the captors of Longueval
59. *as* 23 and 35
60. *as* 31
61. *as* 42
62. *as* 15
63. *as* 20
64. A big mine explosion

Series IX (b & w)
65. *as* 2 and 37
66. Bringing in wounded—an early morning scene
67. *as* 28
68. *as* 9 and 47
69. Night scene on British Front. July 1st, 1916
70. *as* 39
71. 'Back to Blighty'. Boarding the leave boat
72. A British sentry in Flanders

■237a

Pub. Daily Mail. *Official War Photographs series. No. 4. 'Tommy at home in German dug outs'. No. 29. Period 3* £1

Series X
73. *as* 27
74. *as* 3 and 41
75. *as* 4 and 36
76. *as* 33
77. *as* 17
78. *as* 18
79. *as* 19
80. *as* 40

Series XI, 'The King at the Front' (col.) (81—88)
and
Series XII (photogravure—sepia) (89—96)
81, 89. 'The smile of Victory'—An historic group
82, 90. King George and King Albert enjoy an amusing anecdote
83, 91. A talk to Peasants
84, 92. The King meets a hospital matron
85, 93. Attending Church Service in the Field
86, 94. At the grave of a fallen hero
87, 95. Outside a captured German dug-out
88, 96. A greeting from the troops

Series XIII (col.) (97—104)
and
Series XVI (photogravure—sepia) (121—128)
97, 121. One of our Monster Guns
98, 122. A Present for the Kaiser
99, 123. A British Chaplain writing home for Tommy
100, 124. King inspecting RNAS Officers
101, 125. East Yorks going into the trenches
102, 126. Queen of the Belgians as photographer
103, 127. A captured dug-out near La Boiselle
104, 128. A London Heavy Battery in action (on packet)
104.   Anti-Aircraft Gunners spotting a Hun plane (on postcard)

Series XIV (col.) (105—112)
and
Series XVII (photogravure—sepia) (129—136)
105, 129. Anti-aircraft gunners spotting a Hun plane (on packet)
105.   London Heavy Battery in Action (on postcard)
106, 130. British Labour Battalion at work
107, 131. An advanced Field Ambulance

108, 132. King George greets Wounded Officers
109, 133. Captured German Guns
110, 134. An Indian Hotchkiss Gun at work
111, 135. A wiring party going up to the trenches
112, 136. Clearing the way through Contalmaison

Series XV (col.) (113—120)
and
Series XVIII (photogravure—sepia) (137—144)
113, 137. Hot Work by Australian Gunners
114, 138. Black Watch returning to Camp
115, 139. Loading a Trench Mortar
116, 140. Keeping a sharp look-out
117, 141. Australian heavy gun at work
118, 142. Wounded waiting for the Field Ambulances
119, 143. King George in a Gun Pit
120, 144. Observation balloon ascending

Series XIX (photogravure—sepia) 'Anzacs in France'
145. Machine Gunners out of the trenches
146. Back from Pozieres
147. Cheers for the King
148. Hot work in hot weather
149. A Burial on the Battlefield
150. A visit from the King
151. Drawing water for the gun crew
152. 'Some' shave

Series XX (photogravure—sepia) 'Anzacs in France'
153. Off to the trenches
154. New Zealanders loading Ammunition
155. New Zealanders cheer the King
156. Bringing up a gun
157. Bread and jam
158. A Brawny Maori Butcher
159. New Zealand Premier's visit
160. A Queue to the Field Canteen.

Series XXI (photogravure—sepia)
161. Beaumont Hamel. The Railway Station
162. Main Street of Combles
163. Ruins of Flers
164. High Street of Guillemont
165. Last State of Morval
166. Main Street, Longueval
167. Amont the Ruins of Montauban
168. Church at Albert

Series XXII. (photogravure-sepia) 'An Attack'
169. Awaiting the Signal
170. Over the Top
171. Crossing No Man's Land
172. Reserves Moving Up
173. A Wiring Party going forward
174. Railway Laying on Captured Ground
175. Moving up a Big Gun
176. A 'Bag' of Prisoners.
The higher price applies to the later, more
    elusive numbers. A large premium accrues
    for the complete set in the original
    album .. .. 75p/**£1**/£1.50

Damage. Individual cards are of little interest
unless they include close-up detail of military
equipment. Booklets containing detachable cards
showing damage, by publishers such as Louis
Lévy (Fr) (over 20 different booklets), E. Thill
(Belg) and E. Le Deley (Fr) may be valued at 10p
per card.
Equipment & Vehs .. .. £1/**£1.25**/£1.50
Front Line Life. ■239a .. .. 50p/**75p**/£1.25

Irish Rebellion May 1916 .. .. 75p/**£1**/£2
Pub. Baudinière (Fr) .. .. .. –/**50p**/75p
Pub. Bohlgemuth & Lissner (Ger) .. –/**50p**/75p
Pub. Christensen, A. (Fr). Artist Georges
    Scott .. .. 75p/**£1**/£1.25
Pub. Deffrène (Fr) **50p**
Pub. Deley, E. Le (Fr) (ELD) .. –/**50p**/£1
Pub. Delta Fine Art Co. **50p**
Pub. Friends of the Army Museum Paris
    (Fr) **50p**
Pub. Goosens, J. A. (Belg). Artistic
    impressions .. .. –/**50p**/75p
Pub. Imperial War Museum (per 2 cards)
    .. .. **50p**
Pub. Katz, A. H. (Fr) **50p**
Pub. L.V.C. (Fr) .. .. .. –/**50p**/75p
Pub. Lapina, I. (Fr) **50p**
Pub. Laureys (Fr) **50p**
Pub. Levy Fils .. .. .. –/**75p**/£1.25
Pub. Neurdein Frères (Fr) .. –/**50p**/£1
Pub. Newspaper Illustrations Ltd. **50p**
Pub. Noyer, A. (Fr) .. .. –/**50p**/£1
Pub. Official War Committee (USA)
    .. .. –/**50p**/£1
Pub. Photochrom **50p**
Pub. Pictorial Newspaper Co. .. **50p**
Pub. Pikowsky, M. Odessa (Russ). Artistic
    impressions .. .. –/**50p**/75p
Pub. Pulman, G. & Sons. Artist Louis
    Raemaekers .. .. 75p/**£1**/£1.50
Pub. Rathjen, H. Hamburg (Ger) .. –/**50p**/75p

Pub. Schmidt, Karl Dresden (Ger) –/**50p**/75p
Pub. *Sketch, The* **50p**
Pub. *Sphere, The* .. .. .. –/**50p**/75p
Pub. *Tit Bits* **50p**
Pub. Tuck. 'At the Front'. Series I & II.
    Artistic impressions .. .. 75p/**£1**/£1.50
Pub. Tuck. 'European War 1914' series
    .. .. **50p**
Pub. Tuck. 'Types of Allied Armies' series
    .. .. 50p/**75p**/£1
Pub. Tuck. Others **50p**
Pub. Vaugirard, Paris (Fr) **50p**
Pub. War Photogravure Publications
    .. .. **50p**

Prisoners of War. Cards were frequently published at home to raise funds for POW's and these
are listed under 'Fund Raising/Welfare'. This
section is concerned primarily with photographic
origin cards.

Published by captors showing POW in
    camps—British POW .. .. 50p/**75p**/£1
Published by captors showing POW in
    camps—German POW .. ..75p/**£1**/£1.50
Published by captors showing POW moving
    under escort .. .. ..50p/**£1**/£1.25
Published in the camps for the prisoners—
    British POW .. .. .. £1/**£1.50**/£2.50
Published in the camps for the prisoners—
    German POW .. .. .. £1.50/**£2**/£3
Tanks. Close-up views .. .. 50p/**£1**/£2
Weapons—Artillery, flame-throwers, ma-
    chine guns, mortars, etc. .. .. –/**50p**/£1.75
Wounded—Groups, home or overseas
    .. .. **50p**

Official Cards

British troops were issued with Field Service
postcards when the rations were brought up.
Doubtless it was the same for the other armies.

■239a
*Pub. Baudinière (Fr). 'The Great War
1914/15/16' series. 'The Belgian Front—a good
meal in the trenches'. No. 905. Period 3* .. 50p

The British cards were often of the 'cross out the message you don't want' variety, and had an official stationery number—Army Form A2042. They also carried details of the month and year of printing, e.g. 7/17 represents July 1917, as well as the number of that batch produced, e.g. 4,500,000. No embellishment was allowed on British cards, although some regiments produced their own with designs on from time to time for greeting purposes. The Germans, French and Italians, however, often issued official field post-cards with coloured drawings, i.e. pictures. The plain cards are worth little. Value is added by designs and pictures. Messages should be read carefully, particularly on French cards which seem subject to less careful censorship. The value added by Field Post Office cancellations and censorship cachets is the subject of separate reference works.

British Army. Field Service postcard. Army
form A2042 .. .. **50p**
British Army. Hospitalisation card. Army
Form W3229 .. .. **50p**
British Army. Regimentally produced greet-
ings cards **75p**
Church Army Recreation Hut card **50p**
German Army. With picture of captured
locality .. ..75p/**£1.50**/£3
Italian Army. With coloured flags of the
Allies .. .. –/**50p**/75p
French Army. With coloured flags, no
border .. .. –/**50p**/£1
With coloured flags, coloured border
.. ..50p/**£1**/£1.50
YMCA with HM Forces on Active Service
.. .. –/**50p**/75p

Patriotism/Propaganda/Sentiment

National patriotic fervours in 1914 ran very high in every nation. Postcards in their millions carried waving flags and pretty ladies symbolising allies and alliances. As the war progressed propaganda became more thoughtful, more specific. The Germans and French had a strong thread of hate running through their cards, with much play by the latter on the barbaric effects of German *Kultur*. The British cards reflect the national charac-teristic of poking fun both at the enemy and at one's own misfortunes. There is, therefore, con-siderable overlapping with 'Humour' and both there and in this section are considered cards which refer to conditions on the home front. The French, more openly demonstrative than either the British or the Germans, balanced the hate in their propaganda by millions of stylised senti-mental cards (such as those published by Hamine)

invoking the mystical elements of *honneur* and *La Patrie*. The nearest British equivalents are the song cards published by Bamforth, perhaps the major British sentimental card publisher. Values of cards in this section have a generally low base, but where well-known artists such as Brunelleschi, Raemaekers or Sager are involved, or when there is detailed satirical or social content in the card, values increase. Similarly, there are certain sets, themes and publishers which are collected. The classifications set out to reflect these interests. Silk and woven cards have their own section 'Silk/Woven/Embroidered'.

Artists († = *see also* ARTISTS *for more details*)
Armitage, William (Lion's head and mane).
■240a .. .. –/**50p**/75p
Arus, Raoul (Fr) .. ..75p/**£1**/£1.50
Averell, Joyce .. .. –/**50p**/75p
Barribal, W.† .. .. £1.50/**£2**/£3
Beerts, Albert (Fr) .. .. .. 50p/**75p**/£1
Bertle, H. (Aust) .. .. .. £1/**£1.50**/£2
Biggar, J. L. .. .. –/**50p**/75p
Boileau, Philip† (USA) .. £1.50/**£2**/£2.50
Bone, Muirhead .. .. .. £1/**£1.25**/£1.50
Boulanger, M. (Fr) .. .. ..75p/**£1**/£1.50
Brinsley, E. C. .. .. .. 50p/**75p**/£1.50
Brunelleschi (It).† .. .. .. £15/**£25**/£30
Butcher, Arthur .. .. –/**50p**/75p
Canivet, H. (Fr) .. .. –/**50p**/75p
Cartill, T. (Fr) **50p**
Corbella (It)† .. .. £1/**£1.50**/£2
Dupuis, Emile (Fr) .. .. £1/**£1.25**/£1.50
Ellam† .. .. –/**50p**/75p
English, Archibald† (A.E.) .. .. –/**50p**/75p
Freiertag, F. (Aust) .. .. £1/**£1.50**/£2
Gilson, T.† .. .. –/**£50p**/75p
Gunn, Archie (USA) .. .. £1/**£1.50**/£2
Hirleman (Belg) .. .. .. –/**50p**/£1
Hofer, A. (Fr) **75p**
Hoffman, R. J. (Ger) .. .. .. £2/**£3**/£5

■240a

Pub. Boots the Chemist. Artist William Armitage. Patriotic series. 'A Tribute to our Colonies' ..50p

Holland, Frank	£1/**£2**/£2.50
Ibbetson, Ernest†	..75p/**£1**/£1.50
Joseph, Karl (Ger)	£3/**£4**/£5
Jung, F. R. (Aust)	£1/**£1.25**/£1.50
Larwin, H. (Aust)	£1/**£1.25**/£1.50
Lenhard (Ger)	£3/**£7**/£10
Mailik (Ger)†	£1/**£1.50**/£2
Martini, Alberto† (It)	£3/**£5**/£8
Mauzan, Achille (It)	£2/**£3**/£5
Meschine, G. (It)	£2/**£4**/£5
Pastien, Emil (Belg)	£1/**£1.50**/£2.50
Payne, Harry†	£2/**£3**/£5
Pearse, A.	£1/**£2**/£3
Poulbot† (Fr) (drawings of children in tragic situations)	..50p/**£1**/£1.50
Raemaekers, Louis† (Du) ..	..75p/**£1**/£2.50
Ravenhill, L.	50p/**£1**/£2
Richardson, Agnes†..	..75p/**£1**/£1.50
Riss, Th. (Ger)..	50p/**75p**/£1
Rubino, R. (It)	£2/**£3**/£5
Sager, X. (Fr)	£1/**£2**/£3
Scott, Georges (Fr)	£1/**£1.50**/£2
Shepheard, G. E.†	..50p/**£1**/£1.50
Tauzin, Louis (Fr)	..50p/**£1**/£1.50
Thomas, Bert†	..75p/**£1.50**/£2
Wennerburg, Brynolf† (Ger) ..	£1.50/**£2**/£3
Wilson, Oscar	–/**50p**/75p
Wood, Lawson† (Patriotic series for Dobson Molle)	£1/**£1.50**/£2
Others	**50p**

Bamforth

This company is mostly known for song cards of which it produced some 250 sets during WW1. Most sets are of 3 cards, though some have 1, 2 or 4 and the earliest WW1 sets start with Series Numbers around 4740.

All varieties. ■241a	**50p**
Original packets listing current titles	**50p**

Publishers

Listed below are the publishers of the most collectable cards in this category.

Adlington, A.
Birn Bros.
Brown & Calder
Boots the Chemists
Coquemer (Fr)
Dobson Molle
Faulkner, C. W.
Fontane, C. (published composite sets) (Fr)
Gale & Polden
Heininger, Henry (USA)
Hemine (Fr)

Henderson, James (*see* 'Sets' below)
Illustrated Postal Card and Novelty Co. (USA)
Inter-Art Co. (very prolific including a 'Patriotic Series'. *Also see* 'Sets' below)
Jarrold (*see* 'Sets' below)
Mansell, Vivian (*see* 'Sets' below)
Merval Corp. (USA)
Noyer (Fr)
Photochrom
Radiguet, M. (Swiss)
Reinthal & Newman (USA)
Rotary
Rubel, Phillipp (Ger)
Salmon
Schulz, M. (Ger)
Sevampez (Fr)
Sharpe, W. N.
Smith Bros.
Ternois, A. (Fr) (publishers of Poulbot cards)
Tuck
Valentine (also published song cards)
Wildt & Kray
Zerreiss (Ger)

Sets

Some sets stand out as collectable for a variety of reasons. The cards may be by a particular artist, form part of a composite picture, represent a fixed number of Allies or simply be an attractive or numbered series. The listing is alphabetical by the name commonly used to describe the sets. Valuations remain per card unless otherwise stated. A complete set should command at least a 10% premium over the total of the individual values of the cards in the set.

■241a

Pub. Bamforth. Series 4742. 'It's a Long Way to Tipperary'. No. 2. Period 3 .. .. 50p

Aesop's Fables. Set of 6. Pub. Tuck. Artist
F. Sancha .. .. £3/**£4**/£5

'Britain at War'. B & w reproductions of
drawings by Muirhead Bone. At least 2
series—'The Grand Fleet' and 'Making
Munitions' .. .. £1/**£1.25**/£1.50

Butterflies 'Aux Alliés' or 'Les Alliés' series,
printed by L. Geligne (Fr) or L. Marotte
(Fr). Ladies shown as butterflies
representing individual nations, at least
24 cards in set .. .. £2/**£2.50**/£3

Composite set of 6. Pub. I. Lapina (Fr). Also
marked 'IML' or 'Croissant' and/or 'Fontane'. Kaiser's head formed by cards
showing German atrocities. Price per set:
  Brown and white .. .. .. £6/**£10**/£12
  Coloured .. .. £10/**£15**/£20

Cavell, Edith. Set of 6 Italian published
cards showing the Cavell story—
skeletons, etc. Artist Corbella (It)
.. .. £5/**£7**/£8

Devil's Own. At least 5 cards showing
commissioning of devilled officer cadets in
the Inns of Court Training Corps (1917)
.. .. £1/**£1.50**/£2

Dupuis Heads. Pub. Color (Fr). Coloured
soldiers' heads signed and dated represen-
ting individual nations. Artist Emile
Dupuis.
  Leurs Caboches .. .. .. £1/**£2**/£3
  Nos Alliés .. ..75p/**£1**/£1.50
  Nos Poilus .. ..75p/**£1**/£1.50

Girls' Heads representing individual nations
by head and shoulder drawings of girls in
national dress. Listed by publishers. Les
Femmes Héroiques. Pub. Color (Fr).
Artist Emile Dupuis, small rectangular
frames of girls' heads representing national type .. .. .. 75p/**£1.50**/£2.50

Inter-Art 'United Six' series .. .. −/**50p**/£1

James Henderson 'The Allies' series
.. .. £1/**£1.50**/£2

Vivian Mansell. A few are numbered and
signed .. .. 50p/**75p**/£1

Out for Victory. Series of drawings by L.
Ravenhill showing individuals such as
'Tommy' (card 501), 'The Destroyer
Captain' (511), and 'The Allotment
Holder' (513). At least 15 cards in series,
all numbered .. .. .. £1.25/**£1.50**/£2

Punch War Cartoons. Pub. Jarrold.
Reproductions of *Punch* cartoons. At least
4 sets. Twelve cards to a set, numbered
consecutively to no. 48 .. ..50p/**£1**/£1.50

Raemaekers, Louis. Reproductions of acidic
cartoons by artist Raemaekers from the
De Telegraaf newspaper of Amsterdam.
Frequently sold in booklet form of 10
cards and as fund-raisers for the Red
Cross and wounded soldiers. At least 2
series. .. ..75p/**£1.50**/£2

Themes
Certain events provided ideal ammunition for
propaganda, e.g. the execution of Edith Cavell
and the sinking of the *Lusitania*. Catch words and
phrases—'Ils Ne Passeront Pas', 'Gott Mit Uns',
'Are We Downhearted?—No!' and so on—provided emotive patriotic rallying themes. This
section lists thematic reasons for collecting.
Cavell, Edith (*see* 'Sets' above). ■242a
  .. .. £1/**£1.50**/£2.50

Hatred:
British .. .. £2/**£3**/£5
French .. ..75p/**£1**/£2.50
German .. .. £1/**£2**/£3

Home Front. Direct references to rationing,
national insurance, air raids, etc.
.. ..50p/**£1**/£1.50
King & Country .. .. .. −/**50p**/£1
Kultur:
Allied Cards .. .. −/**50p**/£1
German Defence of .. .. .. 50p/**£1**/£2
Lusitania .. .. £1.50/**£2**/£2.50
Quotations. National leaders, Kitchener,
Kaiser, etc. .. .. −/**50p**/75p
Recruiting:
Artistic references to .. .. −/**50p**/£1
Photographic origin, rallies, etc. .. £1.50/**£2**/£3

■242a
*Pub. Phot. Belg (Belg). Period 3. Photo Em.
Basilien. Miss Edith Cavell* £2.50

Sentiment:

American	**50p**
British	–/**50p**/75p
French (two cards)	**50p**
German	–/**50p**/75p
Italian	50p/**75p**/£1

Slogans:

Are we downhearted? No!	–/**50p**/75p
Deutschland Über Alles	50p/**75p**/£1
Gott Strafe England .. .. ·..	50p/**75p**/£1
Ils Ne Passeront Pas	–/**50p**/75p
On Les Aura	**75p**
Poor Little Belgium/Serbia	–/**50p**/75p
Verdun	75p/**£1**/£1.50
Others	**50p**

Peace/Victory

There was rejoicing everywhere when the war ended—for a while anyway. Here we are concerned only with the period immediately after the war, when references to it continued. Thus we are now in Period 4. Values are low.

Memorials

Views (four cards)	**50p**
Unveilings with crowd details ..	**75p**

National Thanksgiving Service 1919

Photographic origin with detail .. .. ·..	£1/**£1.50**/£1.75
Frank O'Salisbury picture. ■243a	75p/**£1.50**/£2

Personalities

Fund raising or similar. Value according to personality	–/**75p**/£1

Victory Parades (close-up detail only)

British	**50p**
Other. ■243b	**50p**

Pin-Ups

During WW1 the soldiers pinned up saucy postcards to relieve the horrors of trench life. The ladies became known as pin-ups. Many cards of this type are artists impressions produced in France. The leading exponent was Raphael Kirchner, an Austrian domiciled in Paris, who like Hérouard, Maurice Millière, Xavier Sager and Suzanne Meunier continued the art form developed on posters and in magazines like *La Vie Parisienne* around the turn of the century. The most prolific pin-up artist is Xavier Sager (see

also ARTISTS). Collecting is mainly centered around artists' signatures and we have listed cards in that way. All cards are Period 3.

■243a
Pub. Fine Arts Pub. Co. Period 4. Artist Frank O'Salisbury. National Peace Thanksgiving Service (1919) **£2**

■243b
Pub. E. Le Deley (Fr). Period 4. General Mangin at victory celebrations, Paris 14 July 1919 .. 50p

■243c
Pub. Delta Paris. Period 3. Artist Ney, 'A sa toilette' No. 145 of series 29 .. .. **£6**

Déshabillé

Cards showing ladies in various forms of undress. These are generally valued more highly than glamour cards.

Bonzagni, Aroldo (It)	£3/**£6**/£12
Calderara, C. (It)	£2/**£4**/£6
Fabiano (Fr)	£2/**£3**/£4
Fontan, Léo (Fr)	£2/**£4**/£5
Hérouard (Fr)	£2/**£3**/£4
Jarach, A. (Fr)	£3/**£5**/£6
Kirchner, Raphael (Fr domicile). ..	£8/**£12**/£15
Maréchaux, C.	£2/**£3**/£5
Meunier, Suzanne (Fr)	£1/**£3**/£5
Millière, M. (It)	£3/**£5**/£6
Ney (Fr). ■243c	£2/**£3**/£6
Peltier (Fr)	£1.50/**£3**/£4.50
Penot, A. (Fr)	£2/**£3**/£5
Pépin, Maurice (Fr)..	£1/**£2**/£4
Sager, Xavier (Fr), e.g. 'Les Obus Pacifiques' series	£2/**£4**/£6
San Marco (It)	£1.50/**£3**/£5
Anonymous	75p/**£1**/£2

Glamour

Cards showing attractive ladies but not undressed, undressing or over-exposing.

Barribal	£2/**£2.50**/£3.50
Bianchi, Alberto (It)	£1.50/**£2**/£3
Boileau, Philip (USA)	£2/**£2.50**/£3
Bompard, Luigi (It)	£2/**£3**/£4
Busi, Adolfo (It)	£2/**£3**/£5
Colombo (Fr)	£2/**£2.50**/£3
Corbella (Fr)	£1.50/**£2.50**/£4
English, Archibald (A.E.) ..	75p/**£1**/£1.50
Fidler, Luella (USA)	75p/**£1**/£1.50
Fuchs, R. (Ger)	75p/**£1**/£1.50
Leonnec (Fr)	£2/**£3**/£5
Mauzan, Achille (It)	£2/**£4**/£6
Nanni (It)	£2/**£3**/£4
Rappini (It)	£2/**£2.50**/£3.50
Anonymous	75p/**£1**/£1.50

Queen Mary's Collection

Her Late Majesty Queen Mary was presented with a quantity of confiscated picture postcards by a postal censor. They are mostly German and Dutch. The total number of cards in the collection, now housed in Windsor, is about 100. The following cards are included in that collection.

Artists

Bernsden (Du). Anti-war cartoons with bulls and dragons	£2/**£3**/£5
Heckel, Dora (Ger). Small child in toy uniform says 'Come with me' (to war)	£1/**£2**/£3

Hollart, F. (Hung). Artistic French scenes	75p/**£1**/£1.50
Landgrebe, H. (Ger). Slogan 'Gott Mit Uns' showing dramatic soldier. Fund-raiser	£2/**£3**/£5
Mermagen, I. (Ger). Patriotic bare-chested youth with flag	£3/**£5**/£7
Schulz, Curt (Ger). Glorious charges like A. Pearse did for Britain	£1/**£2**/£3

Publishers

Bering, Essen (Ger). Fund-raiser for Dierhagen school	£2/**£3**/£4
Doring & Huning, Berlin (Ger). Slogans 'Gott Mit Uns'. (*See* Landgrebe above)	£2/**£3**/£5
Eberle, Josef (Ger). Slogan 'Gott Strafe England'. Zeppelin shown above England, with a burning London below ..	£8/**£10**/£12
Fink, Albert, Berlin (Ger). Kaiser & Kaiserin each paying homage at a soldier's grave. Artist drawn. ■244a	£1/**£2**/£3
Fischer & Uninger, Salzburg (Ger). Name of Allies cooked in different ways, e.g. Englishman with cabbage ..	75p/**£1**/£1.25
Köhn, Brüder (Ger). Slogan 'Gott Strafe England und vernichte Italien'. A flaming sword and a Zeppelin are seen above drowning figures	£4/**£6**/£8
Luhn, Peter (Ger). Slogan 'Gott Mit Uns'. (*See* Landgrebe above)	£2/**£3**/£5
Niedersedlitz, Dresden (Ger). Drawing of a beer mug as a collecting box. Fund-raiser for the Red Cross	75p/**£1**/£1.50

■244a

Pub. Albert Fink (Ger). Period 3. Kaiserin paying homage at a soldier's grave £3

Sea Warfare

The war at sea was a continuous assault by German U-boats upon Allied merchant shipping interspersed by a number of surface actions. In the early months actions were often fully reported on postcards, but Germany soon censored these and Britain followed suit in June 1916. Few cards are found after that date although Britain's best known series by Photochrom showing scenes from the Admiralty film *Britain Prepared* was issued in June 1916. Cards produced prior to 1916 tend to be photographic in origin, whilst those produced later tend to be artistic impressions. The dates given below are those on which the actions began:

Actions

Bombardment—Dardannelles. 18 Mar. 1915	£1/**£1.50**/£2
Bombardment—Scarborough. 16 Dec. 1914	75p/**£1**/£1.25
Coronel—1 Nov. 1914	75p/**£1**/£1.50
Falkland Island—8 Dec. 1914	75p/**£1**/£1.50
Heligoland—28 Aug. 1914 ..	50p/**75p**/£1
Jutland (Skagerrak)—31 May 1916	75p/**£1.50**/£2
Others	−/**50p**/75p

Artists

Most artistic impressions rate less than cards of photographic origin; exceptions are:

Baumgarten, E. V. (Ger)	£3/**£4**/£5
Bohrdt, Professor Hans (Ger).	£2/**£3**/£4
Gribble, Bernard F.	50p/**75p**/£1

Ships

HMAS *Sydney* (*see* SMS *Emden*)	50p/**75p**/£1
HMS *Aboukir* (*see* U9)	75p/**£1.50**-£2
HMS *Cressy* (*see* U9)	75p/**£1.50**/£2
HMS *Hogue* (*see* U9)	75p/**£1.50**/£2
Lusitania 7 May 1915. *See* 'Patriotism/ Propaganda/Sentiment' ..	£1/**£1.50**/£2.50
SMS *Emden* (sunk by HMAS *Sydney* on 9 Nov. 1914)	50p/**75p**/£1.50
U Deutschland (sailed to America in June 1916)	£1/**£2**/£3
U9 (sank Aboukir, Cressy & Hogue on 22 Sept. 1914)	75p/**£1.50**/£2
Others	−/**75p**/£1

Silks

We consider three types of cards—embroidered, printed and woven. The majority of silk cards were made in France and Belgium during WW1, although the type originated in Germany late in Period 1. Classification here is first by publisher and then by major categories. Anonymous cards otherwise of good quality may be valued at 60% of the prices given below.

Embroidered

There is an extraordinary range of embroidered cards but it can be covered by the 5 main classifications below:

Badges:

British Air units including RNAS	£8/**£10**/£12
British Corps	£2/**£3**/£4
British Line Regiments. ■245a ..	£10/**£12**/£15
British Naval units including ships	£8/**£10**/£12
Other Corps	£1/**£2**/£3
Other Line Regiments	£1/**£2**/£4

Inserts: found in embroidered cards with pockets; valuations for sentimental designs:

Card	50p/**£1**/£2
Celluloid	£1/**£2**/£3
Silk hankies	£2/**£3**/£4
Without insert	75p/**£1**/£1.25

■245a
Period 3. Embroidered silk 'The Buffs' £10

■245b
Period 3. Embroidered silk with aeroplane design and card insert £6

Military Designs:

Air/Land/Sea. ■245b	£2/**£4**/£6
Barracks	£8/**£12**/£15
Comfort organisations, e.g. Red Cross	£10/**£12**/£15
Equipment/Weapons	£3/**£5**/£7
Flames	£5/**£8**/£10
Men	£3/**£5**/£7

Personalities:

Inset photographs are often found stuck within an embroidered design. The values below are for single photos. Double photos rate up to 50% above the single valuation.

Albert, King of the Belgians	£3/**£5**/£10
Cavell, Edith	£2.50/**£4**/£7
Elisabeth, Queen of the Belgians ..	£3/**£5**/£10
Foch, Maréchal	£4/**£6**/£12
French, Sir John	£2/**£4**/£8
George V, King	£2/**£4**/£8
Haig, Sir Douglas	£3/**£5**/£10
Joffre	£2.50/**£4**/£7
Kitchener, Lord	£3/**£5**/£10
Nicholas, Tsar of Russia..	£3/**£5**/£10
Pershing, General	£4/**£6**/£12
Poincaré, President of France ..	£3/**£5**/£10
Sarrail, General	£2.50/**£4**/£7
Victor Emmanuel	£2/**£3**/£6

Sentimental:

Flags	£1/**£2**/£3
Flowers	75p/**£1.50**/£2
Greetings	50p/**£1**/£1.50

Printed

This is the smallest category of silk cards. A prominent publisher was Editions Gabriel of Paris and their initials may often be found on the silk.

Personalities:

Cavell, Edith	75p/**£1.50**/£2
Kitchener, Lord	50p/**75p**/£1

Flames:

Albert	£3/**£5**/£7.50
Arras	£4/**£6**/£8
Dixmuide	£3/**£5**/£7.50
Nieuport	£5/**£7**/£10
Rheims	£3/**£5**/£7.50
Ypres	£2/**£3**/£6

Woven

Bertrand & Boiran. This publisher produced landscape layout cards with small silk pictures in arched or rectangular frames.

Personalities:

Albert, King of the Belgians ..	£20/**£30**/£35
Cavell, Edith	£20/**£30**/£35
Foch, Maréchal	£15/**£25**/£30
George V, King	£15/**£25**/£30
Jellicoe, Admiral	£20/**£30**/£35
Joffre	£15/**£25**/£30
Kitchener, Lord	£15/**£25**/£30
Poincaré, President of France ..	£15/**£25**/£30
Sarrail, General	£20/**£30**/£35
Others	£10/**£20**/£25

Deffrene, E. (Fr). This publisher together with Neyret Frères produced most of the French cards. They are considered jointly. The initials NF may be woven into the picture.

Flames. Pictures depicting French and Belgian towns burning:

Albert	£8/**£10**/£12
Amiens Cathedral	£10/**£15**/£20
Arras	£8/**£10**/£12
Bapaume	£10/**£15**/£20
Cambrai	£10/**£15**/£20
Dixmuide	£8/**£10**/£12
Douai	£10/**£15**/£20
Dunkerque	£8/**£10**/£12
Gand	£10/**£15**/£20
Nieuport	£8/**£10**/£12
Peronne	£8/**£10**/£12
Pervyse. ■246a	£10/**£12**/£15
Rheims	£10/**£12**/£15
Verdun	£8/**£10**/£12
Vimy	£15/**£20**/£25
Ypres	£8/**£10**/£12
Others	£7/**£9**/£15

Patriotism/Propaganda/Sentiment:

American	£15/**£20**/£25
Belgian	£15/**£20**/£25
British	£20/**£25**/£30
French	£15/**£20**/£25
Others	£12/**£15**/£20

■246a
Pub. Deffrène (Fr). Period 3. Woven silk, Pervyse in flames £15

Personalities:

Albert, King of the Belgians	£10/**£12**/£15
Cavell, Edith, without flower	£8/**£10**/£15
Cavell, Edith, with flower ..	£20/**£35**/£45
Clemenceau	£15/**£25**/£30
Elisabeth, Queen of the Belgians	£15/**£25**/£30
Foch, Maréchal	£12/**£15**/£18
French, Sir John .. .:	£15/**£18**/£20
George V, King	£10/**£12**/£15
Haig, Sir Douglas	£10/**£12**/£15
Joffre	£10/**£12**/£15
Kitchener, Lord	£10/**£12**/£15
Lloyd George, David ..	£25/**£30**/£40
Pétain	£12/**£15**/£20
Poincaré, President of France ..	£10/**£12**/£15
Wilson, President of America ..	£20/**£30**/£35

Slogans:

Notre 75	£8/**£10**/£12
On Les Aura	£10/**£15**/£18
On Ne Passe Pas. ■247a ..	£15/**£18**/£20

Grant, W. H. This publisher is usually named on the front of the card together with the words 'Woven in Pure Silk'. There is also a black or green line border.

Personalities:

French, Sir John	£30/**£35**/£45
George V, King	£25/**£30**/£35
Jellicoe, Admiral	£20/**£25**/£30
Kitchener, Lord	£18/**£20**/£25
Mary, Queen	£25/**£35**/£40
Others	£10/**£20**/£40

Stevens, Thomas. This publisher embossed the front border of his cards, stated 'Woven in Silk' together with (in most cases) 'by T. Stevens' and used a variety of coloured inks.

Personalities:

French, Sir John	£40/**£80**/£100
George V, King	£40/**£80**/£100
Kitchener, Lord	£40/**£80**/£100
Mary, Queen	£40/**£80**/£100

Women at War

As the men went to fight so women had to take over their jobs. Interest centres around women performing men's jobs and any reference to female emancipation. Major publishers who issued cards on this theme include Art & Humour, Inter-Art, Noyer (Fr), Photochrom and Tuck. The French issued thousands of coloured posed photograph (Bamforth type) cards usually showing women as nurses. Nursing is the most common theme. († = *see also* ARTISTS for more details.)

Artists

Butcher, Arthur	50p/**75p**/£1
Coppins, Harold	50p/**75p**/£1
Dupius, Emile (Fr)	75p/**£1**/£1.50
Edmunds, Kay	–/**50p**/£2
Horsfall, Mary†	50p/**75p**/£1.50
Leroy (Fr).	£1/**£1.50**/£2
Sager, Xavier† (Fr)	£1/**£2**-£2.50
Skinner, E. F. ■247b	50p/**75p**/£2
Spurgin, Fred†	50p/**75p**/£1.50
Wennerburg, B.†	£1.50/**£3**/£4
White, Flora.†	–/**50p**/75p
Emancipation	£2/**£3**/£5

Men's Jobs
Artist drawn:

British	75p/**£1**/£1.25
German	–/**£1**/£1.50
Others	–/**50p**/£1

Photographic:

Clear detail	£2/**£2.50**/£3
French posed (Bamforth type) (2 cards)	**50p**

■247a
Pub. Neyret Freres (Fr). Period 3. On Ne Passe Pas! £20

■247b
Period 3. Artist E. F. Skinner. Women file cutters at Cammell Laird £1.25

Series

'For the Cause' Pub. Tuck	**60p**
'La Femme and La Guerre'. Pub. Gallais (Fr). Artist Leroy (at least 10 cards).	75p/**£1**/£2
Pub. Merval Corp. (US). Unnamed drawn series showing women at war work (at least 10 cards). ■248a	50p/**75p**/£1
'Our Own Girls' Pub. Inter-Art. Artist Arthur Butcher	–/**50p**/75p

SPANISH CIVIL WAR (17 JULY 1936–28 MARCH 1939)

After some years of internal conflict General Franco headed a military revolt against the left wing popular front government. Germany and Italy supported Franco, while Russia and various International Brigades sided with the popular front. The government was eventually overthrown. No detailed listing of cards is currently available. Information would be gratefully welcomed.

Artist drawn	£5/**£7**/£8
General Franco propaganda. ■248b	£3/**£9**/£10
Photographic origin	£6/**£8**/£12

WORLD WAR 2 (3 SEPT. 1939–7 MAY 1945) PERIOD 5

The Second World War was a war of machines. Fighting in the air dominated the early years particularly during the Battle of Britain period. Later tanks, submarines and secret weapons became emotive symbols of the conflict. Picture postcards of WW2 are only just beginning to be recognised. Nazi material has been collected for some years but there are as many postcard categories in Period 5 as there are in Period 3. It is the change of emphasis from man to machine which is the fundamental difference. Cards are much more preoccupied with the mechanics of war than they are with waving banners, sentimental messages or stirring slogans. Once again the British reliance upon a sense of humour to see them through is reflected in the fact that humorous cards form the largest single category. However, these cards offer much more than humour to today's collector, for they reflect the conditions experienced both by the front line soldier and those on the home front. Amongst the jokes are to be found ration books, gas masks, endless queues, spies, petrol rationing, clothing coupons ... a detailed record of the 1940s. We have used the following sub-divisions:

AIR WARFARE
CONCENTRATION CAMPS
FUND RAISING/WELFARE
HEROES/PERSONALITIES/SOLDIERS
HUMOUR
LAND WARFARE
MUNICH
OFFICIAL CARDS
PATRIOTISM/PROPAGANDA/SENTIMENT
PEACE/VICTORY
PIN-UPS
SEA WARFARE
SILKS
WOMEN AT WAR

Air Warfare

Aeroplanes
These are classified according to their publisher.

German. Official and other cards drawn by von Axster-Heudtlass .. .. £3/**£7**/£10

Photochrom
'Britain Prepared' photo series. Black and white .. .. £1/**£2**/£2.50

■248a

Pub. Merval Corp. (USA). Lady farm worker £1

■248b

General Franco. Period 4. Official card celebrating the first anniversary of the revolution. Posted 17 July 1937 .. .. £10

'Britain Prepared' photographic origin
  series. Brown and white, about 50 cards
  .. .. 50p/**£1**/£1.25
'Colour Photograph' series. Prime Minister's
  slogan on the back .. .. .. **–/50p**/75p

P.C. Paris (Fr)
'Aviation Britannique' series. Deckle edge,
  about 12 cards .. .. 50p/**£1**/£1.25

Salmon
Artistic coloured impressions by A. F. D. Bannister, about 100 designs all numbered consecutively from no. 4839.
Full out pictures, details on back. ■249a
  .. .. £1.50/**£2**/£3
Details in white strip on the front £1/**£1.50**/£2

Valentines
'Real Photograph' series, numbered on front,
  black and white, about 100 cards, action
  and other scenes. ■249c .. .. £1/**£2**/£2.50
'Real Photograph' series with coloured Union
  Jack overprint .. .. .. 50p/**£1**/£1.25
Other Publishers .. .. 50p/**75p**/£1

Barrage Balloons
Drawn .. .. £1/**£1.50**/£1.75
Photographic origin .. .. .. £1/**£2**/£2.50

Ground Activity
Valuations given are for cards of photographic origin. The more detail, the higher the value. Drawn pictures command about 30% less.
Airfields .. .. £2/**£3**/£4
Anti-aircraft guns/predictors/searchlights
  .. .. £1.50/**£2.50**/£2
Crashes .. .. £2/**£5**/£7
V1. Flying Bomb .. .. .. £5/**£8**/£10
V2. Ballistic Missile. ■249b .. .. £4/**£6**/£8

Concentration Camps
It was only as the Allied armies advanced across Europe that the full horror of these camps became known. Soon special funds were set up to help the victims and specially designed postcards were sold in exchange for donations.
First Anniversary. Period 6 (1946). French
  .. .. £8/**£12**/£15
Ditto. German. ■249d .. .. .. £10/**£15**/£20
Named Camps .. .. £4/**£6**/£8
Others (*see also* COMMEMORATIVE) 50p/**£1**/£3

■249a
Pub. Salmon. Period 5. Artist A. F. D. Bannister. Spitfire fighters. No. 4841 .. .. £3

■249b
Pub. Allis (Du). Period 5. V2 .. .. .. £5

■249c
Pub. Valentine. Period 5. 'Real Photograph' series. Wellington bombers. No. 38A–45A .. £2

■249d
Pub. Information Office, Dachau. Period 6. 29.4.1946. First Anniversary of the liberation of Dachau £18

Fund Raising/Welfare

The British made little use of postcards as fund raisers compared to the Germans who issued many official postcards for that purpose. German and Italian designs are often coloured, dramatic and are oversize (o/s) cards.

British Fund Raisers
Academy Patriotic Publications, photo-
    graphs of personalities, o/s   ..   £1/**£1.50**/£2
Tuck. 'In a World of Space' series   50p/**£1**/£1.25
Others   ..   ..   50p/**75p**/£1

German
'Tag der—' ('Day of—') cards. Official
    cards and fieldpost, o/s   ..   ..   £3/**£4**/£6
'Wandkalender' (Wall calendar) artist-
    drawn action scenes   ..   ..   £6/**£9**/£10
Others   ..   ..   £2/**£2.50**/£3

Italian
Coloured artist war scenes, o/s   ..   £3/**£4**/£5
Coloured other, o/s   ..   ..   £1.50/**£2**/£3

US Treasury Department
'Buy War Bonds'. ■250a   ..   ..   £2/**£2.50**/£3

Welfare Organisations
NAAFI, Montgomery Club, Red Cross,
    YMCA, etc. usually given away, show
    views of facilities   ..   ..   £1/**£1.50**/£2

Heroes/Personalities/Soldiers

Publicising individuals as heroes was done far less in WW2 than in WW1. Probably the only significant British 'Heroes' series is that of VC winners issued by the Overseas League in their tobacco parcels. Politicians, Royals and fighting commanders of all countries appear in photographic and artistic poses. Unless stated valuations are for cards of photographic origin.

Belgian
Col. artist drawn portraits.   ..   ..   £2/**£3**/£5

British
Pub. G.P.D. 'For Freedom' series
   ..   ..   £1.50/**£2.50**/£3
Pub. G.P.D. 'Victory' series   ..   £1.50/**£2**/£3
Pub. Gale & Polden. Artist Ernest Ibbetson
   ..   ..   £1.50/**£2**/£2.50
Pub. Overseas League. VC series.
   ..   ..   £1.50/**£2**/£2.50
Pub. Photochrom   ..   ..   £1/**£1.50**/£2

Pub. Tuck:
'Real Photograph' series   ..   ..   £1.50/**£2**/£3
'Royal Portrait' series   ..   ..   £1.50/**£2**/£3.50

Others. ■250b   ..   ..   £1/**£2**/£2.50

French
Pub. André Leconte. Artist Paul Barbier.
    'Armée Française' series   ..   £1.50/**£2**/£3

German
Artist W. Willrich. Col. o/s   ..   £5/**£12**/£15

Pub. Hoffman, photo series
Goebbels   ..   ..   £4/**£7**/£8
Hess   ..   ..   £7/**£10**/£12
Skorzeny   ..   ..   £7/**£10**/£12
Others   ..   ..   £4/**£6**/£8

Italian
Col. Artist drawn o/s   ..   ..   £1.50/**£2**/£4

■250a
Pub. US Treasury Department. Period 5   ..   £2

■250b
Pub. Tuck. Period 5. President Roosevelt as a grandfather. French caption £2

Humour

British cards overwhelm those of every other nation. The value of a card that simply makes a joke is negligible. Here we value cards that deliberately—or otherwise—make a direct reference to wartime conditions, e.g. gas masks, blackouts, queues, Hitler, the home front and so on. Collecting is best defined by identifying artist signed cards. Cards without a signature are valued at the end of the alphabetical list of artists names below as 'Unsigned'. Cards depicting Hitler attract the highest values. († = *see also* ARTISTS for more details.)

Artists

Akki	50p/**75p**/£1
Attwell, Mabel Lucie†	..50p/**£1**/£1.50
Bairnsfather, Bruce†	..75p/**£1**/£1.50
Barlog (Ger)	£1.50/**£2**/£3
Birch, Norah Annie	50p/**75p**/£1
Bizuth (Belg)	£1/**£2**/£2.50
Boudart, Bob (Belg)	..75p/**£1**/£1.25
Breger, Dave (US)	£1/**£1.50**/£2
Carter, Reg.†	50p/**75p**/£1
Cheneval (Belg)	..60p/**£1**/£1.20
Cheval, Jean (Fr)	..75p/**£1**/£1.50
Christie, G. F.†	£1/**£1.50**/£1.75
Comicus†	**50p**
Cooper, Phyllis†	**50p**
Dean, Dora	**50p**
Delanchy (Fr)	−/**50p**/£1
Dinah. ■251a	50p/**75p**/£1
Driscoll	−/**50p**/75p
Faizant, Jacques (Fr)	£1/**£2**/£2.50
Forres, Kit	..75p/**£1**/£1.50
Geesink, Joop (Belg)	£1/**£1.50**/£2
Grimes	..75p/**£1**/£1.50
Groth, John	..75p/**£1**/£1.50
Havenstein, Bill (US)	£1/**£1.50**/£1.75
Hemard, Joseph (Fr)	50p/**75p**/£1
Henry (Belg)	£1/**£1.50**/£1.75
Howe, A. Ian	..75p/**£1**/£1.25
Kem, ...	..75p/**£1**/£1.50
Kern, L. (Fr)	−/**50p**/75p
Leclerc (Fr)	..75p/**£1**/£1.50
Long, Wilf (Can)	50p/**£1**/£4
Mallet, Beatrice	£1/**£1.25**/£1.50
Manning, Reg. (US)	£1/**£1.25**/£1.50
Maurice, Reg.	−/**50p**/75p
McGill, Donald† (new comics) ..	−/**50p**/75p
Owen, Will	£2.50/**£3**/£4
Paris (US)	£1/**£1.50**/£2
Paterson, Vera. ■251b	50p/**75p**/£1
Pearson, J. G. (US)	−/**50p**/75p
Purser, Phyllis	−/**50p**/75p

Rémy, P. (Fr)	£1.50/**£2**/£2.50
Richardson, Agnes†	..75p/**£1**/£1.25
Rigby, Cecil T.	**50p**
Saroukhan (Egypt)	£1/**£1.50**/£2
Schnebelen, Jean (Fr)	£1.50/**£2**/£3
Shaw, Stocker	£1/**£1.50**/£1.75
'Strube'	..75p/**£1**/£1.50
Studdy, G. E.†	£1/**£1.50**/£2
Tayler, Laurie	..60p/**£1**/£1.20
Taylor, Arnold	−/**60p**/£1
Tempest, D.	−/**60p**/£1
Thomas, Bert† (ITMA)	£1/**£1.50**/£1.75
Tobey, Barney (US)	£1/**£1.25**/£1.50
White, Brian	**50p**
Wilkin, Bob	**50p**
Wilkinson, Gilbert	..75p/**£1**/£1.50
Williams, Madge	50p/**75p**/£1
Zec, Donald	..75p/**£1**/£1.50

Unsigned

British	−/**50p**/75p
French	**50p**
German	50p/**£1**/£2
Italian	−/**50p**/75p
US	25p/**£1**/£3

■251a

Pub. Tuck. Period 5. Artist Dinah. 'Ladies in Waiting' £1

■251b

Pub. Humoresque. Period 5. Artist Vera Paterson. No. 4899 .. .. 80p

Land Warfare

Most British and French cards in this section were published during the phoney war period and are photographic in origin. Photochrom issued a 'Britain Prepared' series which roughly equates to the *Daily Mail* cards of WW1. Artistic impressions of warfare are more the province of the Italians and the Germans, such cards usually being issued for fund raising or propaganda purposes. They are, therefore, to be found in their appropriate sections. Cards listed here imply a direct connection with active service:

Armoured vehicles. Carriers, self-propelled
    guns, tanks, etc. ■252a .. .. £1/**£1.50**/£2
Combat scenes. .. .. £1/**£2**/£2.50
Damage. Atomic bomb .. .. £2/**£3**/£4
Damage. Other .. ..50p/**£1**/£1.50
Front line life .. .. £1/**£1.50**/£2
Prisoners of War. In camp. .. £1/**£1.50**/£1.50
Prisoners of War. Under escort. .. £1/**£1.50**/£2
Soft-skinned vehicles. Cars, jeeps, trucks,
    etc.■252b .. .. 50p/**75p**/£1
Weapons .. .. £1/**£1.50**/£2

Munich

Cards of photographic origin for September
    1938 (Period 4). Hoffmann RP cards rate
    highest .. .. £1/**£1.50**/£3

Individuals
Chamberlain .. ..75p/**£1**/£1.50
Daladier .. .. 50p/**75p**/£1
Hitler .. .. £2/**£3**/£5
Mussolini .. .. £2/**£3**/£4

Groups
General .. .. £2/**£3**/£5
Showing all signatories above. .. £6/**£8**/£15
Showing two signatories above. .. £4/**£6**/£12

Official Cards

The Germans used their fieldpost cards to carry propaganda pictures and to raise money, thus there are entries in those sections. Otherwise, apart from some American issues, official cards tend to be dull and not highly valued.

Air raid casualty. Card No. G. & S.
    704 .. .. **50p**
Divisional/Regimental cards .. ..50p/**£1**/£1.50
Fieldpost. German (with pictures) £2/**£4**/£5
Fieldpost. Others .. .. .. 50p/**75p**/£1
US Army leave sections .. .. £1/**£1.50**/£2
US Navy 'V' for Victory cards .. –/**50p**/75p

Patriotism/Propaganda/Sentiment

In WW1 'Sentiment' was a major theme on postcards. In WW2 the emphasis passed to propaganda. With Italy and Germany it is almost impossible to separate patriotism from propaganda since government policies were based on appeals to nationalistic instincts. Much National Socialist (Nazi) propaganda began in Period 4 in the 1930s, and provided that postcard designs mirrored official policies they did not have to be approved by any official body before printing— even during the war. After capitulation the Allies ordered the destruction of all stocks of propaganda postcards hence those that survive are highly valued. The British once again made use of the art of caricature and ridicule, therefore, there is a great deal of overlapping with HUMOUR particularly in relation to civilian propaganda. Publishing houses were allowed to continue the production of postcards provided that a patriotic message from the King or the Prime Minister was printed on the back. Except where indicated this section's material is artist drawn and collecting currently relates to specific artists and sub-themes.

Anti-Bolshevist. ■253a .. .. .. £10/**£25**/£40
Anti-Capitalist .. .. £10/**£15**/£25
Anti-Semitic .. .. £25/**£50**/£100

*Pub. Valentine. Period 5. 'Covenanter' tanks
.. .. £1.50*

■252b

*Pub. Photochrom. Period 5. 'Britain Prepared'
series. 'Here we are again' 75p*

Artists

(† = *see also* ARTISTS for more details)

Ardizzone, Edward	..50p/**£1**/£1.50
Axster-Heudtlass, von (Ger)	£3/**£7**/£10
Bartholomaus, H. (Ger)	£2/**£3**/£5
Bartoli, Guiseppe (It)	£4/**£7**/£8
Bee, Noah	£3/**£5**/£6
Bloch, Marcel (Fr)	..75p/**£1**/£1.50
Boccasile, Gino (It)	£12/**£20**/£25
Broos, Piet (Du)	£1/**£1.50**/£2.50
Cass (Fr)	£2/**£4**/£6
Crali, Tullio (It)	£7/**£12**/£15
Davis, Marshall (US)	£1/**£2**/£3
D'Ercoli, Masslio (It)	£3/**£7**/£9
Eichhorst, Franz (Ger)	£5/**£8**/£10
Fougasse†	£1.50/**£2**/£3
Gotschke (Ger)..	£3/**£5**/£9
'Guy' (Belg)	£5/**£7**/£8
Igert, Paul (Fr)	£2/**£3**/£5
Klein, Gottfried (Ger)	£10/**£15**/£17
Klein, Richard (Ger)	..£18/**£25**/£40
Pisani, Vittorio (It)	£3/**£5**/£7
Smits (Du)	£3/**£10**/£12
Steen (Du)	£1.50/**£2**/£2.25
Strong, Patience	..50p/**£1.50**/£2
Tafuri, R. (It)	£3/**£7**/£9
Thomas, Bert†	£1/**£3**/£4
Willrich, W. (Ger)†	£5/**£12**/£15
Woude, Sikko van de (Du)	£1/**£2**/£3

British Embassies/Legations Propaganda

Lisbon. Vast series of cards. Highest values for English captions, notable personalities and artist signed cards.

B & w reproductions of anti-Axis cartoons from London papers. Artists include Groth, Kem, Strube and Zec. Signed cards rate highest .. .. ..75p/**£1**/£1.50

Col. Single pictures. Artist drawn. Lettered and numbered prefix '51'. o/s .. £1/**£2**/£2.50

Col. Multi pictures. Artist drawn. Lettered and numbered, prefix '51'. Higher values for English texts. o/s .. .. .. £2/**£3**/£4

GPD 'For Freedom' series .. £1.50/**£2.50**/£3

GPD 'Victory' series .. .. £1.50/**£2**/£3

RP. Fighting vehicles, tanks and troops. Multi-language captions. o/s .. 50p/**75p**/£1

Teheran. Iranian folk tale of the wicked ruler (Hitler) and the three wise men (Churchill, Stalin and Roosevelt). 5 cards in set. Col. o/s. ■253b .. .. £12/**£20**/£25

Dutch

Anti-German .. .. 50p/**£1**/£2

Free Forces

Artistic/designed, French, Polish, etc.
.. .. £2/**£5**/£10

Photographic origin, French, Polish, etc.
.. .. £1/**£1.50**/£2

French

Photographic posed views of Maginot Line
.. .. £1/**£1.50**/£2

German

National Socialist. Full-out pictures:

Period 4	£5/**£10**/£15
Period 5	£6/**£12**/£18
SS	£10/**£15**/£20

■253a

Period 5 (It). Official propaganda card. German and Italian soldiers attack the Russian monster
.. ..£10

■253b

Pub. British Legation, Teheran. Period 5. Anti-Axis Propaganda. Churchill, Stalin and Roosevelt bring in Hitler and Goebbels. Col. o/s ..£20

National Socialist. Photographic detail
.. .. £3/**£6**/£9

National Socialist. Official issues with pictures:
Period 4 .. .. £2/**£5**/£7
Period 5 .. .. £2/**£6**/£8

Olympics (1936) .. .. .. £4/**£8**/£12
Photographic general .. .. £2/**£3**/£5
Hold to Light 'Ou le Tommy est-il resté?'
   Series. German propaganda all dropped
   on Maginot Line in 1939. Twelve cards in
   set. Hold to light .. .. .. £7/**£15**/£20

Italian
Militaristic scenes. ■254a .. .. £5/**£10**/£20
Peaceful scenes .. .. .. £1/**£1.50**/£2

Sentiment
Sentimental designs/song cards and studio
portrait cards for family use.

British .. .. 50p/**£1**/£1.50
French .. .. 50p/**£1**/£1.50
German song cards .. .. .. £1.50/**£3**/£4
US .. .. 50p/**75p**/£1

US Propaganda
There is considerable overlapping between propaganda and humour. In this section the listing is by publisher. The higher values relate to cards whose content is more political than humorous, but that can be a fine judgement to make. Listing by publisher:
Beals. (Des Moines, Iowa) 'Kick' cards. 30
   cards in series, identified by the letters
   'WC' and numbered 1 to 30. 5 cards
   feature Hitler and rate the highest value
   .. .. £1/**£2**/£3
GC (General Comics) series .. 75p/**£1**/£1.50
Curteich. USA series (Army). Over 30 cards
   USN series (Navy). Over 30 cards
   AS series. Probably set of 5
   Price range .. .. 75p/**£1**/£1.50
Graycraft. Artist Dave Breger. 24 cards in
   series .. .. £1/**£1.50**/£2
Kropp, E. C. (Milwaukee, Wisconsin)
   .. .. £1/**£2**/£2.50
Metrocraft (also 'Photo by Acme'). Series of
   24, numbered from 1 and identified by
   the letter 'A' .. .. .. 50p/**£1**/£1.25
Mid States Press (Chicago) .. .. £1/**£1.50**/£2
RHD Corp. Cards on the theme 'The Army's
   Thinking'. Artists used incl. 'Licty'
   (George Licterstein) .. .. £1/**£1.25**/£2.50

Tichnor Bros. (Boston)
   AP (Airplane series). Numbered 1 to
   10 .. .. 50p/**£1**/£1.25
   Hitler Comics. 5 cards in set .. £1.50/**£2**/£3
   Jap Comics. 10 cards in set .. £1/**£2**/£2.50
   M (Military series). Numbered 1 to
   20 .. .. 50p/**£1**/£1.25
   MA (Military Activities). Numbered 1 to
   20 .. .. 50p/**£1**/£1.25

Peace/Victory
As the Western Allies pushed the Germans back so Belgium, Denmark, France and Holland were liberated. They issued cards to celebrate. When the fighting ceased there were victory parades and then the job of restoring Europe to health began. It was called 'Restoration'. There were cards for that too and also for the return of the fighting man to civilian life—'Demobilisation'. As the date of a man's demobilisation drew near he would count the number of 'days to do'. The French celebrated '100 days to do' with *Père Cent* cards. Since the liberation of Europe began in June 1944, this section covers Period 5 and Period 6 cards, including some issued by Germans, happy that the war was over.

Armistice. Photographic cards issued at
   Rheims on 7 July 1945 showing signing of
   armistice at Rheims on 7 May 1945.
   Stamped and date cancelled .. £15/**£25**/£30
Demobilisation. .. .. £1/**£1.50**/£2

Liberation:
Belgium .. .. 50p/**£1.50**/£3
Denmark. ■255a .. .. .. 50p/**£1**/£1.50
France .. .. 75p/**£1.50**/£2
Holland .. .. £1/**£1.50**/£2.50

Père Cent. ■255b .. .. .. £1/**£2**/£4
Photographic detail of liberating forces
   .. .. £1/**£2.50**/£5

■254a

Pub. V. E. Boeri (It). Period 5. 150th Battalion CC.NN £12

Reconstruction	..	..	..	..	75p/**£1**/£1.50
Memorials	..	..	..	..	50p/**75p**/£1
Victory parades	..	..	..	..	50p/**75p**/£1

Pin-Ups

Magazines such as the American *Yank* provided most of the pin-ups for the forces. Postcard pin-ups are far fewer than in WW1. However, film star photographic cards were very popular. The categories 'Déshabillé' and 'Glamour' refer to artist drawn pictures unless stated otherwise.

Déshabillé

Artist Barribal ..	..	..	..	£2/**£3**/£5
Artist Hermond (Fr)	..	..		£1/**£2**/£3
Pub Hoffman. 'House of German Art'				
Nudes ..	..	..	..	£1/**£2**/£2.50
Schönheit der Gymnastik (Beauty of Gymnastics) (Ger)	..	..	..	£2/**£3**/£5
Others	..	..	..	£1/**£1.50**/£2

Glamour

Film star photos. ■255c ..	..	..	50p/**75p**/£1
Others	..	..	..	..60p/**£1**/£1.20

Sea Warfare

Good artistic impressions of ships and battles, or cards showing clear photographic details are most highly valued. Specific actions, such as the sinking of the *Graf Spee*, were sometimes recorded by sets of cards.

Actions

Graf Spee (Ger) sinking. Twelve cards in set. ■255d ..	..	..	..	£2/**£3**/£5
Narvik ..	..	..	..	£5/**£7**/£12
Scapa Flow (Ger). 'Der Adler' series				
..	..	..	..	..	£2/**£3**/£4

Artists

Axster-Heudtlass, von (Ger)	..	£3/**£7**/£10
Bannister, A. F. D. ..	..	..75p/**£1**/£1.50
Church, Bernard W.	..	..75p/**£1**/£1.50
Igert, Paul (Fr)	..	..	£2/**£3**/£5
Venturini, Antonio (It)	..	£3/**£5**/£7
Vicary, P. A. ■256a	..	..75p/**£1**/£1.50
Werner, Carl (Ger) ..	..	£1/**£2**/£3

Ships

Bismarck (Ger)	..	..	..	£1/**£2**/£3
FFNF (Free French Naval Forces)				75p/**£1**/£1.25

■255a
Period 5 (Danish). Liberation of Denmark by British Forces. 'In Montgomery's Image' £1.50

■255b
Pub. G. Picard (Fr). Period 6. Père Cent .. £3

■255c
Pub. L. D. Ltd. Period 5. Lana Turner. .. £1

■255d
Period 5. Graf Spee after the second explosion. No. 8 .. .. £2

HMS *Hood*	£1/**£1.50**/£2
Kriegsopfer-Wandkalender (War victims wall calendar series)	£5/**£7**/£10
Pub. Photochrom. 'Britain Prepared' series. English and French texts ..	£1/**£1.25**/£1.50
Pub. Salmon	75p/**£1**/£1.50
Pub. Tuck. 'Our Navy' series	50p/**75p**/£1
Pub. Valentines. ■256a	75p/**£1**/£1.50

■256a

Pub. Valentine. Period 5. Artist P. A. Vicary.

HMS Ark Royal	£1.50

Silks

Few silk cards were produced in Period 5. Some embroidered cards with year dates exist for 1939, 1940 and 1945, those years that Allied armies were on the continent of Europe. A limited range of embroidered and woven cards was produced during the German occupation. Woven, or combined embroidered/woven cards of this type, have gold frames on grey borders.

Combined Embroidered/Woven

Gold frames	£3/**£4**/£5

Embroidered

German occupation. ■256b	£7/**£10**/£12
Year dates 1939/1940/1945 ..	£1.50/**£2**/£3

■256b

Period 5 (Fr). Embroidered silk birthday postcard made during the German occupation .. £10

Women at War

In WW2 women went to war—again. This time it made less impact on the postcard than it had in WW1. The Germans used the theme of women's help for the war effort as propaganda, the British and Americans still viewed the idea with amusement.

Men's Jobs

Humorous comment. ■256c	–/**50p**/75p
Photographic origin	50p/**75p**/£1

Nursing

Price range	–/**50p**/75p

Series

Arbeitsmädchen. 'Working Girl' series	£3/**£5**/£8
Bund Deutscher Mädchen. 'League of German Maidens'	£3/**£4**/£5
Frauen schaffen für Euch! 'Women are working for you'	£10/**£12**/£15
Free French photo series.	75p/**£1**/£1.25
Pub. Beals (US). Over 25 cards in series.	£1/**£1.50**/£2
Pub. Tuck. 'With the WAAF'. Over 25 cards in series.	50p/**75p**/£1

■256c

Pub. Coastal Cards. Period 5. Splendidly rude card. 'I said kit inspection' 50p

INDEX TO ARTISTS

For biography see page marked in **bold** type

For illustration see page marked in *italic* type

INDEX TO THEMES